Class Activities
to accompany
Mathematics for Elementary Teachers

Class Activities
to accompany
Mathematics for Elementary Teachers

Sybilla Beckmann
University of Georgia

Boston San Francisco New York
London Toronto Sydney Tokyo Singapore Madrid
Mexico City Munich Paris Cape Town Hong Kong Montreal

Photo Credits: p. 103, 241, 242, 273, 308, 367, 370 Courtesy of the author; **p. 240** U.S. Air Force

Class Activity 13H is adapted with permission from *Primary Mathematics*, Vol. 4A, p. 40; Vol. 4B, p. 62; Vol. 5A, pp. 59, 60; Vol. 6B, pp. 64, 67; and from *Primary Mathematics Workbook*, Vol. 4A part 1, p. 62; Vol. 4B part 2, p. 59 by Ministry of Education and Times Media Private Limited.

ISBN 0-321-12378-6

2 3 4 5 6 7 8 9 10 VH 070605

Contents

11 MORE ABOUT AREA AND VOLUME   333

Preface

The class activities in this book are designed to help prospective elementary school teachers develop a deep understanding of elementary school mathematics.

I wrote these activities because I wanted my students to be actively engaged in mathematics in class. Few students seem to get much out of long lectures, and every teacher of math knows that it is not a spectator sport: In order to learn math, you have to *do* math, and you have to *think deeply* about math. Every teacher also knows that when you explain something to someone else, you deepen your own understanding—or you uncover a gap in your understanding. So when students explain their mathematical ideas to each other in class, it helps develop their own thinking.

I have tried to strike a good balance between structure and guidance, on the one hand, and leaving room for students to put their own thinking into the activities, on the other hand.

Although the activities are designed for college-educated adults, many can be adapted easily for use in elementary school. Indeed, I have used a number of them with children myself. Therefore, I hope that prospective teachers will keep these activities in mind for their own teaching.

Sybilla Beckmann
Athens, Georgia

Chapter 1

Problem Solving

1.1 Solving Problems

CLASS ACTIVITY 1A: A *Clinking Glasses* Problem

$$\frac{20 \times 19}{2}$$

Use Polya's four problem-solving steps to solve the following problem:

At a party, someone proposes a toast. Each of the 20 people in the room wants to "clink" glasses with everyone else. How many "clinks" will there be? (There is exactly one "clink" for each pair of people.)

1. Understand the problem.

2. Devise a plan.

3. Carry out the plan. If you get stuck, return to step 2 and think up a new plan.

4. Look back. Does your answer seem sensible? What plan worked best? What if there were 30 people at the party, would your technique work in that case? Did someone in your class or group have a different plan or idea? Are your results compatible? Think of more ways to "look back" and learn from what you've just done.

CLASS ACTIVITY 1B: Problems About Triangular Numbers

The number of dots in a triangular array is called a **triangular number**.

1st = $\widehat{1}$ + 2   2nd = $\widehat{3}$ + 3   3rd = $\widehat{6}$ + 4   4th = $\widehat{10}$ + 5 5th = 15

$$\frac{n}{2}\left(a_1 + a_n\right)$$

$$\frac{25(25+1)}{2} = 325$$

The first triangular number is 1, the second is 3, the third is 6, the fourth is 10, and so on. In general, the Nth triangular number is the number of dots in a triangular array of dots that has N dots on each side.

Use Polya's four problem-solving steps to solve the following problems about triangular numbers:

1. What is the 25th triangular number? What is the 1000th triangular number?
   If you have solved Class Activity 1A, can you identify a relationship between this problem and the "clinking glasses" problem?

$5^{th} = 15$ $+6$
$6^{th} = 21$ $+7$
$7^{th} = 28$ $+8$
$8^{th} = 36$ $+9$
$9^{th} = 45$ $+10$
$10^{th} = 55$ $+11$

$11^{th} = 66$ $+12$
$12^{th} = 78$ $+13$
$13^{th} = 91$ $+14$
$14^{th} = 105$ $+15$
$15^{th} = 120$

2. Is there a triangular number that has 91 dots in its shape? If so, which one is it? In other words, where does it appear in the sequence of triangular numbers? Is it the 5th, the 12th, etc.? Is there a triangular number that has 150 dots in its shape? What about 2000 dots? If so, where are these numbers in the sequence of triangular numbers? If there are no numbers with 150 or 2000 dots, how do you know for sure?

CLASS ACTIVITY 1C: What Is a Fair Way to Split the Cost?

Two friends, Eliza and Margo, go shopping and find a *buy-two-pairs-get-one-pair-free* sale at a shoe store. (The least expensive pair is the free one.) Eliza finds two pairs she'd like to buy: one for $83.95 and one for $67.95. Margo is interested in a pair that costs $59.95. Eliza and Margo decide to buy the three pairs together, so the pair that costs $59.95 will be free.

1. How should Eliza and Margo divide fairly the total cost of the three pairs of shoes?

    First, solve this problem on your own, then discuss your solution with the group. Explain your solution method and explain why you think it is a fair way to split the cost of the shoes.

    Is there only one correct way to solve this problem, or can different people have different solutions that are valid?

2. What if Margo's pair of shoes only cost $24.95, and Eliza's shoes still cost $83.95 and $67.95? Now, how should Margo and Eliza divide the cost?

    As before, solve this problem on your own first, then discuss your solution with the group. Explain your method of solution and explain why you think it is a fair way to split the cost of the shoes.

    Did you recommend a different method for dividing the cost than you did in Part 1 of this activity? If so, why?

1.2 Explaining Solutions

CLASS ACTIVITY 1D: Who Says You Can't Do Rocket Science?

In this class activity, use Polya's problem-solving steps to *make progress* on solving the next problem. Then explain why the conclusions you have reached are true, whether or not your conclusions fully solve the problem.

Problem: A rocket can use two different types of fuel. Rocket scientists know that it takes 30 minutes to fill the fuel tank with type A fuel from a type A hose, whereas it takes 45 minutes to fill the same fuel tank with type B fuel from a type B hose. (The type B hose is smaller than the type A hose.) The rocket's fuel tank will now be filled simultaneously with type A and type B fuels, each flowing out of their own hoses at a constant rate. How long will it take to fill the fuel tank?

Before you attempt to find an exact answer, determine *approximately* how long it should take for the fuel tank to fill. Answer this either with a specific number of minutes, or by saying, "It will take less than . . . minutes, but more than . . . minutes, to fill the tank." In either case, explain your reasoning.

Chapter 2

Numbers and the Decimal System

2.1 Introduction to the Number Systems

2.2 The Decimal System and Place Value

CLASS ACTIVITY 2A: Developing Place Value

Each person participating in this activity needs a bunch of toothpicks or other small objects, such as coffee stirrers. Each person should have less than 100 toothpicks but enough so that they can't see right away how many toothpicks there are. Each person also needs either several small plastic snack bags, or some rubber bands, or both.

The purpose of this activity is to help you understand the development of our way of writing numbers.

1. Determine how many toothpicks you have *without* counting them all one by one. Do this by arranging your toothpicks so that you can *visually see* how many toothpicks you have. Use your plastic snack bags or rubber bands to help you organize your toothpicks. Describe how you arranged your toothpicks.

2. Does the way you arranged your toothpicks in part 1 correspond to the way you write the number that represents how many toothpicks you have? If so, explain how. If not, try to arrange your toothpicks so that you can visually see how many toothpicks you have and so that this way of arranging the toothpicks corresponds to the way we write the number that stands for how many toothpicks you have.

3. Put your toothpicks together with the toothpicks of several other people. Once again, arrange the toothpicks so that you can visually see how many toothpicks there are and so that your way of arranging the toothpicks corresponds to the way we write the number that stands for how many toothpicks there are. Use plastic snack bags or rubber bands to help organize the toothpicks. Describe how you arranged the toothpicks.

4. Repeat part 3, but now with the toothpicks from everyone in the the class. How many toothpicks are there in all?

CLASS ACTIVITY 2B: Showing Powers of Ten

Mrs. Kubrick wants her students to get a feel for the powers of ten so that they can better understand place value. Mrs. Kubrick decides to use small stars printed on paper for this purpose, as shown in the next set of figures. One star, 10 stars, 100 stars, and 1000 stars all fit on one piece of paper. Ten thousand stars fill up two whole pieces of ordinary $8\frac{1}{2}$-by-11-inch paper, as in Figures 2.1 and 2.2.

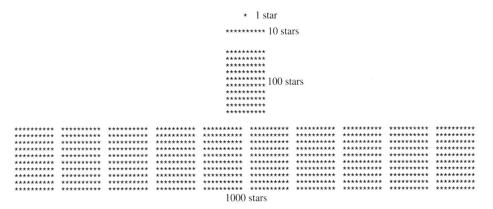

1. How many pieces of paper will Mrs. Kubrick need to show 100,000 stars?

2. How many pieces of paper will Mrs. Kubrick need to show 1,000,000 stars?

3. Mrs. Kubrick's students really want to see one billion stars. How many pieces of paper would Mrs. Kubrick need to show one billion stars?

   A standard package of paper contains 500 sheets. How many packages of paper would Mrs. Kubrick need to show one billion stars? Realistically, can Mrs. Kubrick show one billion stars?

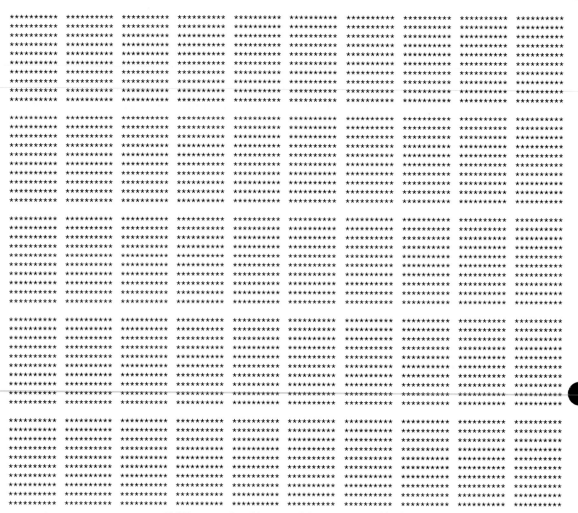

10,000 stars total on this page and the next page combined

FIGURE 2.1
5000 Stars

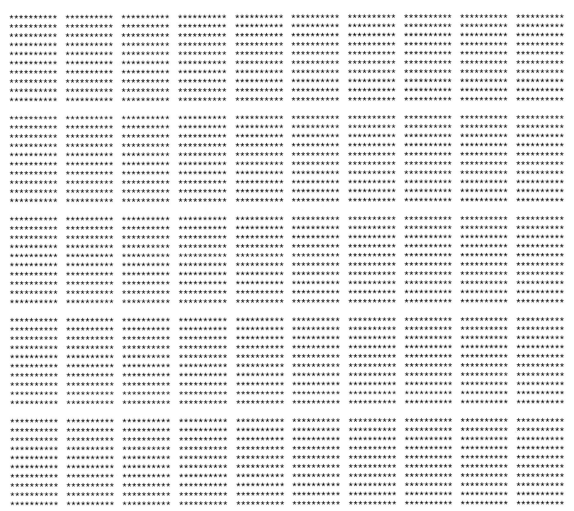

10,000 stars total on this page and the previous page combined

FIGURE 2.2

5000 More Stars

2.3   Representing Decimal Numbers

CLASS ACTIVITY 2C: Representing Decimal Numbers with Physical Objects

1. List at least three different decimal numbers that the blocks pictured below could represent. In each case, state the value of the smallest block.

2. Use either money, bundled toothpicks, or base ten blocks to represent the decimal numbers below. Draw rough pictures to show how you represented these decimal numbers.

    1.2

    1.25

    125

    .034

    .0034

3. Children sometimes mistakenly read the number 1001 as "one hundred one." Why do you think a child would make such a mistake? Draw pictures that indicate how to represent 1001 with either bundled toothpicks or base ten blocks.

4. Explain why the bagged and loose toothpicks pictured below do not represent a decimal number in the manner described in Section **??** of the text. How might you alter the appearance of these bagged and loose toothpicks so that the same total number of toothpicks *does* represent a decimal number?

5. Is it possible to represent the decimal number .1212121212..., where the 1, 2 pattern continues forever, with bundled toothpicks? Why or why not?

CLASS ACTIVITY 2D: Decimal Numbers on Number Lines

1. Label the tick marks on the number lines that follow with appropriate decimal numbers. The second, third, and fourth number lines should be labeled as if they are "zoomed in" on the indicated portion of the previous number line.

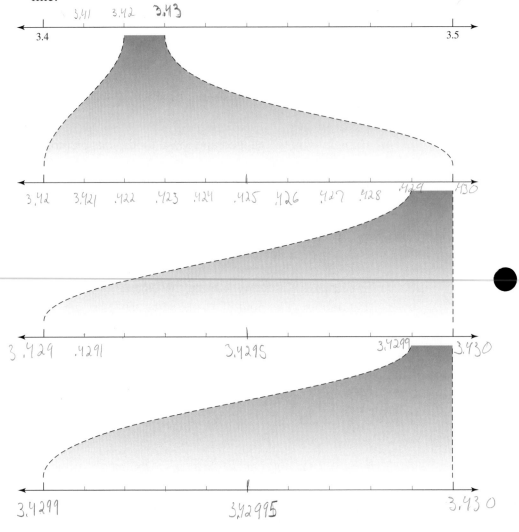

2. Label the tick marks on the next three number lines in three different ways. In each case, your labeling should fit with the fact that the tick marks at the ends of the number lines are longer than the other tick marks. You may further lengthen the tick marks at either end as needed. It may help you to think about "zooming in" on the number line.

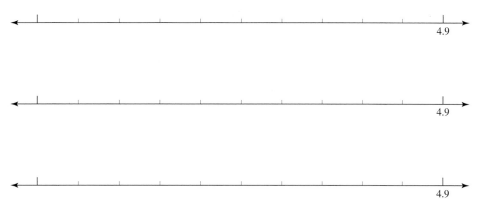

3. Label the tick marks on the next three number lines in three different ways. In each case, your labeling should fit with the fact that the tick marks at the ends of the number lines are longer than the other tick marks. You may further lengthen the tick marks at either end as needed. It may help you to think about "zooming in" on the number line.

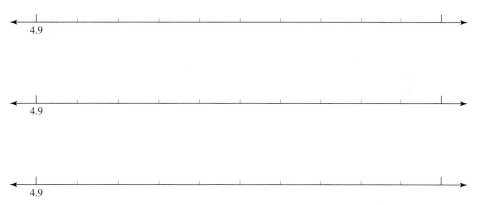

4. Label the tick marks on the next set of number lines with appropriate decimal numbers. Notice that the tick marks on the right and left ends of the number lines are longer than the other tick marks. Therefore, if we think of decimal numbers on number lines as plotted in stages, the decimal numbers plotted at the ends would have been plotted at an earlier stage than those plotted in the middle.

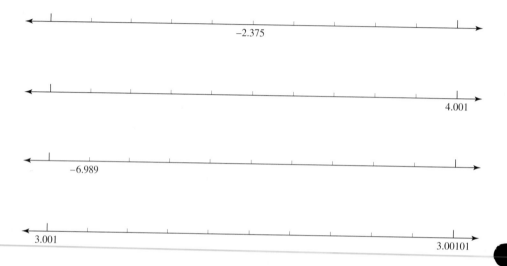

5. Josh says that the unlabeled tick mark on the next number line should be 2.10. Why might Josh think this? Explain to Josh why he is not correct. Describe how you could use physical objects to help Josh determine the correct answer.

2.0   2.1   2.2   2.3   2.4   2.5   2.6   2.7   2.8   2.9

6. Cierral plots the decimal number 7.001 in the location shown on the number line that follows. Is the label legitimate? If so, how should Cierral label the other tick marks? Do any of the tick marks shown need to be lengthened?

7   7.001

Can Cierral plot this ——
decimal here?

7. Juan plots the decimal number 9.999 in the location shown on the number line that follows. Is this label legitimate? If so, how should Juan label the other tick marks? Do any of the tick marks shown need to be lengthened?

9.999   10

—— Can Juan plot this
decimal here?

8. Label the tick marks on the next number line so that the decimal numbers −12.3 and −17 can both be plotted visibly and distinctly. The distance between adjacent tick marks should be a power of ten, such as 0.1, 0.01, or 0.001. The numbers do not necessarily have to fall on tick marks. Plot the two decimal numbers.

9. Label the tick marks on the next number line so that the decimal numbers 4.3572 and 4.3586 can both be plotted visibly and distinctly. The distance between adjacent tick marks should be a power of ten, such as 0.1, 0.01, 0.001, and so on. The numbers do not necessarily have to fall on tick marks. Plot the two decimal numbers.

10. Label the tick marks on the next number line so that the decimal numbers 18.977145 and 18.977638 can both be plotted visibly and distinctly. The distance between adjacent tick marks should be a power of ten, such as 0.1, 0.01, 0.001, and so on. The numbers do not necessarily have to fall on tick marks. Plot the two decimal numbers.

2.4 Comparing Sizes of Decimal Numbers

CLASS ACTIVITY 2E: Finding Smaller and Smaller Decimal Numbers

You can play the following game alone, or with two or more people or teams.

Start by picking any two decimal numbers. Call the lesser one the *target decimal number*. Put the greater decimal number at the top of a list. Take turns placing new decimal numbers on the list. Each new decimal number placed on the list must be *less than* the previous decimal number on the list, but *greater than* the target decimal number. You score a point when you are the first to catch an opponent's mistake.

For example: starting decimal numbers 2, 2.491
Target decimal number: 2
The first few entries in the list could be as follows:

$$2.491$$
$$2.37$$
$$2.085$$
$$2.01$$

1. Play the game several times. Each person should take at least 5 turns each time.

2. Is it possible for the game to be *forced* to end, or is it always possible to continue playing if you want to?

3. Is there a least decimal number that is greater than 2? If yes, show it; if no, explain why not.

CLASS ACTIVITY 2F: Finding Decimals between Decimals

Two people or two teams can play the following game.

Team 1 goes first and picks a decimal number between 1 and 2. Team 2 then picks a different decimal number between 1 and 2. Each team writes its decimal number on a list. For example, the starting lists might look like this:

Team 1: 1.3

Team 2: 1.4

Team 1 takes a turn and writes on its list a new decimal number that is between the decimal numbers on the two lists. Continuing the previous example, Team 1 could write 1.39 on its list because 1.39 is between 1.3 and 1.4. Thus, the two teams' lists would appear as follows:

Team 1: 1.3, 1.39

Team 2: 1.4

Then Team 2 takes a turn and writes on its list a new decimal number that is between the last decimal numbers on the two lists. Continuing the example, Team 2 could write 1.391 on its list because 1.391 is between 1.39 and 1.4:

Team 1: 1.3, 1.39

Team 2: 1.4, 1.391

The teams continue to take turns writing decimal numbers on their lists. The decimal number written on the list must be between the last decimal numbers on the two lists.

A team scores a point when it is the first to catch a mistake made by its opponent.

The game ends when each team has 6 numbers on its list.

1. Play the game several times.

2. Is it possible for the game to be *forced* to end early, or is it always possible for each team to write 6 numbers on its list? Could teams keep playing and write more than 6 numbers on their lists? If so, is there a limit to how many numbers the teams could write on their lists?

3. Is there a decimal number that is "right next to" 1.1? Explain your answer, and explain how you interpret the meaning of "right next to."

CLASS ACTIVITY 2G: Decimals between Decimals on Number Lines

For each of the following pairs of numbers, find a decimal number in between the two numbers. Label the longer tick marks on the number line so that all three numbers can be plotted visibly and distinctly. The distance between adjacent tick marks should be a power of ten, such as 0.1, 0.01, 0.001, and so on. Plot all three numbers. The numbers need not land on tick marks.

1. The numbers 1.6 and 1.7.

Now, describe how to use money to find a decimal number between 1.6 and 1.7.

2. The numbers 12.54 and 12.541.

3. The numbers 2.781 and 2.7342.

4. The numbers 17.3145 and 17.3146.

5. The numbers 23.99 and 24.

6. The numbers 23 and 23.0001.

7. The numbers $\sqrt{3} = 1.73205080757\ldots$ and 1.732379.

CLASS ACTIVITY 2H: "Greater Than" and "Less Than" with Negative Decimal Numbers

1. Explain in two different ways why a negative decimal number is always less than a positive decimal number.

2. Johnny says that $-5 > -2$. Describe two different ways to explain to Johnny why this is not correct.

2.5   Rounding Decimal Numbers

CLASS ACTIVITY 2I: Explaining Why a Procedure for Rounding Makes Sense

This class activity asks you to explain why a common procedure for rounding decimal numbers makes sense based on the meaning of rounding.

To round a given decimal number to the nearest hundred means to find the decimal number closest to your given decimal number that has only zeros in places smaller than the hundreds place. Ties are broken by rounding up.

We often give the following *procedure* for rounding to the nearest hundred:

- Look at the digit immediately to the right of the hundreds place.

  - If the digit to the right of the hundreds place is 5 or more, add 1 to the digit in the hundreds place. (If the digit in the hundreds place is 9, then change it to 0, and add 1 to the digit in the thousands place—if *that* digit is also a 9, change it to 0, and keep moving to the left, changing 9s to 0s until you get to a digit that is less than 9. Add one to that digit.)

  - If the digit to the right of the hundreds place is less than 5, leave the digit in the hundreds place as is.

- Change all digits to the right of the hundreds place to 0s. Leave all digits to the left of the hundreds place as they are.

(This rule can be modified to become a rule for rounding to the nearest ten, one, tenth, etc., by simply changing each occurrence of hundreds to tens, ones, tenths, etc.)

For example, to round 8346 to the nearest hundred, notice that there is a 4 in the tens place. The digit 4 is less than 5, so round 8346 down to 8300. To round 99,967 to the nearest hundred, notice that there is a 6 in the tens place. The digit 6 is greater than 5, so round 99,967 up to 100,000.

$$83\boxed{4}6 \xrightarrow[\text{Because } 4 < 5, \text{ round down.}]{} 8300$$

$$99,9\boxed{6}7 \xrightarrow[\text{Because } 6 > 5, \text{ round up.}]{} 100,000$$

1. Use the procedure described previously to round the numbers 4163, 4129, 4071, and 3955 to the nearest hundred.

   Then use the following number line to help you explain why the procedure for rounding to the nearest hundred makes sense based on the meaning of rounding to the nearest hundred:

2. Use the procedure described previously to round the numbers 59,995; 59,938; 60,048; and 60,093 to the nearest hundred.

   Then use the following number line to help you explain why the procedure for rounding to the nearest hundred makes sense based on the meaning of rounding to the nearest hundred:

CLASS ACTIVITY 2J: Can We Round This Way?

Maureen has made up her own method of rounding. Starting at the rightmost place in a decimal number, she keeps rounding to the value of the next place to the left until she reaches the place to which the decimal number was to be rounded.

For example, Maureen would use the following steps to round 3.2716 to the nearest tenth:

$$3.2716 \rightarrow 3.272 \rightarrow 3.27 \rightarrow 3.3$$

Try Maureen's method on several examples. Is Maureen's method valid? That is, does it always round decimal numbers correctly? Or are there examples of decimal numbers where Maureen's method does not give the correct rounding?

Chapter 3

Fractions

3.1 The Meaning of Fractions

CLASS ACTIVITY 3A: Fractions of Objects

1. Take a blank piece of paper and fold it so that you can shade $\frac{1}{5}$ of the piece of paper. Do this as carefully and precisely as possible without using a ruler or doing any measuring. Explain how you know that your shaded portion of paper is $\frac{1}{5}$ of the whole paper.

   Are there different ways to show $\frac{1}{5}$ of a piece of paper? That is, could two people show $\frac{1}{5}$ of a piece of paper that look different but are both correct?

2. Take a blank piece of paper and imagine that it is $\frac{4}{5}$ of some larger piece of paper. Fold your piece of paper to show $\frac{3}{5}$ of the larger (imagined) piece of paper. Do this as carefully and precisely as possible without using a ruler or doing any measuring. Explain why your answer is correct. Could two people have different-looking solutions that are both correct?

3. Benton used $\frac{3}{4}$ cup of butter to make a batch of cookie dough. Benton rolled his cookie dough out into a rectangle, as shown in the next figure. Now Benton wants to cut off a piece of the dough so that the portion he cuts off contains $\frac{1}{4}$ cup of butter. How could Benton cut the dough? Explain your answer.

4. The next picture shows two pies of different sizes. Make up a story or situation where you would want to determine $\frac{1}{6}$ of the combined amount of the big pie and the little pie. Using your story or situation, determine $\frac{1}{6}$ of the combined amount of the big pie and the little pie, and shade this amount on the pies in the picture.

5. Shade $\frac{5}{6}$ of the combined amount of the big pie and the little pie shown in the next picture. Use the meaning of fractions to explain why your answer is correct.

6. Mireya has a recipe that calls for 5 cups of flour. Mireya wants to make $\frac{3}{4}$ of the recipe. Instead of figuring out what number $\frac{3}{4}$ of 5 is, Mireya measures $\frac{3}{4}$ of a cup of flour 5 times, and uses this amount of flour for $\frac{3}{4}$ of the recipe. Use the meaning of fractions and the following picture to help you explain why Mireya's strategy is valid:

7. Jenny has a large piece of fabric that she has cut into two pieces: a larger piece and a small piece. By laying the pieces of fabric next to each other, Jenny can tell that the small piece of fabric is the same size as $\frac{2}{3}$ of the large piece. What fraction of the original whole piece of fabric (before cutting) is the small piece of fabric? Use the meaning of fractions and a picture to help you explain why your answer is correct.

CLASS ACTIVITY 3B: The Whole Associated with a Fraction

1. Maurice says that the next picture shows that $\frac{1}{3}$ is bigger than $\frac{1}{2}$. The shaded piece representing $\frac{1}{3}$ *is* larger than the shaded piece representing $\frac{1}{2}$, so why is Maurice not correct?

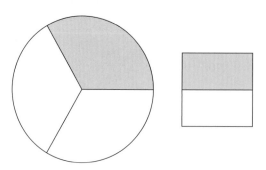

2. Kayla says that the shaded part of the next picture can't represent $\frac{1}{4}$ because there are 3 shaded circles, and 3 is more than 1, but $\frac{1}{4}$ is supposed to be less than 1. What can you tell Kayla about fractions that might help her?

3. When Ted was asked to say what the 4 in the fraction $\frac{3}{4}$ means, Ted said that the 4 is the whole. Explain why it is not completely correct to say, "4 is the whole." What is a better way to say what the 4 in the fraction $\frac{3}{4}$ means?

4. Explain why you can use the fractions in (a), (b), and (c) to describe the shaded region in the next figure. How can three different numbers describe the same shaded region? How must you interpret the shaded region in each case?

a. $\frac{3}{6}$

b. $\frac{3}{2}$

c. $\frac{3}{1}$

5. Suppose a textbook problem asks students to "name the fraction shown in the shaded region of the next figure." Assuming there is no other information given in the problem, explain why the problem is ambiguous. What should the textbook problem clarify?

6. At a neighborhood park, $\frac{1}{3}$ of the area of the park is to be used for a new playground. Swings will be placed on $\frac{1}{4}$ of the area of the playground. What fraction of the neighborhood park will the swing area be? Draw a picture to help you solve the problem and explain your answer. For each fraction in this problem, and in your solution, describe the whole associated with this fraction. In other words, describe what each fraction is *of*. Are all the wholes the same or not?

7. Ben is making a recipe that calls for $\frac{1}{3}$ cup of oil. Ben has a bottle that contains $\frac{2}{3}$ cup of oil. Ben does not have any measuring cups. What fraction of the oil in the bottle should Ben use for his recipe? Draw a picture to help you solve the problem and explain your answer. For each fraction in this problem, and in your solution, describe the whole associated with this fraction. In other words, describe what each fraction is *of*. Are all the wholes the same or not?

CLASS ACTIVITY 3C: Is the Meaning of Equal Parts Always Clear?

1. Matteo says that he can't show $\frac{1}{3}$ of these marbles because some of the marbles are big and some are little. What do you think?

2. A first grade worksheet [6, p. 241] asked children to "show 4 equal parts" and showed a picture like the one on the left in the next figure. Arianna's response is on the right. Although Arianna's work is probably not what the authors had in mind, can it still be considered correct?

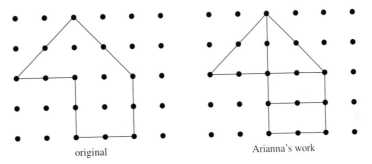

original   Arianna's work

3. The definition of fractions of objects refers to dividing objects into equal parts. Discuss whether the meaning of equal parts is clearly defined in every situation.

CLASS ACTIVITY 3D: Understanding Improper Fractions

1. Enrico says that it doesn't make sense to talk about $\frac{5}{4}$ of a piece of paper because if you divide a piece of paper into 4 equal pieces, then you only have 4 pieces and can't show 5 pieces. What can you tell Enrico that might help him?

2. Show a plot of land that is $\frac{5}{3}$ the area shown on the map in the next figure. Is more than one correct answer possible?

3. On day 1, Denise runs a distance shown on the next diagram. On day 2, Denise runs $\frac{5}{4}$ as far. Show how far Denise runs on day 2. On day 3, Denise runs $\frac{4}{5}$ as far as she ran on day 2. Show how far Denise runs on day 3. Compare the distance Denise ran on day 3 with the distance she ran on day 1. For each fraction in this problem, and in your solution, describe the associated whole. In other words, describe what each fraction is *of*.

———————————————

Denise's running distance

3.2 Equivalent Fractions

CLASS ACTIVITY 3E: Equivalent Fractions

1. Use the meaning of fractions of objects to give a detailed conceptual explanation for why

$$\frac{2}{3}$$

   of a pie is the same amount of pie as

$$\frac{2 \cdot 4}{3 \cdot 4}$$

   of the pie, which is

$$\frac{8}{12}$$

   of the pie. Draw pictures to support your explanation. Discuss how your pictures show the process of multiplying both the numerator and denominator of $\frac{2}{3}$ by 4.

2. Discuss how to modify your explanation for Problem 1 to show that

$$\frac{2}{3}$$

   of a pie is the same amount of pie as

$$\frac{2 \cdot 5}{3 \cdot 5}$$

   of the pie, which is

$$\frac{10}{15}$$

   of the pie.

3. Use the meaning of fractions to explain why

$$\frac{2}{3}$$

of a pie is the same amount of pie as

$$\frac{2 \cdot 127}{3 \cdot 127}$$

of the same pie.

4. Suppose A and B are whole numbers and B is not 0. Also suppose that N is any natural number. Explain why

$$\frac{A}{B}$$

of some object is the same amount of that object as

$$\frac{A \cdot N}{B \cdot N}$$

of the object.

CLASS ACTIVITY 3F: Misconceptions about Fraction Equivalence

1. Anna says,

$$\frac{2}{3} = \frac{6}{7}$$

because starting with $\frac{2}{3}$, you get $\frac{6}{7}$ by adding 4 to the top and the bottom. If you do the same thing to the top and the bottom, the fractions must be equal.

Is Anna right? If not, why not? How might Anna have come up with her rule?

2. Don says that

$$\frac{11}{12} = \frac{16}{17}$$

because both fractions are one part away from a whole. Is Don correct? If not, what is wrong with Don's reasoning?

CLASS ACTIVITY 3G: Common Denominators

1. Write $\frac{1}{2}$ and $\frac{2}{3}$ with two different common denominators. Show each on the pies in the next diagram. In terms of the pictures, what are we doing when we give the two fractions common denominators?

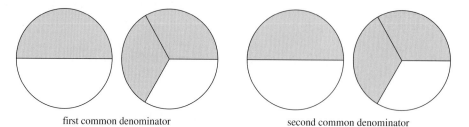

first common denominator   second common denominator

2. Write $\frac{1}{3}$ and $\frac{3}{4}$ with two different common denominators. Show each on the rectangles in the next figure. In terms of the pictures, what are we doing when we give the two fractions common denominators?

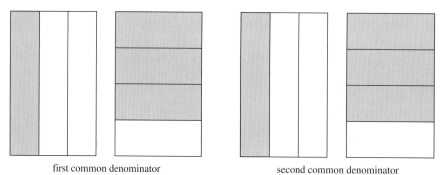

first common denominator   second common denominator

CLASS ACTIVITY 3H: Solving Problems by Changing Denominators

1. Take a blank piece of paper and imagine that it is $\frac{2}{3}$ of some larger piece of paper. Fold your piece of paper to show $\frac{1}{6}$ of the larger (imagined) piece of paper. Do this as carefully and precisely as possible without using a ruler or doing any measuring. Explain why your answer is correct.

   In solving this problem, how does $\frac{2}{3}$ appear in a different form?

   Could two people have different solutions that are both correct?

2. Jeremy first put $\frac{3}{4}$ cup of butter in the sauce he is making. Then Jeremy added another $\frac{1}{3}$ of a cup of butter. How much butter is in Jeremy's sauce? Draw pictures to help you solve this problem. Explain why your answer is correct.

   In solving the problem, how do $\frac{3}{4}$ and $\frac{1}{3}$ appear in different forms?

   For each fraction in this problem, and in your solution, describe the whole associated with this fraction. In other words, describe what each fraction is *of*.

3. Jean has a casserole recipe that calls for $\frac{1}{2}$ cup of butter. Jean only has $\frac{1}{3}$ cup of butter. Assuming that Jean has enough of the other ingredients, what fraction of the casserole recipe can Jean make? Draw pictures to help you solve this problem. Explain why your answer is correct.

In solving this problem, how do $\frac{1}{2}$ and $\frac{1}{3}$ appear in different forms?

For each fraction in this problem, and in your solution, describe the whole associated with this fraction. In other words, describe what each fraction is *of*.

4. One serving of SugarBombs cereal is $\frac{3}{4}$ cup. Joey wants to eat $\frac{1}{2}$ of a serving of SugarBombs cereal. How much of a cup of cereal should Joey eat? Draw pictures to help you solve this problem. Explain why your answer is correct.

In solving the problem, how does $\frac{3}{4}$ appear in a different form?

For each fraction in this problem, and in your solution, describe the whole associated with this fraction. In other words, describe what each fraction is *of*.

CLASS ACTIVITY 31: Simplifying Fractions

1. Use the next diagram to help you explain why the following equations that put $\frac{6}{15}$ in simplest form make sense:

$$\frac{6}{15} = \frac{2 \cdot 3}{5 \cdot 3} = \frac{2}{5}$$

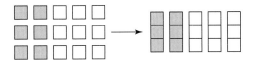

2. Use blocks or snap-together cubes in two different colors, or draw pictures to help you demonstrate why the following equations that put $\frac{8}{12}$ in simplest form make sense:

$$\frac{8}{12} = \frac{2 \cdot 4}{3 \cdot 4} = \frac{2}{3}$$

3. Show two different ways to write equations that put $\frac{12}{18}$ in simplest form. (One way can take several steps to simplify the fraction.)

4. Use blocks or snap-together cubes in two different colors, or draw pictures to help you explain why your equations in part (3) make sense.

CLASS ACTIVITY 3J: When Can We "Cancel" to Get an Equivalent Fraction?

Some people say that

$$\frac{20}{30} = \frac{2}{3}$$

because you can "cancel the zeros" in $\frac{20}{30}$:

$$\frac{2\cancel{0}}{3\cancel{0}}$$

But if you can "cancel the zeros" in $\frac{20}{30}$, then why can't you "cancel the 5s" in

$$\frac{52}{53}$$

and say that

$$\frac{52}{53} = \frac{2}{3}?$$

Can you "cancel the 5s" in

$$\frac{25}{35}$$

and say that

$$\frac{25}{35} = \frac{2}{3}?$$

What is a better way to explain why

$$\frac{20}{30} = \frac{2}{3}$$

than saying that we "cancel the zeros?" What are you really doing when you "cancel the zeros?"

3.3 Fractions as Numbers

CLASS ACTIVITY 3K: Improper Fractions Revisited

1. Discuss the meaning of improper fractions such as $\frac{3}{2}$ and $\frac{5}{4}$ by referring to objects and pictures.

2. If you have only one pie, would it be good to use this pie to talk about the fraction $\frac{5}{4}$? What kinds of things are useful for discussing improper fractions such as $\frac{5}{4}$? Explain.

3. Suppose you use a picture like the next one to talk about the fraction $\frac{5}{4}$. What kind of confusion could arise about this picture? What must we do in order to interpret the shaded region as $\frac{5}{4}$?

4. Now use number lines to discuss the meaning of improper fractions such as $\frac{3}{2}$ and $\frac{5}{4}$.

5. What are the advantages and disadvantages of using objects and pictures to discuss improper fractions? What are the advantages and disadvantages of using number lines to discuss improper fractions?

CLASS ACTIVITY 3L: Plotting Fractions on Number Lines

1. Plot 0, 1, $\frac{1}{4}$, $\frac{7}{4}$, and $\frac{11}{4}$ on the number line for this problem in such a way that each number falls on a tick mark. Lengthen the tick marks of whole numbers.

2. Plot 1, $\frac{2}{3}$, and $\frac{5}{2}$ on the number line for this problem in such a way that each number falls on a tick mark. Lengthen the tick marks of whole numbers.

3. Plot 9, $\frac{55}{6}$ and $\frac{33}{4}$ on the number line for this problem in such a way that each number falls on a tick mark. Lengthen the tick marks of whole numbers.

4. Plot 1, .7, and $\frac{3}{4}$ on the number line for this problem in such a way that each number falls on a tick mark. Lengthen the tick marks of whole numbers.

5. Label the longer tick marks on the number line for this problem so that you can plot $\frac{21}{13}$ and $\frac{55}{34}$ visibly and distinctly. The distance between adjacent tick marks should be a power of ten, such as 0.1, 0.01, 0.001, and so on. Plot both numbers.

CLASS ACTIVITY 3M: Fractions of Line Segments

There is a simple way to divide line segments into equal parts without measuring the length of the line segment. Cut a wide rubber band so that it forms a strip of rubber. Using a ruler, make equally spaced marks on the rubber strip (you might want to stretch the rubber band while doing this to make the marks clearer). Good spacings to use are $\frac{1}{8}$ or $\frac{1}{4}$ of an inch or $\frac{1}{2}$ of a centimeter. To divide a line segment into, say, 5 equal pieces, stretch your marked band so that 5 intervals on the band are the same length as your line segment. The following problems can be done with or without a marked rubber band.

a rubber band, cut open, with equally spaced markings

To divide a line segment into 5 parts, stretch 5 parts
of the band across the line segment.

1. The line segment below is 1 unit long. If available, a marked rubber band can be used to construct a line segment of length $\frac{5}{4}$ units. Otherwise, explain how to subdivide the line segment and possibly add pieces to the line segment to create a segment of length $\frac{5}{4}$ units. Explain how you know your line segment is the correct length.

1 unit

2. The line segment below has length $\frac{3}{2}$ unit. If available, a marked rubber band can be used to construct a line segment of length 1 unit. Otherwise, explain how to subdivide the line segment and possibly add pieces to the line segment to create a segment of length 1 unit. Explain how you know your line segment is the correct length.

$\frac{3}{2}$ unit

3. The line segment below has length $\frac{3}{4}$ unit. If available, a marked rubber band can be used to construct a line segment of length 1 unit. Otherwise, explain how to subdivide the line segment and possibly add pieces to the line segment to create a segment of length 1 unit. Explain how you know your segment is the correct length.

_____
$\frac{3}{4}$ unit

4. The line segment below has length $\frac{4}{5}$ unit. If available, a marked rubber band can be used to construct a line segment of length $\frac{3}{5}$ unit. Otherwise, explain how to subdivide the line segment and possibly add pieces to the line segment to create a segment of length $\frac{3}{5}$ unit. Explain how you know your segment is the correct length.

_____
$\frac{4}{5}$ unit

5. The line segment below has length $\frac{2}{3}$ unit. If available, a marked rubber band can be used to construct a line segment of length $\frac{3}{4}$ unit. Otherwise, explain how to subdivide the line segment and possibly add pieces to the line segment to create a segment of length $\frac{3}{4}$ unit. In either case, do not create a segment of length 1 unit. Explain how you know your segment is the correct length.

_____
$\frac{2}{3}$ unit

6. The line segment below has length $\frac{1}{2}$ unit. If available, a marked rubber band can be used to construct a line segment of length $\frac{3}{5}$ unit. Otherwise, explain how to subdivide the line segment and possibly add pieces to the line segment to create a segment of length $\frac{3}{5}$ unit. In either case, do not create a segment of length 1 unit. Explain how you know your segment is the correct length.

_____
$\frac{1}{2}$ unit

3.4 Comparing Sizes of Fractions

CLASS ACTIVITY 3N: Can We Compare Fractions This Way?

You will need a calculator for part (1a) of this activity.

1. One method for comparing fractions is to determine the decimal representation of each fraction and to compare the decimal numbers.

    When you are asked to compare two fractions to see whether they are equal, your first inclination might be to use a calculator to divide, converting each fraction to a decimal number, so that you can compare the decimal numbers. This usually works well, but watch out, because calculators can only display so many digits.

    Compare

    $$\frac{111,111,111,111}{1,000,000,000,000} \quad \text{and} \quad \frac{111,111,111,111}{999,999,999,999}$$

    by dividing, thereby converting both fractions to decimal numbers. Use a calculator for the second fraction. (If your calculator only holds 8 digits, then work with the fractions $\frac{11,111,111}{100,000,000}$ and $\frac{11,111,111}{99,999,999}$ instead.)

    a. According to your calculator's display, do the two fractions above appear to be equal?

    b. In fact, *are* the two fractions above equal? If not, which is bigger and why? Explain this using the meaning of fractions.

2. Claire says that

$$\frac{4}{9} > \frac{3}{8}$$

because

$$4 > 3 \quad \text{and} \quad 9 > 8$$

Discuss whether or not Claire's reasoning is correct.

3. Conrad says that

$$\frac{4}{11} > \frac{3}{8}$$

because

$$4 > 3 \quad \text{and} \quad 11 > 8$$

Discuss whether or not Conrad's reasoning is correct.

CLASS ACTIVITY 30: Comparing Fractions by Reasoning

Use reasoning other than finding common denominators, cross-multiplying, or converting to decimal numbers to compare the sizes (=, <, or >) of the following pairs of fractions.

$$\boxed{\frac{7}{37}} > \frac{7}{45} \quad \text{Bigger}$$

$$\frac{27}{43} > \frac{26}{45} \qquad 43\overline{)270}^{.627} \quad \text{or} \quad 45\overline{)260}^{.5777}$$

$$\frac{13}{25} > \frac{34}{70} \qquad 25\overline{)130}^{.52} \quad \text{or} \quad 70\overline{)340}^{.0428}$$

$$\frac{17}{18} < \frac{19}{20} \qquad \text{18 in bigger parts so the 1 part missing is bigger}$$

$$\frac{1}{4}\frac{11}{44} < \frac{12}{44} \qquad \times \text{ by 11}$$

$$\frac{51}{53} < \frac{65}{67} \qquad 53 \text{ is a bigger part}$$

$$\frac{16}{144} = \frac{5}{45}$$

$$^{12.5}\frac{13}{25} < \frac{5}{8}^{4.}$$

CLASS ACTIVITY 3P: Rules for Comparing Fractions

In your own words, explain why the following rules for comparing fractions $\frac{A}{B}$ and $\frac{C}{D}$ are true:

$$\frac{A}{B} = \frac{C}{D} \quad \text{exactly when} \quad A \cdot D = C \cdot B$$

$$\frac{A}{B} > \frac{C}{D} \quad \text{exactly when} \quad A \cdot D > C \cdot B$$

$$\frac{A}{B} < \frac{C}{D} \quad \text{exactly when} \quad A \cdot D < C \cdot B$$

3.5 Percent

CLASS ACTIVITY 3Q: Pictures and Percentages

1. For each of the diagrams in Figure 3.1, determine the percent of the diagram
    that is shaded. Give your answer rounded to the nearest multiple of 5, (i.e.,
    5, 10, 15, 20, 25, . . .) and explain your reasoning.

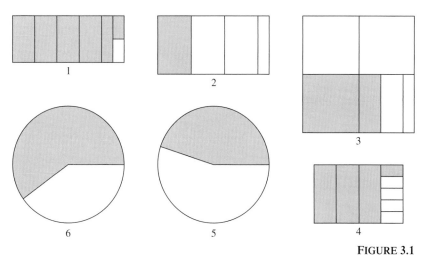

FIGURE 3.1

What Percent of Each Shape Is Shaded?

2. Use a common fraction to help you accurately shade 75% of the region
    inside the circle in the next diagram. Then shade 85% of the circle as
    accurately as you can. Describe your strategy for shading 85% of the
    circle.

3. Use a common fraction to help you determine how to accurately shade 12.5% of the region inside the following circle:

4. Show 125% of the region inside the rectangle that follows as accurately as you can. It may help you to use common fractions.

5. Show 125% of the line segment that follows. Then show 80% of your new line segment. It may help you to use common fractions. How does your final line segment compare with the original line segment?

CLASS ACTIVITY 3R: Calculating Percentages by Using Nearby Common Fractions

Some percentage problems can be made easy to solve mentally by working with a common fraction that is close to the percentage. Pictures can help you understand this technique.

1. Mentally calculate 95% of 80,000 by calculating $\frac{1}{10}$ of 80,000, calculating half of that result, and then taking this last amount away from 80,000. Use the following picture to help you explain why this method makes sense.

2. Mentally calculate 15% of 6500 by first calculating $\frac{1}{10}$ of 6500. Use the following picture to help you explain why this method makes sense.

3. Mentally calculate 60% of 810 by first calculating $\frac{1}{2}$ of 810. Use the following picture to help you explain why this method makes sense.

4. Mentally calculate 55% of 180. Explain why your method makes sense.

5. Mentally determine what percent 660 is of 1200 by first observing that $\frac{1}{2}$ of 1200 is 600. Explain why this method makes sense.

6. Mentally calculate 35% of 160 by first calculating $\frac{1}{4}$ of 160. Explain why this method makes sense.

7. Mentally calculate 35% of 160 in a different way than in part (6). Explain why your method makes sense.

8. Mentally calculate 85% of 120 in two different ways. Explain why your methods make sense.

9. Use a common fraction to help you mentally determine approximately what percent 310 is of 680. Explain why your method makes sense.

10. Use a common fraction to help you mentally determine approximately what percent 1300 is of 4800. Explain why your method makes sense.

CLASS ACTIVITY 3S: Calculations with Percents

1. Suppose that at a certain location, the average daily rainfall in September is $\frac{5}{8}$ of an inch. Last year, the average daily rainfall at that location in September was only $\frac{3}{8}$ of an inch. What percent of the average September daily rainfall fell last year in September? First solve the problem by drawing a picture. Explain how your picture helps you solve the problem. Then solve the problem numerically.

2. Lenny has received 6 boxes of paper, which is 30% of the paper he ordered. How many boxes of paper did Lenny order? First solve the problem by drawing a picture. Explain how your picture helps you solve the problem. Then solve the problem numerically.

3. If 95% of 40,000 voters voted for a referendum, then how many people voted for the referendum? First solve the problem by drawing a picture. Explain how your picture helps you solve the problem. Then solve the problem numerically.

4. A company has bought 3.4 acres of land out of the 4 acres of land that it plans to buy. What percent of the land has the company already bought? First solve the problem by working with common fractions and by drawing a picture. Explain how your picture helps you solve the problem. Then solve the problem numerically.

5. The mayor says that $3.6 million dollars have been spent and that this represents 75% of the money allocated for a project. What was the total amount of money that was allocated for the project? First solve the problem by drawing a picture. Explain how your picture helps you solve the problem. Then solve the problem numerically.

6. Sixty percent of a city's population of 84,000 people live within 5 miles of the library. How many people live within 5 miles of the library? First solve the problem by drawing a picture. Explain how your picture helps you solve the problem. Then solve the problem numerically.

Chapter 4

Addition and Subtraction

4.1 Interpretations of Addition and Subtraction

CLASS ACTIVITY 4A: The Shopkeeper's Method of Making Change

When a patron of a store gives a shopkeeper A for a B purchase, we can think of the change owed to a patron as what is left from A when B are taken away.

In contrast, the shopkeeper might make change by starting with B and handing the customer money while adding on the amounts until they reach A.

1. Describe in detail how a shopkeeper could use this method to give a patron change from a $10 bill on a $3.26 purchase.

2. Describe in detail how a shopkeeper could use this method to give a patron change from a $20 bill on a $7.43 purchase.

   start ab 7.43   − 2 dollars = 10.0
   − 2 pennys = 7.45   − 1 10$ bill = [20.00]
   − nickle = 7.50   what was given
   −2 quarters = 8.00

3. Reconcile the method used by shopkeepers with the view that change is what is left from A when B are taken away. Why is the shopkeeper's method for making change valid?

4.2 Why the Standard Algorithms for Adding and Subtracting Decimal Numbers Work

CLASS ACTIVITY 4B: Understanding the Standard Addition Algorithm

1. Add the following numbers, using the standard paper-and-pencil method. Notice that regrouping is involved.

$$
\begin{array}{r}
147 \\
+\ 195 \\
\hline
\end{array}
$$

2. Use bundles of toothpicks (or other objects) to solve the addition problem $147 + 195$. Draw pictures to show the regrouping process.

3. As in the text, use expanded forms to solve the previous addition problem. First add like terms, and then rewrite (regroup) the resulting number so that it is the expanded form of a number. This rewriting is the regrouping process.

$$1(100) + 4(10) + 7(1)$$
$$+ \ 1(100) + 9(10) + 5(1)$$

← First add like terms, remaining in expanded form.

← Then regroup so that you have the expanded form of a decimal number. You might want to take several steps to do so, as in the text.

4. Describe any similarities you notice in the different ways (standard method, toothpicks, expanded form) of solving the addition problem.

CLASS ACTIVITY 4C: Understanding the Standard Subtraction Algorithm

1. Subtract the following numbers, using the standard paper-and-pencil method. Notice that regrouping is required.

$$\begin{array}{r} 125 \\ -\ \ 68 \\ \hline \end{array}$$

2. Use bundles of toothpicks (or other objects) to solve the subtraction problem 125 − 68, as described in the text. Draw pictures to show how to regroup the 125 toothpicks.

3. As in the text, solve the same subtraction problem, but now use expanded forms. Start by rewriting the number 125 in expanded form. Rewrite the number in several steps, as in the text. This rewriting is the regrouping process.

$$125 = 1(100) + 2(10) + 5(1) =$$

Write your regrouped number here $\rightarrow$

Subtract 68: $- [6(10) + 8(1)]$

4. Describe any similarities you notice in the different ways (standard method, toothpicks, expanded form) of solving the subtraction problem.

CLASS ACTIVITY 4D: Subtracting across Zeros

Some subtraction problems require regrouping "across a 0," as does the problem

$$
\begin{array}{r}
203 \\
- \ \ 86 \\
\hline
\end{array}
$$

Some people like to replace an intermediate 0 with a 9 when regrouping:

$$
\begin{array}{r}
203 \\
- \ \ 86 \\
\hline
\end{array}
\quad \rightarrow \quad
\begin{array}{r}
{\scriptstyle 1\,9\,13} \\
2\!\!\!/0\!\!\!/3 \\
- \ \ 86 \\
\hline
117
\end{array}
$$

Others prefer to regroup in two steps, first changing an intermediate 0 to a 10 and then changing the 10 to a 9:

$$
\begin{array}{r}
203 \\
- \ \ 86 \\
\hline
\end{array}
\rightarrow
\begin{array}{r}
{\scriptstyle 1\,10} \\
2\!\!\!/0\!\!\!/3 \\
- \ \ 86 \\
\hline
\end{array}
\rightarrow
\begin{array}{r}
{\scriptstyle 9} \\
{\scriptstyle 1\,10\,13} \\
2\!\!\!/0\!\!\!/3 \\
- \ \ 86 \\
\hline
117
\end{array}
$$

1. Explain why the first regrouping method described is just a shortcut of the second method.

2. Using bundled toothpicks, explain why both of the regrouping methods described make sense.

3. Subtract the following numbers, using either one of the two regrouping methods just described. By describing the procedure you use in terms of bundled toothpicks, explain why the procedure makes sense.

$$\begin{array}{r} 1002 \\ -\ \ 248 \\ \hline \end{array}$$

4. David solves the subtraction problem $203 - 7$ as follows:

$$\begin{array}{r} {}^{1}\ \ {}^{13} \\ 20\not{3} \\ -\ \ \ \ 7 \\ \hline 106 \end{array}$$

What mistake is David making? Explain why David's method is incorrect.

CLASS ACTIVITY 4E: Regrouping with Dozens and Dozens of Dozens

When we regroup decimal numbers we use the base-10 structure of place value: the value of each place is 10 times the value of the next place to the right. We can also use the regrouping idea in other situations, for example when objects are bundled in groups of a dozen instead of in groups of 10. The following problem asks you to regroup with dozens and dozens of dozens:

A store owner buys small, novelty party favors in bags of one dozen and boxes of one dozen bags (for a total of 144 favors in a box). The store owner has 5 boxes, 4 bags, and 3 individual party favors at the start of the month. At the end of the month, the store owner has 2 boxes, 9 bags, and 7 individual party favors left. How many favors did the store owner sell? Give the answer in terms of boxes, bags, and individual favors.

Solve this problem by working with a sort of *expanded form* for these party favors—in other words, working with the following representation:

$$5(\text{boxes}) + 4(\text{bags}) + 3(\text{individual})$$
$$2(\text{boxes}) + 9(\text{bags}) + 7(\text{individual})$$

Solve this problem by regrouping among the boxes, bags, and individual party favors.

CLASS ACTIVITY 4F: Regrouping with Seconds, Minutes, and Hours

When we regroup decimal numbers we use the base-10 structure of place value: the value of each place is 10 times the value of the next place to the right. We can also use the regrouping idea in other situations, for example with time. Just as 1 hundred is 10 tens and 1 ten is 10 ones, one hour is 60 minutes and one minute is 60 seconds. The following problem asks you to regroup among hours, minutes, and seconds:

Ruth runs around a lake two times. The first time takes 1 hour, 43 minutes, and 38 seconds. The second time takes 1 hour, 48 minutes, and 29 seconds. What is Ruth's total time for the two laps? Give the answer in hours, minutes, and seconds.

Solve this problem by working with a sort of *expanded form* for time, in other words, by working with

$$1(\text{hour}) + 43(\text{minutes}) + 38(\text{seconds})$$
$$1(\text{hour}) + 48(\text{minutes}) + 29(\text{seconds})$$

Solve this problem by regrouping among hours, minutes, and seconds.

4.3 Adding And Subtracting Fractions

CLASS ACTIVITY 4G: Are These Story Problems for $\frac{1}{2} + \frac{1}{3}$?

For each of the following story problems, determine whether the problem can be solved by adding $\frac{1}{2} + \frac{1}{3}$. If not, explain why not, and explain how the problem should be solved if there is enough information to do so. If there is not enough information to solve the problem, explain why not.

1. Tom pours $\frac{1}{2}$ cup of water into an empty bowl. Then Tom pours $\frac{1}{3}$ cup of water into the bowl. How many cups of water are in the bowl now?

    $\frac{3}{6} + \frac{2}{6} = \frac{5}{6}$ cups

2. Tom pours $\frac{1}{2}$ cup of water into an empty bowl. Then Tom pours in another $\frac{1}{3}$. How many cups of water are in the bowl now?

3. Starting at her apartment, Sally runs $\frac{1}{2}$ mile down the road. Then Sally turns around and runs $\frac{1}{3}$ mile back towards her apartment. How far has Sally run since leaving her apartment?

4. Starting at her apartment, Sally runs $\frac{1}{2}$ mile down the road. Then Sally turns around and runs $\frac{1}{3}$ mile back towards her apartment. How far down the road is Sally from her apartment?

    subtraction

5. $\frac{1}{2}$ of the land in Heeltoe County is covered with forest. $\frac{1}{3}$ of the land in the adjacent Toejoint County is covered with forest. What fraction of the land in the two-county Heeltoe–Toejoint region is covered with forest?

    totals are different

6. $\frac{1}{2}$ of the children at Martin Luther King Elementary School say they like to have pizza for lunch. $\frac{1}{3}$ of the children at Martin Luther King Elementary School say they like to have a hamburger for lunch. What fraction of the children at Martin Luther King Elementary School would like to have either pizza or a hamburger for lunch?

7. $\frac{1}{2}$ of the children at Timothy Elementary School like to have pizza for lunch, the other half does not like to have pizza for lunch. Of the children who do not like to have pizza for lunch, $\frac{1}{3}$ like to have a hamburger for lunch. What fraction of the children at Timothy Elementary School like to have either pizza or a hamburger for lunch?

CLASS ACTIVITY 4H: Are These Story Problems for $\frac{1}{2} - \frac{1}{3}$?

For each of the following story problems, determine whether the problem can be solved by subtracting $\frac{1}{2} - \frac{1}{3}$. If not, explain why not, and explain how the problem should be solved if there is enough information to do so. If there is not enough information to solve the problem, explain why not.

1. Zelha pours $\frac{1}{2}$ cup of water into an empty bowl. Then Zelha pours out $\frac{1}{3}$. How much water is in the bowl now?

2. Zelha pours $\frac{1}{2}$ cup of water into an empty bowl. Then Zelha pours out $\frac{1}{3}$ cup of water. How much water is in the bowl now?

3. Zelha pours $\frac{1}{2}$ cup of water into an empty bowl. Then Zelha pours out $\frac{1}{3}$ of the water that is in the bowl. How much water is in the bowl now?

4. Yesterday James ate $\frac{1}{2}$ of a pizza. Today James ate $\frac{1}{3}$ of a pizza of the same size. How much more pizza did James eat yesterday than today?

5. Yesterday James ate $\frac{1}{2}$ of a pizza. Today James ate $\frac{1}{3}$ of the same pizza. Nobody else ate any of that pizza. How much pizza is left?

6. Yesterday James ate $\frac{1}{2}$ of a pizza. Today James ate $\frac{1}{3}$ of the pizza that was left over from yesterday. Nobody else ate any of that pizza. How much pizza is left?

CLASS ACTIVITY 4I: Fraction Addition and Subtraction

1. Use a story problem and a picture or a number line to explain why the procedure for subtracting

$$\frac{3}{4} - \frac{2}{3}$$

   makes sense. In particular, explain why we need common denominators.

2. Use a story problem and a picture or a number line to explain why the procedure for adding

$$\frac{1}{2} + \frac{4}{5}$$

   makes sense. In particular, explain why we need common denominators.

3. When we add fractions, *must* we use the least common denominator? Why or why not? Are there any advantages or disadvantages to using the least common denominator when adding fractions? Illustrate your answers with the example

$$\frac{3}{4} + \frac{1}{6}$$

and with other examples.

4. Patti thinks that it would be easier to add fractions by "adding the tops and adding the bottoms." For example, Patti wants to add $\frac{2}{3}$ and $\frac{4}{5}$ this way:

$$\frac{2}{3} + \frac{4}{5} = \frac{2+4}{3+5} = \frac{6}{8}$$

Patti uses the picture below to explain why her method makes sense. Why is Patti's method not a valid way to add fractions, and why doesn't Patti's picture prove that fractions can be added in her way? Do not just state the proper way to add fractions; explain what is wrong with Patti's reasoning.

CLASS ACTIVITY 4J: Mixed Numbers

1. Draw a picture to show how to convert $2\frac{3}{5}$ to an improper fraction. Relate your picture to the following numerical procedure for converting $2\frac{3}{5}$ to an improper fraction:

$$2\frac{3}{5} = \frac{2 \cdot 5 + 3}{5} = \frac{13}{5}$$

2. Sue showed Ramin the next diagram to explain why $1\frac{3}{4} = \frac{7}{4}$, but Ramin says that it shows $\frac{7}{8}$, not $\frac{7}{4}$. What must Sue and Ramin clarify?

3. Arnold says that $2\frac{2}{3} = \frac{4}{5}$, and he uses the next picture to support his conclusion. What is wrong with Arnold's reasoning? Do not just state the correct way to convert $2\frac{2}{3}$; explain why Arnold's reasoning is not valid.

$2\frac{2}{3}$ Put them together. $\frac{4}{5}$

4. Find at least two different ways to calculate

$$7\frac{1}{3} - 4\frac{2}{5}$$

and to give the answer as a mixed number. In each case, explain why your method makes sense.

4.4 When Do We Add Percentages?

CLASS ACTIVITY 4K: Should We Add These Percentages?

A factory has two vats designed to contain liquid chocolate. At the moment, vat A is 20% full and vat B is 60% full.

1. Explain why we can't calculate the percent of the total capacity for liquid chocolate that the factory currently has by adding $20\% + 60\%$, even though we are combining the amounts of liquid chocolate in the two vats.

2. For each of the three cases in Figure 4.1, determine the percent of its total capacity for liquid chocolate that the factory currently has.

3. Even though this is not a realistic scenario, suppose vat A is huge compared to vat B. Assume that vat A is still 20% full and vat B is still 60% full. Approximately what percent of its total capacity for liquid chocolate would the factory have in this case?

4. Now suppose it's the other way around and vat B is much larger than vat A, but vat A is still 20% full and vat B is still 60% full. Approximately what percent of its total capacity for liquid chocolate would the factory have in this case?

5. Based on your work in parts 1 to 4 above, if you are only given the information that there are two vats, one 20% full and one 60% full, what theoretical range of percentages is possible for the total capacity of liquid chocolate that the factory has?

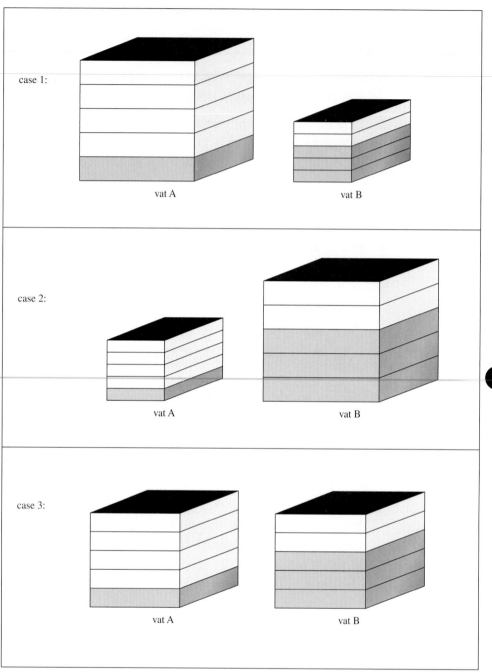

case 1:

vat A   vat B

case 2:

vat A   vat B

case 3:

vat A   vat B

FIGURE 4.1

Vats of Chocolate

4.5 Percent Increase and Percent Decrease

CLASS ACTIVITY 4L: Percent Increase and Decrease

1. Last year's revenues were $7.5 million, this year's revenues are $9 million. By what percent did revenues increase from last year to this year? First solve the problem by drawing a picture. Explain how your picture helps you solve the problem. Then solve the problem numerically.

2. There were 80 gallons of gas in a tank. Now there are only 50 gallons left. By what percent did the amount of gas in the tank decrease? First solve the problem by drawing a picture. Explain how your picture helps you solve the problem. Then solve the problem numerically.

3. The price of a Loungy Chair increased by 40%. The new price is $489.65. What was the price of the Loungy Chair before the increase? Explain why your method of calculation makes sense.

4. The price of a blouse was marked down 15%. The new price is $39.95. What was the price of the blouse before the markdown? Explain why your method of calculation makes sense.

5. Whoopiedoo makeup used to be sold in 4-ounce tubes. Now it's sold in 5-ounce tubes for the same price. Ashlee says the label should read "25% more free," while Carolyn thinks it should read "20% more free." Who is right, who is wrong, and why? Help the person with the incorrect answer understand her error and explain how to correct it. Draw pictures to aid your explanation.

6. The Film Club increased from 63 members to 214 members. By what percent did membership in the Film Club increase?

CLASS ACTIVITY 4M: Percent *Of* versus Percent Increase or Decrease

1. The price of an oven was marked up from $539 to $639. Fill in the blanks and justify your answers.

    a. The new price is ____% of the old price.

    b. The new price is ____% more than the old price.

    c. The old price is ____% lower than the new price.

    d. The old price is ____% of the new price.

    e. Compare your answers to (b) and (c). Why does it make sense that they are *not* the same? (If your answers are the same, go back and rethink your methods.)

2. Explain the difference between the following concepts and give examples to illustrate each one.
    - 200% of an amount

    - a 200% increase in an amount

4.6 The Commutative and Associative Properties of Addition and Mental Math

CLASS ACTIVITY 4N: Mental Math

Try to find ways to make the following problems easy to do *mentally*. In each case, explain your method.

1. $7999 + 857 + 1$

2. $367 + 98 + 2$

3. $153 + 19 + 7$

4. $7.89 + 6.95 + .05$

CLASS ACTIVITY 40: Using Properties of Addition in Mental Math

For each addition problem in this activity, the equations show how one or more property of addition has been used to make the problem easier to do mentally. In each case,

- identify the property or properties that have been used

- describe the strategy that is shown, using groups of marbles, parts of pies, or money.

EXAMPLE:

$$297 + 35 = 297 + (3 + 32)$$
$$= (297 + 3) + 32$$
$$= 300 + 32$$
$$= 332$$

SOLUTION: The associative property was used at the second equal sign to say that

$$297 + (3 + 32) = (297 + 3) + 32$$

If you had 297 marbles and got 35 more marbles, you could first take 3 of the 35 marbles and put them with the 297 marbles to make 300 marbles. Then you could add on the remaining 32 marbles. This shows that you have 332 marbles in all.

1.

$$153 + 19 + 7 = 153 + 7 + 19$$
$$= 160 + 19$$
$$= 179$$

2.

$$687 + 799 = (686 + 1) + 799$$
$$= 686 + (1 + 799)$$
$$= 686 + 800$$
$$= 1486$$

3.

$$2\frac{5}{8} + 6\frac{3}{8} = 2 + \frac{5}{8} + 6 + \frac{3}{8}$$
$$= 2 + 6 + \frac{5}{8} + \frac{3}{8}$$
$$= 8 + 1$$
$$= 9$$

4.

$$3.95 + 2.87 = 3.95 + (.05 + 2.82)$$
$$= (3.95 + .05) + 2.82$$
$$= 4.00 + 2.82$$
$$= 6.82$$

CLASS ACTIVITY 4P: Using Properties of Addition to Aid Learning of Basic Addition Facts

In school, children must learn the basic addition facts from $1 + 1 = 2$ to $10 + 10 = 20$. These are 100 separate facts, but many of these facts are related by properties of addition. By knowing how some facts are related to other facts, children can structure their understanding of the basic facts and can lighten their memorization load.

1. Examine the 4 regions (1 shaded, 3 unshaded) in the addition table in Figure 4.2 on page 79. Describe how the unshaded regions are related to the shaded region and to each other. The shaded region is labeled "core facts" because you can derive the other facts from these core facts.

2. In some countries, children systematically learn to turn an addition problem of the form

   $$\text{smaller number} + \text{larger number}$$

   into a problem of the form

   $$\text{larger number} + \text{smaller number}$$

   and to solve the second problem. For example, if you asked a child to solve $2 + 7$, the child would say

   $$2 + 7 = 7 + 2 = 9$$

   a. Which property of arithmetic does this practice use?

   b. Relate this practice to the addition table on page 79. If children learn this practice then what portion of the addition table must the children focus on memorizing?

3. We can derive each of the facts in the rightmost unshaded region from the core facts (or facts related to core facts by the commutative property) by using the "make-a-10" strategy. For example, to solve $8 + 7$ you can break 7 into $2 + 5$, join the 2 with the 8 to make 10, and add the 5 to make 15. The following dot picture illustrates this strategy:

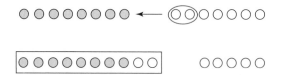

Pick several facts from the rightmost unshaded region of the addition table in Figure 4.2. In each case, do the following:

a. Explain how you can derive that fact from core facts (or facts related to core facts by the commutative property) by using a make-a-10 strategy.

b. Draw a dot picture like the previous one to illustrate the make-a-10 strategy you described in part (a).

c. Write equations that go along with the make-a-10 strategy you described in part (a). Which property of arithmetic does your equation illustrate?

Observe that the make-a-10 strategy requires children to know the core facts "forwards and backwards." In other words, to use the make-a-10 strategy, a child must know not only that $7 + 2 = 9$ but also that 9 decomposes into 7 plus 2 or 2 plus 7.

core facts

1 + 1 = 2	1 + 2	1 + 3	1 + 4	1 + 5	1 + 6	1 + 7	1 + 8	1 + 9	1 + 10
2 + 1 = 3	2 + 2 = 4	2 + 3	2 + 4	2 + 5	2 + 6	2 + 7	2 + 8	2 + 9	2 + 10
3 + 1 = 4	3 + 2 = 5	3 + 3 = 6	3 + 4	3 + 5	3 + 6	3 + 7	3 + 8	3 + 9	3 + 10
4 + 1 = 5	4 + 2 = 6	4 + 3 = 7	4 + 4 = 8	4 + 5	4 + 6	4 + 7	4 + 8	4 + 9	4 + 10
5 + 1 = 6	5 + 2 = 7	5 + 3 = 8	5 + 4 = 9	5 + 5 = 10	5 + 6	5 + 7	5 + 8	5 + 9	5 + 10
6 + 1 = 7	6 + 2 = 8	6 + 3 = 9	6 + 4 = 10	6 + 5	6 + 6	6 + 7	6 + 8	6 + 9	6 + 10
7 + 1 = 8	7 + 2 = 9	7 + 3 = 10	7 + 4	7 + 5	7 + 6	7 + 7	7 + 8	7 + 9	7 + 10
8 + 1 = 9	8 + 2 = 10	8 + 3	8 + 4	8 + 5	8 + 6	8 + 7	8 + 8	8 + 9	8 + 10
9 + 1 = 10	9 + 2	9 + 3	9 + 4	9 + 5	9 + 6	9 + 7	9 + 8	9 + 9	9 + 10
10 + 1 = 11	10 + 2 = 12	10 + 3 = 13	10 + 4 = 14	10 + 5 = 15	10 + 6 = 16	10 + 7 = 17	10 + 8 = 18	10 + 9 = 19	10 + 10 = 20

FIGURE 4.2

Basic Addition Facts

CLASS ACTIVITY 4Q: Writing Correct Equations

The following are hypothetical examples of student work. In each case, the student has a good idea for how to solve the problem, but doesn't use the equal sign correctly. Describe the student's strategy in words and explain briefly why the strategy makes sense. Then rewrite the student's work, using the same ideas, but using the = sign correctly.

1. The problem: $136 + 57$

STUDENT SOLUTION: **YOUR CORRECTION:**
$$136 + 50 = 186 + 7$$
$$= 193$$

2. The problem: $378 - 102$

STUDENT SOLUTION: **YOUR CORRECTION:**
$$378 - 100 = 278 - 2$$
$$= 276$$

3. The problem: $235 - 65$

STUDENT SOLUTION: **YOUR CORRECTION:**
$$235 - 5 = 230 - 30$$
$$= 200 - 30$$
$$= 170$$

4. The problem: $416 + 99$

STUDENT SOLUTION: **YOUR CORRECTION:**
$$416 + 100 = 516 - 1$$
$$= 515$$

5. The problem: $114 - 97$

STUDENT SOLUTION: **YOUR CORRECTION:**
$$97 + 3 = 100 + 14$$
$$= 114$$
So the answer is:
$$3 + 14 = 17$$

CLASS ACTIVITY 4R: Writing Equations That Correspond to a Method of Calculation

Write equations that correspond to the following solution strategies that are described in words. In each case explain briefly why the strategy makes sense. In problems 1 and 2, write your equations in the following form:

$$\begin{aligned} \text{original problem} \quad &= \quad \text{some expression} \\ &= \quad \text{some expression} \\ &= \quad \vdots \\ &= \quad \text{final answer} \end{aligned}$$

1. *Problem:* $268 + 496$
   Solution: $268 + 500 = 768$, but that's 4 too many, so take away 4. The answer is 764.

2. *Problem:* $123 - 58$
   Solution: $120 - 60 = 60$, plus 3 is 63. I took away 2 too many, so add on 2 to make 65.

3. *Problem:* $153 - 76$
   Solution: 76 and 4 make 80, and 20 make 100, and 53 make 153. So the answer is $4 + 20 + 53$, which is 77.

CLASS ACTIVITY 4S: Other Ways to Add and Subtract

1. John and Anne want to solve $253 - 99$ by first solving $253 - 100$. They calculate

$$253 - 100 = 153$$

   John says that they must now *subtract* 1 from 153, but Anne says that they must *add* 1 to 153.

   a. Draw a number line (which need not be perfectly to scale) to help you explain who is right and why. Do not just say which answer is numerically correct; use the number line to help you explain why the answer must be correct.

   b. Explain in another way who is right and why.

2. Jamarez says that he can solve $253 - 99$ by adding 1 to both numbers and solving $254 - 100$ instead.

   a. Draw a number line (which need not be perfectly to scale) to help you explain why Jamarez's method is valid.

   b. Explain in another way why Jamarez's method is valid.

   c. Could you adapt Jamarez's method to other subtraction problems, such as to the problem $324 - 298$? Explain, and give several examples.

3. Find ways to solve the following addition and subtraction problems *other than* using the standard addition or subtraction algorithms. In each case explain your reasoning and also write equations that correspond to your line of reasoning.

   a. $183 + 99$

   b. $268 + 52$

   c. $600 - 199$

   d. $164 - 70$

   e. $999 + 9999$

   f. $\$10.00 - \$2.99$

CLASS ACTIVITY 4T: A Third Grader's Method of Subtraction

When asked to compute $423 - 157$, Pat (a third grader) wrote the following:

    $4-$

    $30-$

    $34-$

    300

    266

"You can't take 7 from 3; it's 4 too many, so that's negative 4. You can't take 50 from 20; it's 30 too many, so that's negative 30, and with the other 4, it's negative 34. 400 minus 100 is 300, and then you take the 34 away from the 300, so it's 266."[1]

1. Discuss Pat's idea for calculating $423 - 157$. Is her method legitimate? If so, write equations corresponding to Pat's ideas.

2. Could you use Pat's idea to calculate $317 - 289$? If so, write what you think Pat might write, and also write corresponding equations.

This is taken from [1, p.263]

Chapter 5

Multiplication

5.1 The Meaning of Multiplication and Ways to Show Multiplication

CLASS ACTIVITY 5A: Showing Multiplicative Structure

1. A rug is 3 feet wide and 4 feet long. How many square feet is the rug? Recall that a square foot is the area of a square that is 1 foot wide and 1 foot long.

   Use the meaning of multiplication to explain why you can solve the problem by multiplying.

2. Fran has 3 pairs of pants, pants 1, 2, and 3, that coordinate perfectly with 4 different shirts, shirts A, B, C, and D. How many different outfits consisting of a pair of pants and a shirt can Fran make from these clothes?

   Show how to solve this problem by using an organized list and a tree diagram. Use the meaning of multiplication to explain why you can solve the problem by multiplying.

3. You have two bags. The bag on the left contains an orange marble, a red marble, and a purple marble. The bag on the right contains a yellow marble, a green marble, and a blue marble. How many ways are there to pick two marbles simultaneously: one out of the bag on the left and one out of the bag on the right?

Show how to solve this by using an organized list and a tree diagram. Use the meaning of multiplication to explain why you can solve the problem by multiplying.

Suppose we simply wanted to find out how many marbles were in the two bags altogether. How would this problem be like or unlike finding the different combinations of marbles selected from the two bags?

4. Jenna and Katie work on the previous problem (part 3) about picking pairs of marbles from two bags.

   Jenna draws the tree diagram in Figure 5.1 and says that there are 6 ways to pick a pair of marbles from the two bags. What's wrong with Jenna's reasoning?

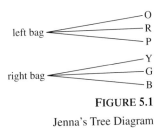

FIGURE 5.1

Jenna's Tree Diagram

Katie draws the tree diagram in Figure 5.2 and counts all the labels (letters) on her tree diagram. Katie says that there are

$$3 + 9 = 12$$

ways to pick a pair of marbles from the two bags. What's wrong with Katie's reasoning?

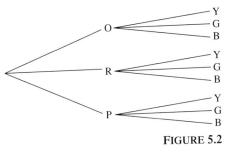

FIGURE 5.2

Katie's Tree Diagram

5. A bakery makes four different kinds of cake. Each cake can have three different kinds of frosting. Each frosted cake can be decorated in two different ways. How many ways are there of ordering a decorated, frosted cake?

   Show how to solve the problem using an organized list and a tree diagram. Use the meaning of multiplication to explain why you can solve the problem by multiplying.

6. Suppose that a certain type of small key is made with two notches and that each notch is either deep, medium, or shallow. How many different possible keys can be made this way?

   What if the key is made with four notches, and each notch is either deep, medium, or shallow?

   Show how to solve the preceding problems by using organized lists and tree diagrams. Use the meaning of multiplication to explain why you can solve the problems by multiplying.

5.2 Why Multiplying Decimal Numbers by 10 Is Easy

CLASS ACTIVITY 5B: If We Wrote Numbers Differently, Multiplying by 10 Might Not Be So Easy

Multiplying by 10 is easy with decimal numbers because of the special structure of the decimal system. What if we wrote numbers differently?

Let's consider a different way of writing numbers. We'll call our new system for writing numbers **money notation**. To write a whole number in money notation, use the coins and bills of *largest value* to represent that many cents. Then write down from right to left how many cents, nickels, dimes, quarters, fifty-cent pieces, dollar bills, 5 dollar bills, etc., are needed to make the given number of cents. A few examples will illustrate:

DECIMAL NOTATION	MONEY NOTATION	EXPLANATION
27	1002	1 quarter, 0 dimes, 0 nickels, and 2 pennies make 27 cents.
85	11100	1 fifty-cent piece, 1 quarter, 1 dime, 0 nickels, and 0 pennies make 85 cents.
149	101204	1 dollar, 0 fifty-cent pieces, 1 quarter, 2 dimes, 0 nickels, and 4 pennies make 149 cents.

Notice that even though you can also make 27 cents with 2 dimes and 7 cents, you shouldn't write 27 as "207" in money notation. This is because you should always use the *largest value* coins and bills possible.

1. Write the following numbers in money notation:

34

68

180

2. In decimal notation, to multiply a number by 10, we shift each digit one place to the left. Does this same procedure work when we write numbers in money notation?

    Write the following numbers in money notation:

    340

    680

    1800

    Compare these results to the results of shifting the digits in your answers to question (1) one place to the left.

3. Why is it that to multiply a number in decimal notation by 10 we only have to shift each digit one place to the left, but the same procedure does not work for numbers written in money notation? What creates this difference in the two systems?

CLASS ACTIVITY 5C: Multiplying by Powers of 10 Explains the Cycling of Decimal Representations of Fractions

When you use a calculator or long division you will find that

$$\frac{1}{7} = .142857142857142857\ldots$$

Notice the repeating pattern—it turns out that it continues forever.

1. Look carefully at the sequence of digits in the decimal representations of the fractions listed. For $\frac{1}{7}$, this sequence is

$$1,\ 4,\ 2,\ 8,\ 5,\ 7,\ 1,\ 4,\ 2,\ 8,\ 5,\ 7,\ldots$$

How does the sequence of digits in these other decimal representations compare to this sequence?

$\frac{1}{7} = .142857142857\ldots$

$\frac{2}{7} = .285714285714\ldots$

$\frac{3}{7} = .428571428571\ldots$

$\frac{4}{7} = .571428571428\ldots$

$\frac{5}{7} = .714285714285\ldots$

$\frac{6}{7} = .857142857142\ldots$

2. By way of comparison, look at the decimal representations for various fractions with denominator 37. How is this similar to and how is this different from the situation in question (1)?

$$\frac{1}{37} = .027027027027\ldots$$

$$\frac{2}{37} = .054054054054\ldots$$

$$\frac{3}{37} = .081081081081\ldots$$

$$\frac{4}{37} = .108108108108\ldots$$

$$\frac{5}{37} = .135135135135\ldots$$

$$\frac{10}{37} = .270270270270\ldots$$

$$\frac{26}{37} = .702702702702\ldots$$

The next several parts will be used to explain why the relationships you discovered in question (1) exist.

3. Calculate the following without the use of a calculator:

$10 \times .142857142857142857\ldots =$

$100 \times .142857142857142857\ldots =$

$1,000 \times .142857142857142857\ldots =$

$10,000 \times .142857142857142857\ldots =$

$100,000 \times .142857142857142857\ldots =$

$1,000,000 \times .142857142857142857\ldots =$

4. Write the following numbers as mixed numbers, in other words, with a whole number and a fractional part:

$10 \times \frac{1}{7} = \frac{10}{7} = 1\frac{3}{7}$

$100 \times \frac{1}{7} = \frac{100}{7} =$

$1,000 \times \frac{1}{7} = \frac{1000}{7} =$

$10,000 \times \frac{1}{7} = \frac{10,000}{7} =$

$100,000 \times \frac{1}{7} = \frac{100,000}{7} =$

$1,000,000 \times \frac{1}{7} = \frac{1,000,000}{7} =$

5. What is the relationship between the lists of numbers in questions (3) and (4)? How are the fractional parts in question (4) related to your answers in question (3)? Use this to explain the relationship you discovered in question (1).

5.3   Multiplication and Areas of Rectangles

CLASS ACTIVITY 5D: Areas of Rectangles in Square Yards and Square Feet

1. One yard is 3 feet. Does this mean that one square yard is 3 square feet? Draw a picture to show how many square feet are in a square yard. Use the meaning of multiplication to explain why you can determine the number of square feet in a square yard by multiplying.

2. A rug is 5 yards long and 4 yards wide. What is the area of the rug in square yards? What is the area of the rug in square feet? Show two different ways to solve this problem. In each case, refer to the meaning of multiplication.

3. A room has a floor area of 35 square yards. What is the floor area of the room in square feet? Explain your answer, referring to the meaning of multiplication.

CLASS ACTIVITY 5E: Using Multiplication to Estimate How Many

1. Use multiplication to estimate how many curlicues there are below.

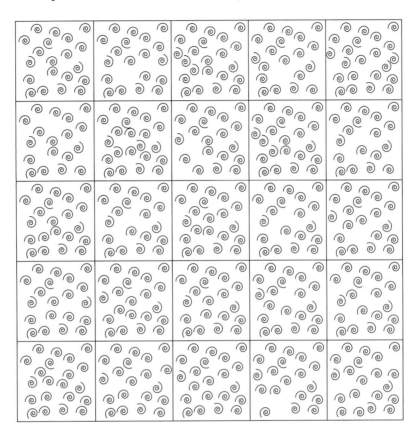

2. Use multiplication to estimate how many dots there are below. Describe your strategy.

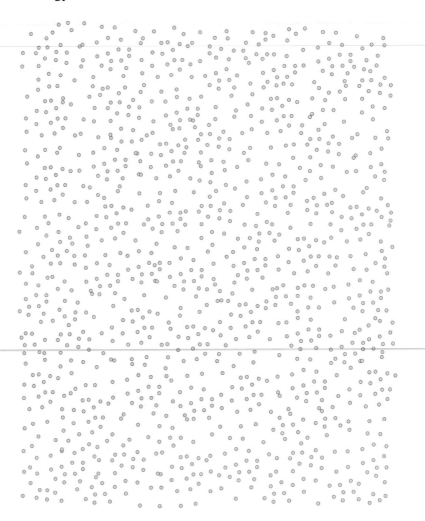

3. Describe a *realistic* strategy for determining approximately how many hairs are on a person's head. If possible, carry out your strategy.

5.4 The Commutative Property of Multiplication

CLASS ACTIVITY 5F: Explaining the Commutative Property of Multiplication

You will need small square tiles for part (1) of this activity.

1. Using small square tiles, make a rectangle that is 4 tiles long and 3 tiles wide. By showing groups in your rectangle, explain why

$$4 \times 3 = 3 \times 4$$

2. A third-grade math book explained the commutative property of multiplication by using a number line to show that

$$5 + 5 + 5$$

    is equal to
$$3 + 3 + 3 + 3 + 3$$

    Why is this not a good explanation? Why would it be better to make a rectangle out of tiles, as in part (1), or to draw an array like the one below?

    ☆ ☆ ☆ ☆ ☆
    ☆ ☆ ☆ ☆ ☆
    ☆ ☆ ☆ ☆ ☆

3. A marching band is arranged in 20 rows of 4. Everybody in the band turns 90° to their left. Now how is the band arranged? How can you use the marching band to illustrate the commutative property of multiplication?

CLASS ACTIVITY 5G: Using the Commutative Property of Multiplication

1. There are 21 bags with 2 marbles in each bag. Ben calculates the number of marbles there are in all by counting by 2s 21 times. Kaia calculates $21 + 21 = 42$ instead. Why is Kaia's approach legitimate?

2. This problem will help you investigate the following question. Which of the following two options will result in the lower price for a pair of pants?

   • The price of the pants is marked up by 10% and then marked down 20% from the increased price.

   • The price of the pants is marked down by 20% and then marked up by 10% from the discounted price.

   Both options involve marking up by 10% and marking down by 20%. The difference is the order in which the marking up and marking down occurs.

   a. Before you do any calculations, make a guess about which of the two ways should result in a lower price.

   b. Determine which of the two ways will result in a lower price using the fact that if a price increases by 10%, then you can find the increased price by multiplying by 1.10 (which is $100\% + 10\% = 110\%$), and if a price decreases by 20%, then you can find the decreased price by multiplying by 0.80 (which is $100\% - 20\% = 80\%$).

   c. Explain how the commutative property of multiplication is relevant to the question of which of the two ways results in a lower price of the pair of pants.

5.5 Multiplication and Volumes of Boxes

CLASS ACTIVITY 5H: Ways to Describe the Volume of a Box with Multiplication

You will need a set of blocks for parts 1 and 2 of this activity.

1. If you have cubic-inch blocks available, build a box that is 3 inches wide, 2 inches deep, and 4 inches tall. It should look like this:

2. Subdivide your box into natural groups of blocks and describe how you subdivided the box. How many groups were there and how many blocks were in each group? Using multiplication, write the corresponding expressions for the total number of blocks in the box. Now repeat, this time subdividing your box into natural groups in a different way.

3. The next two pages show different ways of subdividing a box into groups. If you have built a box from blocks, subdivide your box in the ways shown in the figures. In each case, describe the number of groups and the number of blocks in each group. Then write an expression for the total number of blocks. Your expression should use multiplication, parentheses, and the numbers 2, 3, and 4.

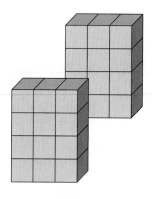

_____ groups of _____ blocks

On the following line, write an expression using multiplication, parentheses, and the numbers 2, 3, and 4 for the total number of blocks:

_____

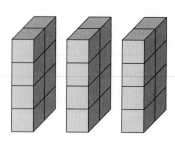

_____ groups of _____ blocks

On the following line, write an expression using multiplication, parentheses, and the numbers 2, 3, and 4 for the total number of blocks:

_____

_____ groups of _____ blocks

On the following line, write an expression using multiplication, parentheses, and the numbers 2, 3, and 4 for the total number of blocks:

_____

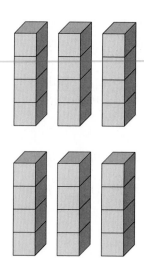

_____ groups of _____ blocks

On the following line, write an expression using multiplication, parentheses, and the numbers 2, 3, and 4 for the total number of blocks:

_____

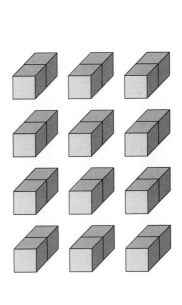

_____ groups of _____ blocks

On the following line, write an expression using multiplication, parentheses, and the numbers 2, 3, and 4 for the total number of blocks:

_____

_____ groups of _____ blocks

On the following line, write an expression using multiplication, parentheses, and the numbers 2, 3, and 4 for the total number of blocks:

_____

CLASS ACTIVITY 5I: Volumes of Boxes in Cubic Yards and Cubic Feet

1. One yard is 3 feet. Does this mean that 1 cubic yard is 3 cubic feet? Describe how to use the meaning of multiplication to determine what 1 cubic yard is in terms of cubic feet.

2. A compost pile is 2 yards high, 2 yards deep, and 2 yards wide. Does this mean that the compost pile has a volume of 2 cubic yards? Describe how to use the meaning of multiplication to determine the volume of the compost pile in cubic yards.

3. Determine the volume in cubic feet of the compost pile described in the previous problem in two different ways. In each case, refer to the meaning of multiplication.

CLASS ACTIVITY 5J: How Many Gumdrops?

You will need a box of cereal and standard kitchen measuring cups or measuring spoons for part 2 of this activity.

1. The container shown below has a square base, so all four vertical sides of the container are identical; the picture shows one of those four sides. Use multiplication to determine approximately how many gumdrops are in the container. Explain your method.

2. Describe several different realistic methods for determining approximately how many pieces of cereal are in a box of cereal. In each case, carry out your method.

5.6 The Associative Property of Multiplication

CLASS ACTIVITY 5K: Explaining and Using the Associative Property

1. By describing the groups, explain how to see the following:

    The next design shows 6 groups of dots with 4×2 dots in each group; this design also shows 6×4 groups of dots with 2 dots in each group.

    Then write an equation to show that you must get the same number of dots, either way you count them.

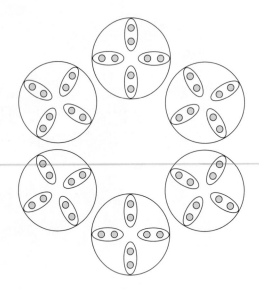

2. Use the next design to help you explain why

$$(5 \times 3) \times 4 = 5 \times (3 \times 4)$$

Your explanation should be general, in the sense that it explains why the equation is true when you replace the numbers 5, 3, and 4 with other counting numbers, and the design is changed accordingly.

3. Which properties of arithmetic are used in the following calculations? Where are the properties used?

$$
\begin{aligned}
8 \times 70 &= (8 \times 7) \times 10 \\
&= 56 \times 10 \\
&= 560
\end{aligned}
$$

4. Which properties of arithmetic are used in the following calculations? Where are the properties used?

$$
\begin{aligned}
60 \times 4000 &= 6 \times 10 \times 4 \times 1000 \\
&= 6 \times 4 \times 10 \times 1000 \\
&= 24 \times 10 \times 1000 \\
&= 240 \times 1000 \\
&= 240{,}000
\end{aligned}
$$

5. When we multiply 4×60 mentally, we multiply 4×6 first, and then we put a 0 at the end to get the answer, 240. Write equations to show that this mental technique uses the associative property of multiplication. Use the next picture to explain why the mental technique makes sense.

‖‖‖‖‖‖‖ ‖‖‖‖‖‖‖ ‖‖‖‖‖‖‖ ‖‖‖‖‖‖‖ ‖‖‖‖‖‖‖ ‖‖‖‖‖‖‖

‖‖‖‖‖‖‖ ‖‖‖‖‖‖‖ ‖‖‖‖‖‖‖ ‖‖‖‖‖‖‖ ‖‖‖‖‖‖‖ ‖‖‖‖‖‖‖

‖‖‖‖‖‖‖ ‖‖‖‖‖‖‖ ‖‖‖‖‖‖‖ ‖‖‖‖‖‖‖ ‖‖‖‖‖‖‖ ‖‖‖‖‖‖‖

‖‖‖‖‖‖‖ ‖‖‖‖‖‖‖ ‖‖‖‖‖‖‖ ‖‖‖‖‖‖‖ ‖‖‖‖‖‖‖ ‖‖‖‖‖‖‖

6. Marcie calculated 30×400 mentally as follows:

    3 times 4 is 12,   10 times 100 is 1000,   12 times 1000 is 12,000.

    Write a sequence of equations that shows why Marcie's method of calculation is valid. Which properties of arithmetic are involved? Write your equations in the following form:

$$
\begin{aligned}
30 \times 400 &= \text{some expression} \\
&= \text{some expression} \\
&= \vdots \\
&= 12{,}000
\end{aligned}
$$

CLASS ACTIVITY 5L: Different Ways to Calculate the Total Number of Objects

1. Use only the numbers 3, 4, and 5, the multiplication symbol × (or ·), and parentheses to write at least two different expressions for the total number of hearts in the next figure. In each case, evaluate your expression to calculate the total number of hearts.

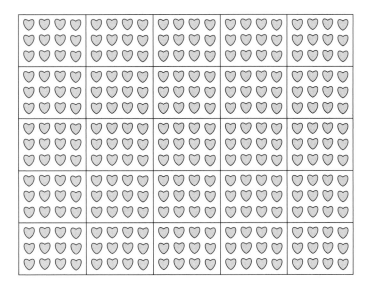

2. Write at least two different expressions for the total number of stars in Figure 5.3. In each case, evaluate your expression in order to calculate the total number of stars.

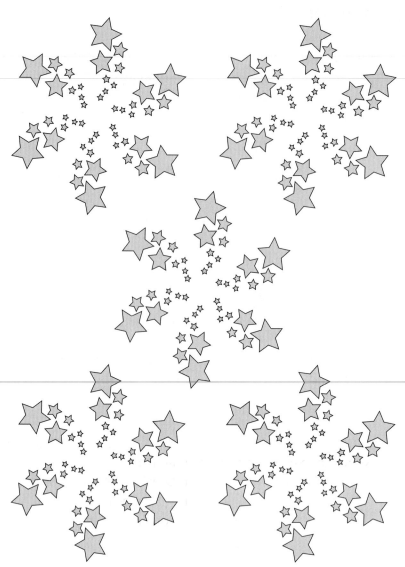

FIGURE 5.3
How Many Stars?

5.7 The Distributive Property

CLASS ACTIVITY 5M: Order of Operations

You will need a calculator for part 1(b) of this activity.

1. **a.** Evaluate the expression $4 \times 5 - 18 \div 3 + 12 \times 10$ without a calculator.

   b. Using a calculator, enter the numbers and operations in the expression $4 \times 5 - 18 \div 3 + 12 \times 10$ in the order in which they appear, pressing the $=$ sign or "enter" button each time after you enter a number. Do you get the correct answer this way? If not, why not?

2. There are 12 goodie bags. Each goodie bag contains 3 eraser tops, 2 pencils, and 4 stickers. Write an expression using the numbers 12, 3, 2, and 4; the symbols $\times$ (or $\cdot$) and $+$; and parentheses, if needed, for the total number of items in the 12 goodie bags. If you use parentheses, explain why you need them; if you do not use parentheses, explain why you do not need them.

3. Tiffany put 4 marbles in each of 5 cups and 3 marbles in each of 6 cups. Write an expression using the numbers 4, 5, 3, and 6; the symbols $\times$ (or $\cdot$) and $+$; and parentheses, if needed, for the total number of marbles that Tiffany put into cups. If you use parentheses, explain why you need them; if you do not use parentheses, explain why you do not need them.

4. For each of the following expressions, write a story problem for that expression and explain briefly why your story problem is appropriate for the expression.

   a. $6 \times 4 + 3$

   b. $6 \times \quad\quad 4 + 3$ Does it matter if there is a big space between the $\times$ and the 4?

   c. $6 \times (4 + 3)$

   d. $6 \times 4 + 3 \times 5$

CLASS ACTIVITY 5N: Explaining and Using the Distributive Property

1. Use the shading shown in the rectangle and use the meaning of multiplication to explain why

$$3 \times (2 + 4) = 3 \times 2 + 3 \times 4$$

   Your explanation should be general in the sense that you could use it to explain why
$$A \times (B + C) = A \times B + A \times C$$

   for *all* counting numbers A, B, and C.

2. On the graph paper shown, draw a rectangle and shade a portion of it to illustrate the equation

$$8 \times (10 + 5) = 8 \times 10 + 8 \times 5$$

3. Use the multiplication facts

$$15 \times 15 \; = \; 225$$
$$2 \times 15 \; = \; 30$$

to help you mentally calculate

$$17 \times 15$$

Explain how your calculation method is related to the following array, which consists of 17 rows of dots with 15 dots in each row:

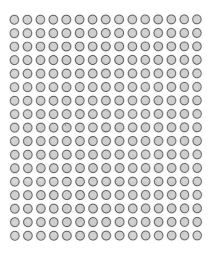

4. Write equations showing how your mental strategy for calculating 17×15 in part 3 involves the distributive property.

5. Write an equation that uses subtraction and the distributive property and that goes along with the following array:

6. Mentally calculate 20×15 and use your answer to mentally calculate 19×15. Write an equation that uses subtraction and the distributive property and that goes along with your strategy. Without drawing all the detail, draw a rough picture of an array that illustrates this calculation strategy.

CLASS ACTIVITY 50: The Distributive Property and FOIL

If you have studied algebra, then you probably learned the FOIL method for multiplying expressions of the form

$$(A + B) \cdot (C + D)$$

FOIL stands for *First, Outer, Inner, Last*, and reminds us that

$$(A + B) \cdot (C + D) = A \cdot C + A \cdot D + B \cdot C + B \cdot D$$

where $A \cdot C$ is *First*, $A \cdot D$ is *Outer*, $B \cdot C$ is *Inner*, and $B \cdot D$ is *Last*.

This class activity will help you explain in several different ways why the FOIL equation is valid.

1. Use the shading shown in the next rectangle and use the meaning of multiplication to explain why

$$(2 + 3) \cdot (7 + 4) = 2 \cdot 7 + 2 \cdot 4 + 3 \cdot 7 + 3 \cdot 4$$

Your explanation should be general in the sense that you could use it to explain why

$$(A + B) \cdot (C + D) = A \cdot C + A \cdot D + B \cdot C + B \cdot D$$

is true for all counting numbers A, B, C, and D.

2. Relate the preceding subdivided rectangle to the following sequence of equations:

$$\begin{aligned}(2 + 3) \cdot (7 + 4) &= 2 \cdot (7 + 4) + 3 \cdot (7 + 4) \\ &= 2 \cdot 7 + 2 \cdot 4 + 3 \cdot 7 + 3 \cdot 4\end{aligned}$$

Which properties of arithmetic do these equations use? Where are the properties used?

3. On the graph paper shown, draw and shade a rectangle to show why the following equation is true:

$$(10 + 3) \cdot (20 + 4) = 10 \cdot 20 + 10 \cdot 4 + 3 \cdot 20 + 3 \cdot 4$$

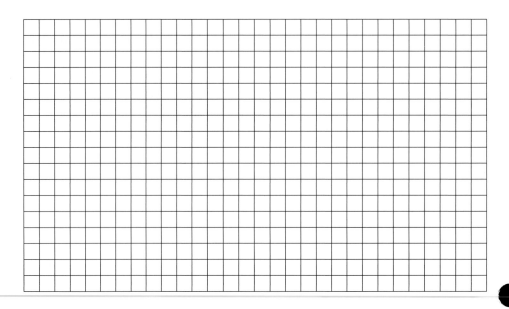

4. Use the distributive property several times to write a sequence of equations which proves that

$$(10 + 3) \cdot (20 + 4) = 10 \cdot 20 + 10 \cdot 4 + 3 \cdot 20 + 3 \cdot 4$$

Your work should be general in the sense that it would remain valid if other numbers were to replace 10, 3, 20, and 4.

5. Relate each step in your sequence of equations in part 4 to the subdivided rectangle you created in part 3 above.

CLASS ACTIVITY 5P: Why Isn't 23 × 23 Equal to 20 × 20 + 3 × 3?

Kylie has an idea for how to calculate 23 × 23. She says:

Twenty times twenty is 400 and 3 times 3 is 9, so 23 × 23 should be 400 plus 9 which is 409.

Is Kylie's method valid? If not, how could you modify her work to make it correct? Don't just start over in a different way, work with Kylie's idea. Use the large square below, which consists of 23 rows with 23 small squares in each row, to help you explain your answer.

CLASS ACTIVITY 5Q: Squares and Products near Squares

If available, a set of square tiles would be helpful for part 2.

The word *square* can refer to a geometric shape or to a related amount of area, such as a "square inch." But there are also square *numbers*. The **square numbers** or **perfect squares** are the counting numbers that can be written as a counting number times itself, for example

$$1 \times 1, \quad 2 \times 2, \quad 3 \times 3, \quad \ldots, \quad 9 \times 9, \quad \ldots$$

are squares. In the multiplication table, the squares are usually easy to remember; the squares lie on a diagonal in the multiplication table below.

×	1	2	3	4	5	6	7	8	9	10
1	1	2	3	4	5	6	7	8	9	10
2	2	4	6	8	10	12	14	16	18	20
3	3	6	9	12	15	18	21	24	27	30
4	4	8	12	16	20	24	28	32	36	40
5	5	10	15	20	25	30	35	40	45	50
6	6	12	18	24	30	36	42	48	54	60
7	7	14	21	28	35	42	49	56	63	70
8	8	16	24	32	40	48	56	64	72	80
9	9	18	27	36	45	54	63	72	81	90
10	10	20	30	40	50	60	70	80	90	100

1. Compare each square in the multiplication table to the entry that is diagonally above and to the right of it (or diagonally below and to the left). For example, compare 49 (which is 7 × 7) to 48 (which is 6 × 8). What pattern do you notice?

2. Use arrays to help you explain why the pattern you described in part 1 exists. If available, use square tiles to make your arrays; rearrange the tiles in order to relate multiplication facts. If tiles are not available, draw the arrays instead.

3. Now apply the distributive property or FOIL to the expression

$$(A - 1) \cdot (A + 1)$$

to explain why the pattern you discovered in part 1 exists.

4. Why are the squares 1×1, 2×2, 3×3, ... called squares?

5. Annie is working on the multiplication problem 19 × 21. Annie says that 19 × 21 should equal 20 × 20 because 19 is one less than 20 and 21 is one more than 20.

Annie has a wonderful idea, but is it correct? If not, use the dots shown to help you explain to Annie why not. There are 20 rows of dots with 21 dots in each row.

6. Mary is working on the multiplication problem 19 × 21. Mary says that 19 × 21 is 21 less than 20 × 21, and 20 × 21 is 20 more than 20 × 20, which she knows is 400. Mary thinks this ought to help her calculate 19 × 21, but she can't quite figure it out.

Discuss Mary's idea in detail. Can you make her explanation work?

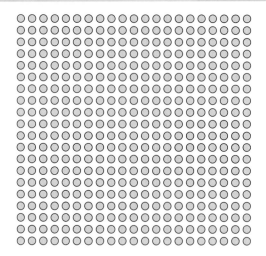

5.8 Mental Math, Properties of Arithmetic, and Algebra

CLASS ACTIVITY 5R: Using Properties of Arithmetic to Aid the Learning of Basic Multiplication Facts

In school, children must learn the basic multiplication facts from $1 \times 1 = 1$ to $10 \times 10 = 100$ (or beyond). These are 100 separate facts, but many of these facts are related by properties of arithmetic. By knowing how some facts are related to other facts, children can structure their understanding of the basic facts in order to learn them better.

$2 \times 2 = 4$	3×2	4×2	5×2	6×2	7×2	8×2	9×2
$2 \times 3 = 6$	$3 \times 3 = 9$	4×3	5×3	6×3	7×3	8×3	9×3
$2 \times 4 = 8$	$3 \times 4 = 12$	$4 \times 4 = 16$	5×4	6×4	7×4	8×4	9×4
$2 \times 5 = 10$	$3 \times 5 = 15$	$4 \times 5 = 20$	$5 \times 5 = 25$	6×5	7×5	8×5	9×5
$2 \times 6 = 12$	$3 \times 6 = 18$	$4 \times 6 = 24$	$5 \times 6 = 30$	$6 \times 6 = 36$	7×6	8×6	9×6
$2 \times 7 = 14$	$3 \times 7 = 21$	$4 \times 7 = 28$	$5 \times 7 = 35$	$6 \times 7 = 42$	$7 \times 7 = 49$	8×7	9×7
$2 \times 8 = 16$	$3 \times 8 = 24$	$4 \times 8 = 32$	$5 \times 8 = 40$	$6 \times 8 = 48$	$7 \times 8 = 56$	$8 \times 8 = 64$	9×8
$2 \times 9 = 18$	$3 \times 9 = 27$	$4 \times 9 = 36$	$5 \times 9 = 45$	$6 \times 9 = 54$	$7 \times 9 = 63$	$8 \times 9 = 72$	$9 \times 9 = 81$

1. Examine the darkly shaded, lightly shaded, and unshaded regions in the preceding multiplication table. Explain how to obtain the unshaded facts quickly and easily from the shaded facts. In doing so, what property of arithmetic do you use?

2. Multiplication facts involving the numbers 6, 7, and 8 are often hard to learn. For each fact in the lightly shaded regions in the table, describe a way to obtain the fact from facts in the darkly shaded region as follows:

a. Draw an array for the fact and show how to subdivide the array in order to relate the fact to one or more other facts. Try to find several different ways to subdivide the array this way.

b. Write equations that correspond to your subdivided array from part (a) and that show how the multiplication fact is related to darkly shaded facts. Specify the properties of arithmetic that your equations used.

For example, we could draw either of the following two subdivided arrays for the fact 3×7 and write the corresponding equations shown underneath them. Both equations use the distributive property.

$$3 \times 7 = 2 \times 7 + 1 \times 7$$
$$= 14 + 7 = 21$$

$$3 \times 7 = 3 \times 3 + 3 \times 4$$
$$= 9 + 12 = 21$$

3. The $5 \times$ *table* is easy to learn because it is "half of the *10 × table*".

$$5 \times 1 = 5 \qquad 10 \times 1 = 10$$
$$5 \times 2 = 10 \qquad 10 \times 2 = 20$$
$$5 \times 3 = 15 \qquad 10 \times 3 = 30$$
$$5 \times 4 = 20 \qquad 10 \times 4 = 40$$
$$5 \times 5 = 25 \qquad 10 \times 5 = 50$$
$$5 \times 6 = 30 \qquad 10 \times 6 = 60$$
$$5 \times 7 = 35 \qquad 10 \times 7 = 70$$
$$5 \times 8 = 40 \qquad 10 \times 8 = 80$$
$$5 \times 9 = 45 \qquad 10 \times 9 = 90$$

a. Use the arrays below for the facts 10×4 and 10×7 to illustrate the statement about the $5 \times$ table being half of the $10 \times$ table.

b. Write an equation showing the relationship between 10×7 and 5×7 that fits with the statement about the $5 \times$ table being half of the $10 \times$ table. Which property of arithmetic do you use?

4. The $9 \times$ *table* is easy to learn because you can just subtract a number that is to be multplied by 9 from that number with a 0 placed behind it, as shown next. Explain why this way of multiplying by 9 is valid.

$$9 \times 1 = 10 - 1 = 9$$
$$9 \times 2 = 20 - 2 = 18$$
$$9 \times 3 = 30 - 3 = 27$$
$$9 \times 4 = 40 - 4 = 36$$
$$9 \times 5 = 50 - 5 = 45$$
$$9 \times 6 = 60 - 6 = 54$$
$$9 \times 7 = 70 - 7 = 63$$
$$9 \times 8 = 80 - 8 = 72$$
$$9 \times 9 = 90 - 9 = 81$$

5. What is another pattern (other than the one described in part 4) in the $9 \times$ *table*?

CLASS ACTIVITY 5S: Solving Arithmetic Problems Mentally

For each of the following arithmetic problems, describe a way to make the problem easy to solve mentally:

1. 4×99

2. 12×125 (Try to find several ways to solve this problem mentally.)

3. $125\% \times 120$

4. $45\% \times 680$

CLASS ACTIVITY 5T: Which Properties of Arithmetic Do These Calculations Use?

The following sequences of equations correspond to efficient mental strategies for solving the arithmetic problems of the previous class activity. In each case, describe the strategy in words. That is, describe what a person who is solving the problem mentally in a way that corresponds to the given equations might say to himself. Also, determine which properties of arithmetic were used, and where they were used. Be specific.

1.

$$
\begin{aligned}
4 \times 99 &= 4 \times (100 - 1) \\
&= 4 \times 100 - 4 \times 1 \\
&= 400 - 4 \\
&= 396
\end{aligned}
$$

2.

$$
\begin{aligned}
12 \times 125 &= 10 \times 125 + 2 \times 125 \\
&= 1250 + 2 \times 100 + 2 \times 25 \\
&= 1250 + 200 + 50 \\
&= 1500
\end{aligned}
$$

3.

$$
\begin{aligned}
12 \times 125 &= (3 \times 4) \times 125 \\
&= 3 \times (4 \times 125) \\
&= 3 \times (4 \times 100 + 4 \times 25) \\
&= 3 \times (400 + 100) \\
&= 3 \times 500 \\
&= 1500
\end{aligned}
$$

4.

$$
\begin{aligned}
125\% \times 120 &= (100\% + 25\%) \times 120 \\
&= 100\% \times 120 + 25\% \times 120 \\
&= 120 + \frac{1}{4} \times 120 \\
&= 120 + 30 \\
&= 150
\end{aligned}
$$

5.

$$
\begin{aligned}
45\% \times 680 &= (50\% - 5\%) \times 680 \\
&= 50\% \times 680 - 5\% \times 680 \\
&= \frac{1}{2} \times 680 - \frac{1}{2} \times 10\% \times 680 \\
&= 340 - \frac{1}{2} \times 68 \\
&= 340 - 34 \\
&= 306
\end{aligned}
$$

6.

$$
\begin{aligned}
16 \times 25 &= (4 \times 4) \times 25 \\
&= 4 \times (4 \times 25) \\
&= 4 \times 100 \\
&= 400
\end{aligned}
$$

7.

$$
\begin{aligned}
16 \times 25 &= 4 \times 4 \times 5 \times 5 \\
&= 4 \times 5 \times 4 \times 5 \\
&= 20 \times 20 \\
&= 400
\end{aligned}
$$

CLASS ACTIVITY 5U: Writing Equations That Correspond to a Method of Calculation

Each arithmetic problem in this activity has a description of the problem solution. In each case, write a sequence of equations that corresponds to the given description. Which properties of arithmetic were used and where? Write your equations in the following form:

$$\text{original} = \text{some expression}$$
$$= \vdots$$
$$= \text{some expression}$$

1. $6 \times 800 = ?$

   6 times 8 is 48, then 48 times 100 is 4800.

2. $51 \times 4 = ?$

   50 times 4 is 200, plus another 4 is 204.

3. $35 \times 2 = ?$

   35 twos is two 35s, which is 70.

4. What is 55% of 120?

   Half of 120 is 60. Ten percent of 120 is 12, so 5% of 120 is half of that ten percent, which is 6. So the answer is 60 plus 6, which is 66.

5. What is 35% of 80?

   25% is $\frac{1}{4}$, so 25% of 80 is one fourth of 80, which is 20. Ten percent of 80 is 8. So 35% of 80 is 20 plus 8, which is 28.

6. What is 90% of 350?

   10% of 350 is 35. Taking 35 away from 350 leaves 315. So the answer is 315.

7. What is $\frac{7}{8}$ of 2400?

   One eighth of 2400 is 300. Taking 300 away from 2400 leaves 2100. The answer is 2100.

CLASS ACTIVITY 5V: Showing the Algebra in Mental Math

For each arithmetic problem in this activity, find ways to use properties of arithmetic to make the problem easy to do mentally. Describe your method in words, and write equations that correspond to your method. Write your equations in the following form:

$$\text{original} \ = \ \text{some expression}$$
$$= \ \vdots$$
$$= \ \text{some expression}$$

1. 9×99 (Try to find several different ways to solve this problem mentally.)

2. 24×25 (Try to find several different ways to solve this problem mentally.)

3. $\frac{7}{8} \times 128$

4. $26\% \times 840$

5. $5\% \times 48$

6. $15\% \times \$44$

5.9 Why the Procedure for Multiplying Whole Numbers Works

CLASS ACTIVITY 5W: The Standard Versus the Partial-Products Multiplication Algorithm

1. Use the standard multiplication algorithm and then the partial-products algorithm to solve the following multiplication problems:

$$
\begin{array}{r}
495 \\
\times\ \ \ 7 \\
\hline
\end{array}
\qquad\qquad
\begin{array}{r}
495 \\
\times\ \ \ 7 \\
\hline
\end{array}
$$

$$
\begin{array}{r}
234 \\
\times\ \ 59 \\
\hline
\end{array}
\qquad\qquad
\begin{array}{r}
234 \\
\times\ \ 59 \\
\hline
\end{array}
$$

2. Compare the two algorithms. How are they the same, how are they different? Why do both produce the same answer? Compare how "carrying" is handled in the two algorithms. Compare how place value is handled in the two algorithms.

CLASS ACTIVITY 5X: Why the Partial-Products Algorithm Gives Correct Answers, Part I

Graph paper would be helpful for part 5 of this activity.

This class activity will help you explain why the partial-products algorithm (and therefore also the standard algorithm) gives correct answers to multiplication problems.

Consider the relatively simple multiplication problem 6×38.

1. Use the partial-products multiplication algorithm to calculate 6×38.

2. The array shown next consists of 6 rows of o's with 38 o's in each row. Subdivide the array into pieces that correspond to the steps in the partial-products algorithm. Use this correspondence to explain why the partial-products algorithm calculates the correct answer to 6×38. Begin your explanation by using the meaning of multiplication to relate the array to the multiplication problem 6×38.

```
oooooooooo   oooooooooo   oooooooooo   oooooooo

oooooooooo   oooooooooo   oooooooooo   oooooooo

oooooooooo   oooooooooo   oooooooooo   oooooooo

oooooooooo   oooooooooo   oooooooooo   oooooooo

oooooooooo   oooooooooo   oooooooooo   oooooooo

oooooooooo   oooooooooo   oooooooooo   oooooooo
```

3. Now solve the multiplication problem 6×38 by working with expanded forms and using the distributive property.

$$6 \times 38 \;=\; 6 \times (30 + 8)$$
$$=$$

Relate the equations you just wrote to the steps in the partial-products algorithm. Use this relationship to explain why the partial-products algorithm calculates the correct answer to 6×38.

4. Compare the two explanations you gave in parts 2 and 3 to show why the partial-products algorithm calculates the correct answer to 6×38.

5. a. Use the partial-products algorithm to calculate 9×26.

   b. Draw an array for 9×26 (if available, use graph paper). Subdivide the array in a natural way so that the parts of the array correspond to the steps in the partial-products algorithm.

   c. Solve 9×26 by writing equations that use expanded forms and the distributive property. Relate your equations to the steps in the partial-products algorithm.

CLASS ACTIVITY 5Y: Why the Partial-Products Multiplication Algorithm Gives Correct Answers, Part II

Graph paper would be helpful for part 5 of this activity.

This class activity will help you explain why the partial-products multiplication algorithm (and therefore also the standard algorithm) gives correct answers to multiplication problems.

Consider the multiplication problem 23×45.

1. Use the partial-products algorithm to calculate

$$
\begin{array}{r}
45 \\
\times\ 23 \\
\hline
\end{array}
$$

2. The next array consists of 23 rows of o's with 45 o's in each row. Subdivide the array into pieces that correspond to the steps in the partial-products algorithm. Use this correspondence to explain why the partial-products algorithm calculates the correct answer to 23×45. Begin your explanation by using the meaning of multiplication to relate the array to the multiplication problem 23×45.

OOOOOOOOOO OOOOOOOOOO OOOOOOOOOO OOOOOOOOOO OOOOO
OOOOOOOOOO OOOOOOOOOO OOOOOOOOOO OOOOOOOOOO OOOOO
OOOOOOOOOO OOOOOOOOOO OOOOOOOOOO OOOOOOOOOO OOOOO
OOOOOOOOOO OOOOOOOOOO OOOOOOOOOO OOOOOOOOOO OOOOO
OOOOOOOOOO OOOOOOOOOO OOOOOOOOOO OOOOOOOOOO OOOOO
OOOOOOOOOO OOOOOOOOOO OOOOOOOOOO OOOOOOOOOO OOOOO
OOOOOOOOOO OOOOOOOOOO OOOOOOOOOO OOOOOOOOOO OOOOO
OOOOOOOOOO OOOOOOOOOO OOOOOOOOOO OOOOOOOOOO OOOOO
OOOOOOOOOO OOOOOOOOOO OOOOOOOOOO OOOOOOOOOO OOOOO
OOOOOOOOOO OOOOOOOOOO OOOOOOOOOO OOOOOOOOOO OOOOO

OOOOOOOOOO OOOOOOOOOO OOOOOOOOOO OOOOOOOOOO OOOOO
OOOOOOOOOO OOOOOOOOOO OOOOOOOOOO OOOOOOOOOO OOOOO
OOOOOOOOOO OOOOOOOOOO OOOOOOOOOO OOOOOOOOOO OOOOO
OOOOOOOOOO OOOOOOOOOO OOOOOOOOOO OOOOOOOOOO OOOOO
OOOOOOOOOO OOOOOOOOOO OOOOOOOOOO OOOOOOOOOO OOOOO
OOOOOOOOOO OOOOOOOOOO OOOOOOOOOO OOOOOOOOOO OOOOO
OOOOOOOOOO OOOOOOOOOO OOOOOOOOOO OOOOOOOOOO OOOOO
OOOOOOOOOO OOOOOOOOOO OOOOOOOOOO OOOOOOOOOO OOOOO
OOOOOOOOOO OOOOOOOOOO OOOOOOOOOO OOOOOOOOOO OOOOO
OOOOOOOOOO OOOOOOOOOO OOOOOOOOOO OOOOOOOOOO OOOOO

OOOOOOOOOO OOOOOOOOOO OOOOOOOOOO OOOOOOOOOO OOOOO
OOOOOOOOOO OOOOOOOOOO OOOOOOOOOO OOOOOOOOOO OOOOO
OOOOOOOOOO OOOOOOOOOO OOOOOOOOOO OOOOOOOOOO OOOOO

3. Now solve the multiplication problem 23×45 by working with expanded forms and using the distributive property several times.

$$23 \times 45 \;=\; (20 + 3) \times (40 + 5)$$
$$=$$

Relate the equations you wrote above to the steps in the partial-products algorithm. Use this relationship to explain why the partial-products algorithm calculates the correct answer to 23×45.

4. Compare the two explanations you gave in parts 2 and 3 to show why the partial-products algorithm calculates the correct answer to 23×45.

5. a. Use the partial-products algorithm to calculate 17×28.

   b. Draw an array for 17×28. (Draw your array by drawing a rectangle on graph paper; if you don't have graph paper, draw a rectangle to represent the array rather than drawing 17 rows of 28 items.) Subdivide the array in a natural way so that the parts of the array correspond to the steps in the partial-products algorithm.

   c. Solve 17×28 by writing equations that use expanded forms and the distributive property. Relate your equations to the steps in the partial-products algorithm.

CLASS ACTIVITY 5Z: Why the Standard Multiplication Algorithm Gives Correct Answers

1. Use the standard multiplication algorithm and the partial-products algorithm to multiply 28×32.

$$\begin{array}{r} 32 \\ \times\ 28 \\ \hline \end{array} \qquad\qquad \begin{array}{r} 32 \\ \times\ 28 \\ \hline \end{array}$$

2. On the graph paper given, draw an array and use your array to explain why the partial-products algorithm calculates the correct answer to 28×32. Then relate your array and the steps in the partial-products algorithm to the steps in the standard algorithm. Use these relationships to explain why the standard algorithm calculates the correct answer to 28×32.

3. Now solve the multiplication problem 28×32 by writing 28 in expanded form and by using the distributive property.

$$28 \times 32 \ = \ (20 + 8) \times 32$$
$$=$$

    Relate the equations you wrote above to the steps in the standard algorithm. Use this relationship to explain why the standard algorithm calculates the correct answer to 28×32.

4. Compare the two explanations you gave in parts 2 and 3 for why the standard products algorithm calculates the correct answer to 28×32.

5. Explain why we place a 0 in the second row when we use the standard algorithm to calculate 28×32.

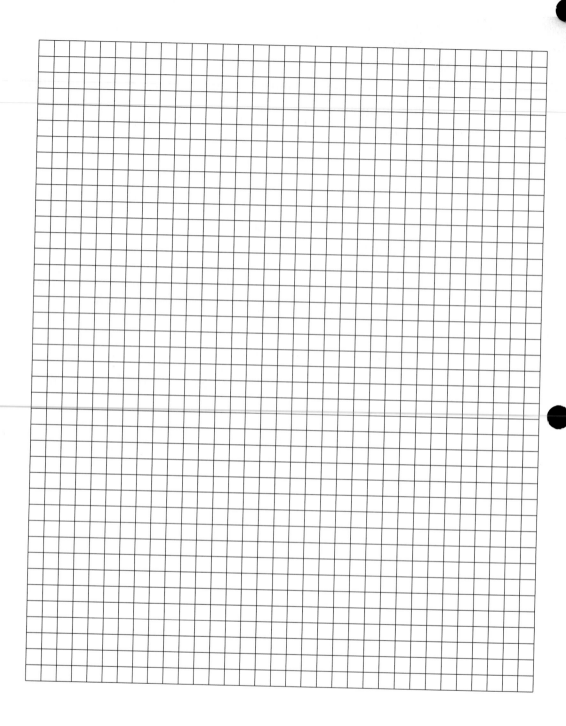

Chapter 6

Multiplication of Fractions, Decimals, and Negative Numbers

6.1 Multiplying Fractions

CLASS ACTIVITY 6A: Writing and Solving Fraction Multiplication Story Problems

Write a story problem for each of the following fraction multiplication problems. Then show how to solve your story problem with the aid of pictures. Verify that the solution you obtain from pictures agrees with the solution you obtain by using the fraction multiplication procedure.

1.

$$2 \cdot \frac{1}{3}$$

2.

$$\frac{1}{2} \cdot \frac{1}{3}$$

3.

$$\frac{1}{3} \cdot 2$$

4.

$$3 \cdot \frac{4}{5}$$

CLASS ACTIVITY 6B: Misconceptions with Fraction Multiplication

1. Maisy draws a picture like the one below to show $3 \cdot \frac{4}{5}$. Maisy concludes from her picture that

$$3 \cdot \frac{4}{5} = \frac{12}{15}$$

because 12 pieces out of 15 are shaded. Is Maisy right? If not, where is her reasoning flawed?

2. Joey, a fourth grader, wanted to figure out how many calories were in a piece of candy. According to the label on the bag, there were 50 calories in 3 pieces. Joey knew he had to find $\frac{1}{3}$ of 50, and he gave the answer $16\frac{2}{6}$. Joey explained his answer this way:

   3 sixteens is 48 and $\frac{1}{3}$ of the other 2 calories is $\frac{2}{6}$.

Joey drew the following picture to explain the $\frac{2}{6}$. What was Joey confused about?

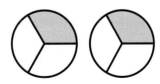

CLASS ACTIVITY 6C: Explaining Why the Procedure for Multiplying Fractions Gives Correct Answers

This class activity will help you explain how the procedure for multiplying fractions comes from the meaning of fractions and the meaning of multiplication.

1. Use the meaning of fractions, the meaning of multiplication, and the next diagram to help you explain why

$$\frac{2}{3} \cdot \frac{5}{8} = \frac{2 \cdot 5}{3 \cdot 8}$$

In particular, explain why it makes sense to multiply the numerators and why it makes sense to multiply the denominators.

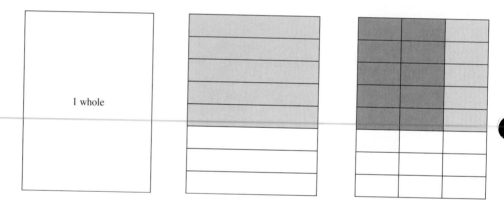

2. Use meaning of fractions, the meaning of multiplication, and the rectangles in the next figure to help you explain why

$$\frac{2}{5} \cdot \frac{3}{7} = \frac{2 \cdot 3}{5 \cdot 7}$$

In particular, explain why it makes sense to multiply the numerators and why it makes sense to multiply the denominators.

1 whole

CLASS ACTIVITY 6D: When Do We Multiply Fractions?

1. Originally there were 3 cubic yards of mulch in a mulch pile. Then $\frac{3}{4}$ of the mulch was removed from the pile. What question about the mulch pile can you answer by calculating $\frac{3}{4} \cdot 3$?

2. Shelley reads that one serving of Sweetblaster cereal will provide 80% of her daily value of vitamin C. Shelley is on a diet, so she decides to eat $\frac{2}{3}$ of a serving of Sweetblaster cereal. What question about Shelley's cereal will be answered by calculating $\frac{2}{3} \cdot \frac{80}{100}$?

3. Which of the following problems are story problems for $\frac{2}{3} \cdot \frac{1}{4}$ and which are not? Why?

   a. Joe is making $\frac{2}{3}$ of a recipe. The full recipe calls for $\frac{1}{4}$ cup of water. How much water should Joe use?

   b. $\frac{1}{4}$ of the students in Mrs. Watson's class go to the after-school program. $\frac{2}{3}$ of those children (those who go to the after-school program) have handed in permission slips to go on the after-school field trip. How many children have permission to go on the field trip? (Assume that the field trip is only open to children enrolled in the after-school program.)

   c. $\frac{1}{4}$ of the students in Mrs. Watson's class go to the after-school program. $\frac{2}{3}$ of those children (those who go to the after-school program) have handed in permission slips to go on the after-school field trip. What fraction of the students in Mrs. Watson's class have permission to go on the field trip? (Assume that the field trip is only open to children enrolled in the after-school program.)

   d. Carla is making snack bags that each contain $\frac{1}{4}$ package of jelly worms. $\frac{2}{3}$ of Carla's grab bags have been bought. What fraction of Carla's jelly worms have been bought?

CLASS ACTIVITY 6E: Multiplying Mixed Numbers

1. Make up a story problem for $2\frac{1}{2} \times 1\frac{1}{2}$.

2. Use pictures and the meaning of multiplication to solve your problem from part 1.

3. Use the distributive property or FOIL to calculate $2\frac{1}{2} \times 1\frac{1}{2}$ by rewriting this product as $(2 + \frac{1}{2}) \times (1 + \frac{1}{2})$.

4. Identify the four terms produced by the distributive property or FOIL (in part 3) in your picture in part 2.

5. Now write the mixed numbers $2\frac{1}{2}$ and $1\frac{1}{2}$ as improper fractions and use the procedure for multiplying fractions to calculate $2\frac{1}{2} \times 1\frac{1}{2}$. How do you see the product of the numerators in your picture in part 2? How can you see the product of the denominators in your picture?

6.2 Powers

CLASS ACTIVITY 6F: Multiplying Powers of 10

Remember that if A is a counting number, the expression

$$10^A$$

stands for A 10s multiplied together:

$$10^A = \underbrace{10 \times 10 \times \cdots \times 10}_{A \text{ times}}$$

1. Use the meaning of powers of ten to show how to write each of the expressions (a), (b), and (c) as a single power of ten (i.e., in the form 10^A for some exponent A). For example, 10^2 means 10×10 and 10^3 means $10 \times 10 \times 10$; therefore,

$$10^2 \times 10^3 = (10 \times 10) \times (10 \times 10 \times 10)$$
$$= 10^5$$

   a. $10^3 \times 10^4$

   b. $10^2 \times 10^5$

   c. $10^3 \times 10^3$

2. In each of (a), (b), and (c) in part 1, relate the exponents in the product with the exponent in the answer. (For the example given at the beginning of part 1, relate 2 and 3 to 5). In each case, how are the three exponents related?

3. Explain why it is always true that $10^A \times 10^B = 10^{A+B}$ when A and B are counting numbers.

6.3 Multiplying Decimals

CLASS ACTIVITY 6G: Where Do We Put the Decimal Point When We Multiply Decimals?

1. Ben wants to multiply 3.46×1.8. He first multiplies the numbers by ignoring the decimal points:

$$\begin{array}{r} 3.46 \\ \times\quad 1.8 \\ \hline 6228 \end{array}$$

Ben knows that he just needs to figure out where to put the decimal point in his answer, but he can't remember the rule about where to put the decimal point. Explain how Ben could reason about the sizes of the numbers in order to determine where to put the decimal point in his answer.

2. Lameisha used a calculator and found that

$$1.5 \times 1.2 = 1.8$$

Lameisha wants to know why the rule about adding the number of places behind the decimal point doesn't work in this case. Why aren't there 2 digits to the right of the decimal point in the answer? Is Lameisha right that the rule about adding the number of places behind the decimal points doesn't work in this case? Explain.

CLASS ACTIVITY 6H: Explaining Why We Place the Decimal Point Where We Do When We Multiply Decimals

1. As indicated in the next diagram, to get from 1.36 to 136, we multiply by 10×10. To get from 2.7 to 27, we multiply by 10. In other words,

$$136 = 10 \times 10 \times 1.36 \quad \text{and} \quad 27 = 10 \times 2.7$$

$$
\begin{array}{r}
1.36 \\
\times\ 2.7 \\
\end{array}
\xrightarrow[\ \times 10\ ]{\ \times 10\ \ \times 10\ }
\begin{array}{r}
136 \\
\times\ \ 27 \\
\hline
952 \\
2720 \\
\hline
3672 \\
\end{array}
$$

therefore,

$$
\begin{array}{r}
1.36 \\
\times\ \ 2.7 \\
\hline
952 \\
2720 \\
\hline

\end{array}
\xleftarrow[\quad ?\quad]{\begin{array}{c}?\\[-2pt]?\end{array}}
\begin{array}{r}
136 \\
\times\ \ 27 \\
\hline
952 \\
2720 \\
\hline
3672
\end{array}
$$

Therefore, what should we do to

$$136 \times 27 = 3672$$

to get back to

$$1.36 \times 2.7?$$

Use your answer to explain the placement of the decimal point in 1.36×2.7.

2. Use the next diagram to help you explain where to put the decimal point in 2.476 × 1.83.

$$2.476 \longrightarrow 2476$$
$$\times\ 1.83 \longrightarrow \times\ 183$$

therefore,

$$2.476 \longleftarrow 2476$$
$$\times\ 1.83 \longleftarrow \times\ 183$$

3. Working with powers of 10 and using the idea of parts 1 and 2, explain why the following makes sense: if you multiply a number that has 3 digits to the right of its decimal point by a number that has 4 digits to the right of its decimal point, you should place the decimal point $3 + 4 = 7$ places from the end of the product calculated without the decimal points.

CLASS ACTIVITY 61: Interpreting Decimal Multiplication with Pictures

Consider the multiplication problem 2.3×1.8. As with whole number and fraction multiplication, 2.3×1.8 means the total number of objects in 2.3 groups if there are 1.8 objects in each group.

1. Using the diagrams in Figure 6.1, explain how the bottom diagram in Figure 6.1 shows 2.3 groups with 1.8 objects in each group.

2. Explain how the bottom diagram of Figure 6.1 shows that 2.3×1.8 has an entry in the hundredths place, but no entries in any smaller places (thousandths, ten thousandths, etc.) Therefore, explain why we place the decimal point in 2.3×1.8 where we do.

3. Cut out Figure A.1 on page 531. Cut Figure A.1 into pieces and rearrange the pieces to show the solution to 2.3×1.8.

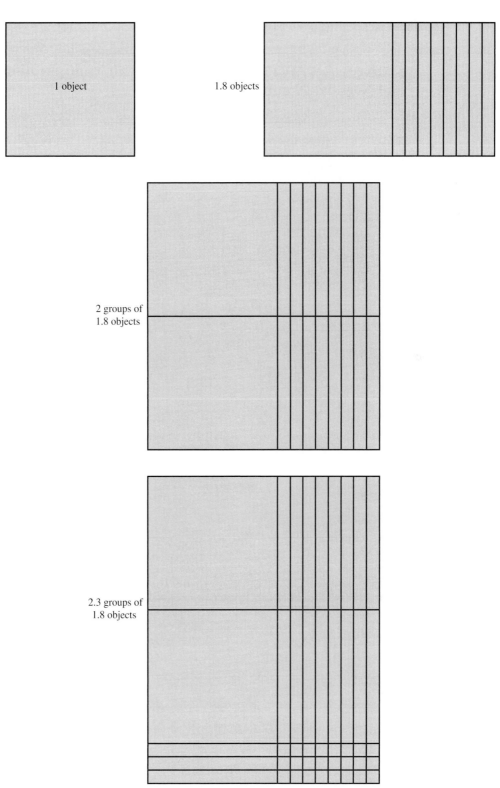

FIGURE 6.1

Showing 2.3 Groups with 1.8 Objects in Each Group

6.4 Multiplying Negative Numbers

CLASS ACTIVITY 6J: Patterns with Multiplication and Negative Numbers

In addition to the discussion in the text, there is another way to see why the rules for multiplying with negatives are reasonable. This is the purpose of this class activity.

For each of the following sets of equations, complete the set so that the pattern of numbers on the right-hand side of the equal signs continues. Describe the patterns.

$$
\begin{array}{rclr}
6 \times 4 & = & 24 \\
6 \times 3 & = & 18 \\
6 \times 2 & = & 12 \\
6 \times 1 & = & 6 \\
6 \times 0 & = & 0 \\
6 \times -1 & = & \\
6 \times -2 & = & \\
6 \times -3 & = & \\
6 \times -4 & = & \\
6 \times -5 & = & \\
\end{array}
\qquad
\begin{array}{rclr}
4 \times 7 & = & 28 \\
3 \times 7 & = & 21 \\
2 \times 7 & = & 14 \\
1 \times 7 & = & 7 \\
0 \times 7 & = & 0 \\
-1 \times 7 & = & \\
-2 \times 7 & = & \\
-3 \times 7 & = & \\
-4 \times 7 & = & \\
-5 \times 7 & = & \\
\end{array}
$$

$$
\begin{array}{rclr}
-8 \times 4 & = & -32 \\
-8 \times 3 & = & -24 \\
-8 \times 2 & = & -16 \\
-8 \times 1 & = & -8 \\
-8 \times 0 & = & 0 \\
-8 \times -1 & = & \\
-8 \times -2 & = & \\
-8 \times -3 & = & \\
-8 \times -4 & = & \\
-8 \times -5 & = & \\
\end{array}
$$

CLASS ACTIVITY 6K: Using Checks and Bills to Interpret Multiplication with Negative Numbers

1. For each of the following transactions, compare the amount of money you will have before and after the transaction takes place:

   a. You get 3 checks, each for $5.

   b. You get 3 bills, each for $5.

   c. You give away 3 checks, each for $5.

   d. You give away 3 bills, each for $5.

2. Write a consistent set of multiplication problems that describe how the amount of money you have changes due to the transactions in part 1. Use negative numbers wherever it makes sense to do so.

CLASS ACTIVITY 6L: Does Multiplication Always Make Larger?

1. In ordinary language, the term "multiply" means "make larger," as in:

    Go forth and multiply.

    In mathematics, does multiplying always make a quantity larger? Give some examples to help you explain your answer.

2. For which numbers, N, is $N \times 3$ greater than 3? In other words, for which numbers, N, is

    $$N \times 3 > 3$$

    Consider all kinds of numbers for N: fractions, decimals, positive, negative. Investigate this question by trying a number of examples and by thinking about the meaning and rules of multiplication.

3. For which numbers, N, is $N \times -3$ greater than -3? In other words, for which numbers, N, is

    $$N \times -3 > -3$$

    Consider all kinds of numbers for N: fractions, decimals, positive, negative. Investigate this question by trying a number of examples and by thinking about the meaning and rules of multiplication.

6.5 Scientific Notation

CLASS ACTIVITY 6M: Scientific Notation versus Ordinary Decimal Notation

1. A $1.3 trillion tax cut was approved. Write 1.3 trillion in scientific notation and in ordinary decimal notation.

2. The population of the U.S. is approximately 280 million. Write 280 million in scientific notation and in ordinary decimal notation.

3. Use a calculator to multiply

$$123,456,789 \times 987,654,321$$

a. Does your calculator's display show all the digits in the product $123,456,789 \times 987,654,321$? If not, why not? What does your calculator's display mean?

b. Based on your calculator's display, what can you determine about the ordinary decimal representation of the product $123,456,789 \times 987,654,321$?

c. Can you use the calculator's display to determine how many digits the decimal representation of the product $123,456,789 \times 987,654,321$ has? Explain.

d. Explain how you can "break up" the numbers $123,456,789$ and $987,654,321$ and use the distributive property or FOIL in conjunction with a calculator in order to determine all the digits in the product $123,456,789 \times 987,654,321$. Do not just multiply longhand.

CLASS ACTIVITY 6N: How Many Digits Are in a Product of Counting Numbers?

When you multiply two counting numbers, how many digits does the product have? This class activity will help you discover the answer to this question.

1. Multiply many 2-digit counting numbers with 3-digit counting numbers. How many digits do the products have?

Multiply many 3-digit counting numbers with 4-digit counting numbers. How many digits do the products have?

Multiply many 2-digit counting numbers with 4-digit counting numbers. How many digits do the products have?

In your examples, how are the number of digits in the two factors related to the number of digits in the product? (Your answer should involve "either ... or ...".)

2. Based on your results in part 1, predict what will happen in other situations. If you multiply a 9-digit counting number with an 11-digit counting number, how many digits will the product have? In general, if you multiply an n-digit counting number with an m-digit counting number, how many digits will the product have? Give "either ... or ..." answers.

CLASS ACTIVITY 60: Explaining the Pattern in the Number of Digits in Products

This class activity continues the previous activity. In this activity, you will explain why the pattern you found in the previous class activity must hold. The key is to relate the number of digits in a counting number to the exponent on the 10 when the number is written in scientific notation.

1. Based on what you discovered in the previous class activity, predict how many digits the product

$$123,456,789 \times 23,456,789$$

has.

2. Now use a calculator to compute $123,456,789 \times 23,456,789$. Use the calculator's display to determine how many digits the product $123,456,789 \times 23,456,789$ has.

3. In general, what is the relationship between the number of digits of a counting number and the exponent on the 10 when that number is written in scientific notation? Explain.

4. Write the numbers 123,456,789; 23,456,789; and the product 123,456,789 × 23,456,789 in scientific notation. Look carefully at the exponents on the 10s. What relationship do you notice among these three exponents?

5. Take another pair of whole numbers and write them and their product in scientific notation. What is the relationship among the exponents on the 10s? Do this many times, with many pairs of numbers. Do you always get the same relationship as in the last problem or not?

6. What happens when we multiply numbers that are in scientific notation? Fill in the correct exponents for the 10s on the right in the following equations:

$(1.2 \times 10^3) \times (3.7 \times 10^5) \quad = \quad (1.2 \times 3.7) \times 10^3 \times 10^5 = \quad (1.2 \times 3.7) \times 10—$

$(7.63 \times 10^4) \times (8.14 \times 10^6) = (7.63 \times 8.14) \times 10^4 \times 10^6 = (7.63 \times 8.14) \times 10—$

$(4.5 \times 10^7) \times (5.2 \times 10^8) \quad = \quad (4.5 \times 5.2) \times 10^7 \times 10^8 = \quad (4.5 \times 5.2) \times 10—$

7. Now put the numbers from the previous problem in scientific notation. In some cases, the exponent on the 10 changes. Why?

$$(1.2 \times 3.7) \times 10— \; =$$
$$(7.63 \times 8.14) \times 10— \; =$$
$$(4.5 \times 5.2) \times 10— \; =$$

8. Suppose you have a 7-digit counting number and an 8-digit counting number. What will they look like in scientific notation? Use this to explain why the product of a 7-digit counting number with an 8-digit counting number will have 14 or 15 digits.

Chapter 7

Division

7.1 The Meaning of Division

CLASS ACTIVITY 7A: The Two Interpretations of Division

1. Use both interpretations of division to explain why $14 \div 2 = 7$ and $8 \div 3 = 2\frac{2}{3}$. Make up a story problem for each case. Draw diagrams to illustrate.

2. For each of the following problems, write the corresponding division problem and decide which interpretation of division is involved (the "how many groups?" or the "how many in each group?", with or without remainder). Draw diagrams to help you decide.

    a. Gloria has 28 candies to distribute equally among 5 children. How many candies will each child get, and how many candies will be left over?

    b. Bill has a muffin recipe that calls for 2 cups of flour. How many batches of muffins can Bill make if he has 9 cups of flour available? How much flour will be left over? What if Bill is willing to make a fraction of a batch, then how many batches of muffins can Bill make?

    c. If 6 limes cost one dollar, then how much should one lime cost (assuming that all limes are priced equally).

d. If 8 cups of ice cream cost $3, then how many cups of ice cream could you buy for $1?

e. One foot is 12 inches. If a piece of rope is 100 inches long, then how long is it in feet?

f. Francine has 20 yards of rope that she wants to cut into 8 equal pieces. How long will each piece be?

g. A gallon of water weighs 8 pounds. How many gallons is 500 pounds of water?

h. If you drive 250 miles at a constant speed and it takes you 4 hours, then how fast did you go?

CLASS ACTIVITY 7B: Remainder, Mixed Number, or Decimal Answer to a Division Problem: Which Is Most Appropriate?

Which of the three types of answers to a division problem are appropriate in the following situations? (In some cases more than one answer is appropriate.)

1. For purposes of maintenance, a 58-mile stretch of road will be divided into 3 equal parts. How many miles of road are in each part?

2. For purposes of maintenance, a 58-mile stretch of road will be divided into sections of 15 miles. Each section of 15 miles will be the responsibility of a particular road crew. How many road crews are needed?

3. You have 75 pencils to give out to a class of 23 children who insist on fair distribution. How many pencils will each child get?

4. You have 7 packs of chips to share equally among 4 hungry people. How many packs of chips will each person get?

CLASS ACTIVITY 7C: Why Can't We Divide by Zero?

1. Make up story problems for the two interpretations of $2 \div 0$. Use your problems to explain why $2 \div 0$ is not defined.

2. Why can't we just say that $2 \div 0$ is 0, remainder 2? If we did, would that fit with the way we defined division with remainder?

3. A division problem (without remainder)

$$A \div B = ?$$

can always be rewritten as a multiplication problem, namely, as

$$? \times B = A$$

or as

$$B \times ? = A$$

Use the fact that every division problem can be rewritten as a multiplication problem to explain why $2 \div 0$ is not defined.

4. Make up story problems for the two interpretations of $0 \div 2$. Use your problems to explain why $0 \div 2$ *is* defined. Explain the difference between $2 \div 0$ and $0 \div 2$.

5. Explain why $0 \div 0$ is undefined. Can you give the same explanation as for why $2 \div 0$ is not defined? If not, how are the explanations different?

CLASS ACTIVITY 7D: Can We Use Properties of Arithmetic to Divide?

In Chapter 4, we often used properties of arithmetic to solve multiplication problems. Think carefully about each of the following:

1. Is division commutative? Explain your answer.

2. Is division associative? Explain your answer.

3. Is the following statement true?

$$200 \div 45 = 200 \div 40 + 200 \div 5$$

Why, or why not? Explain your answer carefully, including diagrams if possible.

4. Is the following statement true?

$$365 \div 7 = 300 \div 7 + 60 \div 7 + 5 \div 7$$

Does it depend on how you express the answer (as a whole number with remainder, a mixed number, or a decimal)?

CLASS ACTIVITY 7E: Reasoning about Division

1. Even though

$$25 \div 12 = 2, \text{ remainder } 1$$

and

$$21 \div 10 = 2, \text{ remainder } 1$$

would it be correct to say that

$$25 \div 12 = 21 \div 10?$$

Explain.

2. **a.** Write and solve a simple story problem for $600 \div 20$.

    b. Use the situation of your story problem in part (a) to help you solve $600 \div 19$ without a calculator or long division by modifying your solution to $600 \div 20$.

    c. Use the situation of your story problem in part (a) to help you solve $600 \div 21$ without a calculator or long division by modifying your solution to $600 \div 20$.

CLASS ACTIVITY 7F: Rounding to Estimate Solutions to Division Problems

1. Suppose you want to estimate

$$615 \div 29$$

by rounding 29 up to 30. Both $600 \div 30$ and $630 \div 30$ are easy to calculate mentally. Use reasoning about division to determine which division problem, $600 \div 30$ or $630 \div 30$, should give you a better estimate to $615 \div 29$. Then check your answer by solving the division problems.

2. Suppose you want to estimate

$$615 \div 31$$

by rounding 31 down to 30. Both $600 \div 30$ and $630 \div 30$ are easy to calculate mentally. Use reasoning about division to determine which division problem, $600 \div 30$ or $630 \div 30$, should give you a better estimate to $615 \div 31$. Then check your answer by solving the division problems.

3. Suppose you want to estimate $527 \div 48$. What is a good way to round the numbers 527 and 48 so as to obtain an easy division problem that will give a good estimate to $527 \div 48$? Explain, drawing on what you learned from problems 1 and 2.

4. Suppose you want to estimate $527 \div 52$. What is a good way to round the numbers 527 and 52 so as to obtain an easy division problem that will give a good estimate to $527 \div 52$? Explain, drawing on what you learned from problems 1 and 2.

7.2 Understanding Long Division

CLASS ACTIVITY 7G: Dividing without Using a Calculator or Long Division

1. Antrice is working on the following problem: There are 260 pencils to be put in packages of 12. How many packages of pencils can we make, and how many pencils will be left over? Here are Antrice's ideas:

   10 packages will use up 120 pencils. After another 10 packages, 240 pencils will be used up. After 1 more package, 252 pencils are used. Then there are only 8 pencils left, and that's not enough for another package. So the answer is 21 packages of pencils with 8 pencils left over.

   Explain why the equations

$$10 \cdot 12 + 10 \cdot 12 + 1 \cdot 12 + 8 \ = \ 260 \qquad (7.1)$$
$$(10 + 10 + 1) \cdot 12 + 8 \ = \ 260 \qquad (7.2)$$
$$21 \cdot 12 + 8 \ = \ 260 \qquad (7.3)$$

   correspond to Antrice's work and explain why the last equation shows that $260 \div 12 = 21$, remainder 8.

2. Maya is working on the division problem $245 \div 15$. She writes the following:

$$
\begin{array}{r}
15 \\
\times\ 2 \\
\hline
30
\end{array}
\qquad 8 \times 30 = 240 \qquad 8 \times 2 = 16 \qquad \boxed{16\ \text{R}\ 5}
$$

   a. Explain why Maya's strategy makes sense. It may help you to work with a story problem for $245 \div 15$.

   b. Write equations like Equations 7.1, 7.2, and 7.3 which correspond to Maya's work and which demonstrate that $245 \div 15 = 16$, remainder 5. One side of each equation should be 245.

3. Ashley is working on the division problem $245 \div 15$. She writes

$$15 \times 15 = 225 \qquad \begin{array}{r} 225 \\ +\ \ 15 \\ \hline 240 \\ +\ \ \ 5 \\ \hline 245 \end{array} \qquad 15 + 1 = 16 \ \text{remainder } 5$$

    a. Explain why Ashley's strategy makes sense. It may help you to work with a story problem for $245 \div 15$.

    b. Write equations like Equations 7.1, 7.2, and 7.3 which correspond to Ashley's work and which demonstrate that $245 \div 15 = 16$, remainder 5.

4. Zane is working on the division problem $245 \div 15$. He writes

$$\begin{array}{r} 15 \\ \times\ \ 2 \\ \hline 30 \\ \times\ \ 2 \\ \hline 60 \\ \times\ \ 4 \\ \hline 240 \\ 5 \text{ left} \end{array} \qquad 2 \times 2 \times 4 = 16 \text{ R } 5$$

    a. Explain why Zane's strategy makes sense. It may help you to work with a story problem for $245 \div 15$.

    b. Write equations like Equations 7.1, 7.2, and 7.3 which correspond to Zane's work and which demonstrate that $245 \div 15 = 16$, remainder 5.

5. Assume that you don't have a calculator and have forgotten how to do any longhand division method. Explain how you can calculate $2783 \div 125$.

CLASS ACTIVITY 7H: Understanding the Scaffold Method of Long Division

1. Interpret each of the steps in the next scaffold in terms of the following story problem:

> You have 3475 marbles and you want to put these marbles into bags with 8 marbles in each bag. How many bags of marbles can you make and how many marbles will be left over?

$$
\begin{array}{r}
4 \\
30 \\
400 \\
8\,)\overline{3475} \\
-\,3200 \\
\hline
275 \\
-\,240 \\
\hline
35 \\
-\,32 \\
\hline
3
\end{array}
$$

2. Explain how the equations

$$3475 - 400 \times 8 - 30 \times 8 - 4 \times 8 = 3$$
$$3475 - (400 + 30 + 4) \times 8 = 3$$
$$3475 - 434 \times 8 = 3$$

relate to the scaffold and to the story problem in part 1. Then explain why the last equation shows that $3475 \div 8 = 434$, remainder 3.

3. Use the scaffold method to calculate $8321 \div 6$. Interpret each step in your scaffold in terms of the following story problem:

> You have 8321 pickles and you want to put these pickles in packages with 6 pickles in each package. How many packages can you make and how many pickles will be left over?

4. Write equations like those in part 2 for your scaffold in part 3. Explain how your equations relate to the scaffold and to the story problem of part 3.

5. Cassie writes the following scaffold to calculate $7549 \div 12$:

$$
\begin{array}{r}
1 \\
8 \\
20 \\
100 \\
500 \\
\hline
12 \overline{)7549} \\
- \ 6000 \\
\hline
1549 \\
- \ 1200 \\
\hline
349 \\
- \ 240 \\
\hline
109 \\
- \ 96 \\
\hline
13 \\
- \ 12 \\
\hline
1
\end{array}
$$

Then Cassie writes the following:

$$500 + 100 + 20 + 8 + 1 = 629, \text{ so } 7549 \div 12 = 629, \text{ remainder } 1.$$

a. Describe how Cassie could have written a scaffold with fewer steps to solve $7549 \div 12$.

b. Even though Cassie used more steps than she had to, is her method still legitimate? In other words, is her method based on sound reasoning? Explain.

6. Manuel calculates $427 \div 11$ using the following reasoning:

> 10 elevens is 110. After another 10 elevens and another 10 elevens I'm up to 330. After another 5 elevens, I'm up to 385. One more eleven makes 396. Then one more eleven makes 407. One more eleven makes 418. Then there are 9 left. So the answer is 38, remainder 9.

Write a scaffold for $427 \div 11$ that is based on Manuel's reasoning. The arithmetic in the scaffold will not correspond exactly to Manuel's. Why not?

7. Use the scaffold method and the standard long division method to calculate $3895 \div 14$. Discuss how the two methods are related.

CLASS ACTIVITY 71: Interpreting Standard Long Division from the "How Many in Each Group?" Viewpoint

If available, bundled toothpicks (or other bundled objects) would be useful for part (1).

1. Use standard long division to calculate $137 \div 3$. Interpret each step in your calculation in terms of the following problem:

> You have 137 toothpicks arranged in bundles as 1 hundred, 3 tens, and 7 individual toothpicks. If you divide the 137 toothpicks into 3 equal groups, how many toothpicks will be in each group and how many toothpicks will be left over?

> If available, demonstrate the steps of the long division calculation with bundled toothpicks.

2. Use standard long division to calculate $10,347 \div 6$. Interpret each step in your calculation in terms of the following problem:

> You have 10,347 toothpicks arranged in bundles as 1 ten-thousand, 0 thousands, 3 hundreds, 4 tens, and 7 individual toothpicks. If you divide the 10,347 toothpicks into 6 equal groups, how many toothpicks will be in each group and how many toothpicks will be left over?

CLASS ACTIVITY 7J: Zeros in Long Division

1. Describe the error in the following division calculation:

$$
\begin{array}{r}
39 \\
12\overline{)3711} \\
-36 \\
\hline
111 \\
-108 \\
\hline
3
\end{array}
$$

2. Use the scaffold method to calculate $3711 \div 12$. Discuss why it is easier to avoid the error of part 1 when using the scaffold method than when using standard long division.

7.3 Fractions and Division

CLASS ACTIVITY 7K: Can Fractions be Defined in a Different Way?

In the article *Understanding Teaching/Teaching for Understanding*, teacher Anne Marie O'Reilley [8] describes the following situation that arose in her class when she wrote $\frac{1}{2}$ on the board and asked her class what the top and bottom numbers in the fraction represented:

> I was not prepared for David's answer:
> 1   thing
> -   cut into
> 2   pieces
> David made it clear, as he drew the horizontal bar in the air with his finger, that the line took the place of the words "cut into."

Most of the students agreed with David's definition, even though it's not standard. The incident was unsettling for O'Reilley both because the students didn't give the answer she expected and because she was uncertain whether David's idea gave a definition equivalent to the usual one. Does it? We will now explore this question.

David might say that $\frac{3}{4}$ of a pie is 3 pies cut into 4 pieces. To put it more precisely, according to David, $\frac{3}{4}$ of a pie is the amount of pie each person should get if 3 pies are divided equally among 4 people.

Our definition of $\frac{3}{4}$ of a pie is the amount of pie in 3 pieces when 1 pie is cut into 4 equal pieces. Is it the same amount of pie either way? Explain your answer clearly and in such a way that your explanation could be used when other numbers replace 3 and 4 in $\frac{3}{4}$.

What does your explanation allow you to conclude about how $\frac{3}{4}$ and $3 \div 4$ are related?

CLASS ACTIVITY 7L: Mixed-Number Answers to Division Problems

1. Describe how to get the mixed-number answer to $14 \div 3$ from the whole-number-with-remainder answer. Explain why your method makes sense by interpreting it in terms of dividing 14 large cookies equally among 3 people.

2. Describe how to use division to write the improper fraction $\frac{17}{6}$ as a mixed number and explain why the procedure you describe makes sense.

CLASS ACTIVITY 7M: Using Long Division to Calculate Decimal-Number Answers to Whole-Number Division Problems

1. Use long division to determine the decimal-number answer to $2674 \div 3$ to the hundredths place.

2. Interpret each step in your long-division calculation for part 1 in terms of dividing $2674 equally among 3 people by imagining that you distribute the money in stages: first distribute hundreds, then tens, then ones, then dimes (tenths), then pennies (hundredths).

CLASS ACTIVITY 7N: Using Division to Calculate Decimal Representations of Fractions

1. Use long division to show that the decimal representation of $\frac{3}{4}$ is 0.75.

2. Interpret each of your long-division steps in part 1 in terms of dividing $3 equally among 4 people using only dollars, dimes, and pennies.

3. Interpret each of your long-division steps in part 1 in terms of dividing the 3 large squares below into 4 equal parts.

4. Use long division to determine the decimal representation of $\frac{1}{8}$.

5. Interpret each of your long-division steps in part 4 in terms of dividing $1 equally among 8 people using dollars, dimes, and pennies. (Note that you will not be able to divide evenly without being able to split a penny.)

6. Interpret each of your long-division steps in part 4 in terms of dividing the following large square into 8 equal parts:

7. Use long division to determine the decimal representation of $\frac{1}{6}$ to the thousandths place.

8. Interpret the steps down to the hundredths place in your long division for part 7. Think in terms of dividing $1 equally among 6 people using dollars, dimes, and pennies.

9. Interpret each of your long-division steps in part 7 in terms of dividing the following large square into 6 equal parts:

CLASS ACTIVITY 70: Errors in Decimal Answers to Division Problems

1. Given that the answer to a whole number division problem is 4, remainder 1, can you tell what the decimal answer to the division problem is without any additional information? If not, what other information would you need to determine the decimal answer?

2. Ben has been making errors in his division problems. Here are some of Ben's answers:

$$251 \div 6 = 41.5$$
$$269 \div 7 = 38.3$$
$$951 \div 21 = 45.6$$

Use long division to calculate the correct answers to Ben's division problems. Based on your work, determine what Ben is likely to be confused about.

7.4 Dividing Fractions

CLASS ACTIVITY 7P: Explaining "Invert and Multiply" by Relating Division to Multiplication

Every division problem is equivalent to a multiplication problem:

$A \div B = ?$ is equivalent to $? \times B = A$.

Assume that you don't know the "invert and multiply" procedure for fraction division but that you do know how to multiply fractions. Solve each of the following division problems by first rewriting the problem as a multiplication problem:

1. $1 \div \frac{4}{5} = ?$

2. $1 \div \frac{3}{7} = ?$

3. $\frac{A}{B} \div \frac{4}{5} = ?$

4. $\frac{A}{B} \div \frac{3}{7} = ?$

5. $\frac{A}{B} \div \frac{C}{D} = ?$

CLASS ACTIVITY 7Q: "How Many Groups?" Fraction Division Problems

1. **a.** Write a "how many groups?" story problem for $6 \div 2$.

   b. Write a "how many groups?" story problem for $6 \div \frac{3}{4}$. (If it works, you may modify your story problem from part (a).)

   c. Assume that you don't know the "invert and multiply" method for dividing fractions. Solve your story problem for $6 \div \frac{3}{4}$ in a simple and concrete way, for example, by drawing pictures. Explain your solution.

   d. Use the "invert and multiply" procedure to calculate $6 \div \frac{3}{4}$. Verify that the answer agrees with your answer in part (c).

2. Tonya and Chrissy are trying to understand $1 \div \frac{2}{3}$ using the following story problem:

> One serving of rice is $\frac{2}{3}$ of a cup. I ate 1 cup of rice. How many servings of rice did I eat?

To solve the problem, Tonya and Chrissy draw a diagram of a large cup divided into three equal pieces, and they shade two of those pieces.

Tonya says, "There is one $\frac{2}{3}$-cup serving of rice in 1 cup and there is $\frac{1}{3}$ cup of rice left over, so the answer should be $1\frac{1}{3}$."

Chrissy says, "The part left over is $\frac{1}{3}$ cup of rice, but the answer is supposed to be $\frac{3}{2} = 1\frac{1}{2}$. Did we do something wrong?"

Help Tonya and Chrissy.

3. a. Write a "how many groups?" story problem for $8 \div 3$. Choose your story problem so that a mixed-number answer makes sense.

b. Write a "how many groups?" story problem for $1\frac{1}{2} \div \frac{2}{3}$. (If it works, you may modify your story problem from part (a).)

c. Assume that you don't know the "invert and multiply" method for dividing fractions. Solve your story problem for $1\frac{1}{2} \div \frac{2}{3}$ in a simple and concrete way, for example, by drawing pictures. Explain your solution.

d. Use the "invert and multiply" procedure to calculate $1\frac{1}{2} \div \frac{2}{3}$. Verify that the answer agrees with your answer in part (c).

4. a. Write a "how many groups?" story problem for $\frac{1}{3} \div \frac{3}{4}$.

b. Assume that you don't know the "invert and multiply" method for dividing fractions. Solve your story problem for $\frac{1}{3} \div \frac{3}{4}$ in a simple and concrete way, for example, by drawing pictures. Explain your solution.

c. Use the "invert and multiply" procedure to calculate $\frac{1}{3} \div \frac{3}{4}$. Verify that the answer agrees with your answer in part (b).

CLASS ACTIVITY 7R: "How Many in One Group?" Fraction Division Problems

1. **a.** Write a "how many in one group?" story problem for $6 \div 2$.

    b. Write a "how many in one group?" story problem for $3 \div \frac{1}{4}$. (If it works, you may modify your story problem from part (a).)

    c. Assume that you don't know the "invert and multiply" method for dividing fractions. Solve your story problem for $3 \div \frac{1}{4}$ in a simple and concrete way, for example, by drawing pictures. Explain your solution.

    d. Solve $3 \div \frac{1}{4}$ numerically by "inverting and multiplying," in other words, by multiplying 3 by $\frac{4}{1}$. Explain how your solution in part (c) shows this process of multiplying 3 by $\frac{4}{1}$.

2. a. Write a "how many in one group?" story problem for $6 \div \frac{3}{4}$.

b. Assume that you don't know the "invert and multiply" method for dividing fractions. Solve your story problem for $6 \div \frac{3}{4}$ in a simple and concrete way, for example, by drawing pictures. Explain your solution.

c. Solve $6 \div \frac{3}{4}$ numerically by "inverting and multiplying," in other words, by multiplying 6 by $\frac{4}{3}$. Explain how your solution in part (b) shows this process of multiplying 6 by $\frac{4}{3}$.

3. a. Write a "how many in one group?" story problem for $2 \div 3$. Choose your story problem so that a mixed number answer (in this case, a fraction answer) makes sense.

b. Write a "how many in one group?" story problem for $\frac{1}{2} \div \frac{2}{3}$. (If it works, you may modify your story problem from part (a).)

c. Assume that you don't know the "invert and multiply" method for dividing fractions. Solve your story problem for $\frac{1}{2} \div \frac{2}{3}$ in a simple and concrete way, for example, by drawing pictures. Explain your solution.

d. Solve $\frac{1}{2} \div \frac{2}{3}$ numerically by "inverting and multiplying," in other words, by multiplying $\frac{1}{2}$ by $\frac{3}{2}$. Explain how your solution in part (c) shows this process of multiplying $\frac{1}{2}$ by $\frac{3}{2}$.

CLASS ACTIVITY 7S: Are These Division Problems?

Which of the following are story problems for the division problem $\frac{3}{4} \div \frac{1}{2}$? For those that are, which interpretation of division is used? For those that are not, determine how to solve the problem if it can be solved.

1. Beth poured $\frac{3}{4}$ cup of cereal in a bowl. The cereal box says that one serving is $\frac{1}{2}$ cup. How many servings are in Beth's bowl?

2. Beth poured $\frac{3}{4}$ cup of cereal in a bowl. Then Beth took $\frac{1}{2}$ of that cereal and put it into another bowl. How many cups of cereal are in the second bowl?

3. A crew is building a road. So far, the road is $\frac{3}{4}$ mile long. This is $\frac{1}{2}$ the length that the road will be when it is finished. How many miles long will the finished road be?

4. A crew is building a road. So far, the crew has completed $\frac{3}{4}$ of the road, and this portion is $\frac{1}{2}$ mile long. How long will the finished road be?

5. If $\frac{3}{4}$ cup of flour makes $\frac{1}{2}$ a batch of cookies, then how many cups of flour are required for a full batch of cookies?

6. If $\frac{1}{2}$ cup of flour makes a batch of cookies, then how many batches of cookies can you make with $\frac{3}{4}$ cup of flour?

7. If $\frac{3}{4}$ cup of flour makes a batch of cookies, then how much flour is in $\frac{1}{2}$ of a batch of cookies?

7.5 Dividing Decimals

CLASS ACTIVITY 7T: Quick Tricks for Some Decimal Division Problems

1. Describe a quick way to calculate $32.5 \div 0.5$ mentally. Hint: Think in terms of fractions or in terms of money.

2. Describe a quick way to calculate $1.2 \div 0.25$ mentally.

3. Describe a quick way to calculate $7.2 \div 0.333$ mentally.

CLASS ACTIVITY 7U: Understanding Decimal Division

1. The problem

    "How many $0.25 are in $12.37?"

    is a story problem for the division problem

    $$12.37 \div 0.25$$

    Modify the story problem so that it retains its same meaning, but becomes a story problem for

    $$1237 \div 25$$

    What can you conclude about how the two division problems

    $$0.25 \overline{)12.37} \quad \text{and} \quad 25 \overline{)1237}$$

    are related?

2. Explain how Figure 7.1 can be interpreted as the following:

    $$12 \div 3.5 = ?$$

    Explain how the same figure can be interpreted as follows:

    $$120 \div 35 = ?$$

    What other division problems can Figure 7.1 illustrate? Use Figure 7.1 to help you give an approximate answer to $12 \div 3.5$.

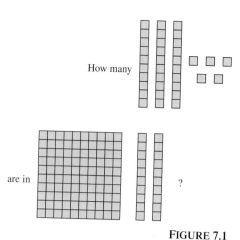

FIGURE 7.1

A Diagram for $12 \div 3.5$, for $120 \div 35$, and for
Other Division Problems

3. Draw a picture like Figure 7.1 for the following division problem:

    $$2.3 \div 0.75 = ?$$

    What other division problems can your picture illustrate? Use your picture to help you give an approximate answer to $2.3 \div 0.75 = ?$

4. Fran must calculate $2.45 \div 1.5$ longhand, but she can't remember what to do about decimal points. Instead, Fran solves the division problem $245 \div 15$ longhand and gets the answer 16.33. Fran knows that she must shift the decimal point in 16.33 somehow to get the correct answer to $2.45 \div 1.5$. Explain how Fran could reason about the sizes of the original numbers to determine where to put the decimal point.

7.6 Ratio and Proportion

CLASS ACTIVITY 7V: Ratios, Fractions, and Division

For a certain shade of orange paint, the ratio of red to yellow is 3 to 5. For each of the following fractions and division problems, write a question about the orange paint that will be answered by the given fraction or by solving the associated division problem.

1. $\frac{3}{8}$ or $3 \div 8$

2. $\frac{5}{8}$ or $5 \div 8$

3. $\frac{3}{5}$ or $3 \div 5$

4. $\frac{5}{3}$ or $5 \div 3$

5. $\frac{8}{3}$ or $8 \div 3$

6. $\frac{8}{5}$ or $8 \div 5$

CLASS ACTIVITY 7W: Equivalent Ratios

1. Driving at a constant speed, you drove 14 miles in 20 minutes. In the table that follows, fill in different distances and times that would give you the same speed. Use simple, logical reasoning about multiplication and division.

Drive _____ miles in _____ minutes.

Drive _____ miles in _____ minutes.

Drive _____ miles in 1 minute.

Drive 1 mile in _____ minutes.

2. Tracy mixed 3 tablespoons of lemonade concentrate with $\frac{3}{4}$ cup of water to make lemonade. In the table that follows, fill in other amounts of lemonade concentrate and water you could mix to make lemonade that tastes the same as Tracy's. Use simple, logical reasoning about multiplication and division.

Mix _____ tablespoons concentrate with _____ cups water.

Mix _____ tablespoons concentrate with _____ cups water.

Mix 1 tablespoon concentrate with _____ cups water.

Mix _____ tablespoons concentrate with 3 cups water.

3. For a certain shade of pink paint, the ratio of white paint to red paint is 3 to 2. In the table that follows, fill in different amounts of red and white paint that you could mix to get the same shade of pink paint. Use simple, logical reasoning about multiplication and division.

Use _____ cups white paint   for   _____ cups red paint   to make   _____ cups pink paint.

Use _____ cups white paint   for   _____ cups red paint   to make   _____ cups pink paint.

For   1 cup white paint   use   _____ cups red paint   to make   _____ cups pink paint.

Use _____ cups white paint   for   1 cup red paint   to make   _____ cups pink paint.

Use _____ cups white paint   for   _____ cups red paint   to make   1 cup pink paint.

CLASS ACTIVITY 7X: Making and Comparing Mixtures

Blue and yellow paint in squeeze bottles, containers for paint mixtures, water, and spoons or paintbrushes for mixing paint will be useful for part 1 and necessary for part 2 of this activity.

1. Will the following paint mixtures make the same shade of green? Why or why not? If not, how will the shades of green differ? Try to find several different elementary ways of reasoning to answer these questions.

   • 5 drops yellow and 2 drops blue

   • 8 drops yellow and 5 drops blue

   (All drops of paint should be the same size.) If possible, make the mixtures and check your answers. If you thin the paint with water, the colors might be easier to see.

2. Work with a partner or a group. Challenge your partner or another group by doing the following: Make two or three different shades of green paint by mixing blue paint with yellow paint. Write down the recipes for your paint mixtures and keep track of which recipe goes with which paint. On a piece of paper, paint a swatch of the different shades of green you made. Write the recipe for each shade underneath it, but hide the recipe by covering it with a sticky note or a piece of paper. Show your partner or another group your paint swatches and your recipes and ask them to figure out which recipe goes with which paint swatch.

3. Here are two ways to make lemonade using lemonade crystals:
   - Mix 2 tablespoons lemonade crystals with 9 tablespoons water.

   - Mix 3 tablespoons lemonade crystals with 10 tablespoons water.

   Jenny thinks that the mixtures will taste the same because you add one tablespoon of lemonade crystals and also one tablespoon of water to the first mixture to get the second mixture. Jenny says these added parts "cancel" each other. Ben says that the mixtures will taste the same because in both mixtures there are 7 tablespoons more water than lemonade crystals.

   a. Is Jenny's reasoning correct? Is Ben's reasoning correct? If not, why not?

   b. Should the two lemonade mixtures taste the same? If not, which one should be more lemony? Try to find several different elementary ways of reasoning to answer these questions.

CLASS ACTIVITY 7Y: Solving Proportions With Multiplication and Division

1. If you mix 3 cups of blue paint with 5 cups of yellow paint to make a green paint, then how many cups of yellow paint will you need if you want to make the same shade of green paint using 4 cups of blue paint? Use multiplication, division, and logical reasoning to explain how to fill in the blanks in the following table, thereby solving this paint problem:

	BLUE PAINT		YELLOW PAINT
For	3 cups blue paint,	use	5 cups yellow paint.
For	1 cup blue paint,	use	_____ cups yellow paint.
	Use your answer on the previous line to solve the following:		
For	4 cups blue paint,	use	_____ cups yellow paint.

2. Describe the strategy for solving the paint problem that the table in part 1 helps you use. What is the idea behind the way the table was created?

3. If you mix 3 cups of blue paint with 5 cups of yellow paint to make a green paint, then how many cups of blue paint and how many cups of yellow paint will you need if you want to make 10 cups of the same shade of green paint? Use multiplication, division, and logical reasoning to explain how to fill in the blanks in the following table thereby solving this paint problem:

	BLUE PAINT		YELLOW PAINT		GREEN PAINT
For	3 cups blue paint	use	5 cups yellow paint	to make	8 cups green paint.
For	_____ cups blue paint	use	_____ cups yellow paint	to make	1 cup green paint.
Use your answer on the previous line to solve:					
For	_____ cups blue paint	use	_____ cups yellow paint	to make	10 cups green paint.

4. Describe the strategy for solving the paint problem that the table in part 3 helps you use. What is the idea behind the way the table was created?

5. If you mix $\frac{3}{4}$ cup of red paint with $\frac{2}{3}$ cup of yellow paint to make an orange paint, then how many cups of red paint and how many cups of yellow paint will you need if you want to make 15 cups of the same shade of orange paint? Use multiplication, division, and logical reasoning to explain how to fill in the blanks in the following table, thereby solving this paint problem. For each line in the table, use your answer for that line to help you answer the next line.

	RED PAINT		YELLOW PAINT		ORANGE PAINT
For	$\frac{3}{4}$ cup red paint	use	$\frac{2}{3}$ cup yellow paint	to make	_____ cups orange paint.
For	_____ cups red paint	use	_____ cups yellow paint	to make	17 cups orange paint.
For	_____ cups red paint	use	_____ cups yellow paint	to make	1 cup orange paint.
For	_____ cups red paint	use	_____ cups yellow paint	to make	15 cups orange paint.

6. Describe the strategy for solving the paint problem that the table in part 5 helps you use. What is the idea behind the way the table was created?

7. Chandra made a milkshake by mixing $\frac{1}{2}$ cup of ice cream with $\frac{3}{4}$ cup of milk. Use the the most elementary reasoning you can to determine how many cups of ice cream and milk Chandra should use if she wants to make 3 cups of the same kind of milkshake.

8. Russell was supposed to mix 3 tablespoons of weed killer concentrate with $1\frac{3}{4}$ cups of water to make a weed killer. By accident, Russell put in an extra tablespoon of weed killer concentrate, mixing 4 tablespoons of weed killer concentrate with $1\frac{3}{4}$ cups of water. How much water should Russell add to his mixture so that the ratio of weed killer concentrate to water will be the same as in the correct mixture? Use the most elementary reasoning you can to solve this problem.

CLASS ACTIVITY 7Z: Solving Proportions by Cross-Multiplying Fractions

Read the following recipe problem:

A recipe that serves 6 people calls for $2\frac{1}{2}$ cups of flour. How much flour will you need to serve 10 people, assuming that the ratio of people to cups of flour remains the same?

One familiar way to solve this problem is by setting up and solving a proportion as follows: First, we let x be the amount of flour we need to serve 10 people. Then we set two fractions equal to each other:

$$\frac{x}{10} = \frac{2\frac{1}{2}}{6}$$

In setting these fractions equal to each other, we think "x is to 10 as $2\frac{1}{2}$ is to 6." Next, we "cross-multiply" to obtain the equation

$$6 \cdot x = 10 \cdot 2\frac{1}{2}$$

Finally, we solve for x by dividing both sides of the equation by 6. Therefore,

$$x = \frac{10 \cdot 2\frac{1}{2}}{6} = \frac{10 \cdot \frac{5}{2}}{6} = \frac{25}{6} = 4\frac{1}{6}$$

and we see that $4\frac{1}{6}$ cups of flour are needed to serve 10 people.

This class activity will help you understand the rationale for this method of solving proportions.

1. In the solution we just found, we worked with two fractions:

$$\frac{x}{10} \quad \text{and} \quad \frac{2\frac{1}{2}}{6}$$

Interpret the meaning of these fractions in terms of the recipe problem at the beginning of this activity. Explain why these two fractions should be equal.

2. After setting two fractions equal to each other, the next step in solving the proportion was to "cross-multiply." Why does it make sense to cross-multiply? What is the rationale behind the procedure of cross-multiplying?

3. In the preceding solution, we set up the proportion

$$\frac{x}{10} = \frac{2\frac{1}{2}}{6}$$

What is another way to set up a proportion so that the unknown amount of flour, x, is in the numerator of one of the fractions? Interpret the two fractions in your new proportion in terms of the recipe problem. Use your interpretations to explain why the two fractions should be equal.

4. Now solve the recipe problem in a different way by using logical thinking and by using the most elementary reasoning you can. Explain your reasoning clearly.

CLASS ACTIVITY 7AA: Can You Always Use a Proportion?

Sometimes a problem that looks as if it could be solved by setting up a proportion actually can't be solved that way. Before you set up a proportion to solve a problem, ask the following question about quantities in the problem: if I double one of the quantities, should the other quantity also double? If the answer is "no," then you cannot solve the problem by setting up a proportion.

1. Ken used 3 loads of stone pavers to make a circular (i.e., circle-shaped) patio with a radius of 10 feet. Ken wants to make another circular patio with a radius of 15 feet, so he sets up the proportion

$$\frac{3 \text{ loads}}{10 \text{ feet}} = \frac{x \text{ loads}}{15 \text{ feet}}$$

Is this correct? If not, why not? Is there another proportion that Ken could set up to solve the problem? (The area of a circle that has radius r units is πr^2 square units.)

2. In a cookie factory, 4 assembly lines make enough boxes of cookies to fill a truck in 10 hours. How long will it take to fill a truck if 8 assembly lines are used? Is the proportion

$$\frac{10 \text{ hours}}{4 \text{ lines}} = \frac{x \text{ hours}}{8 \text{ lines}}$$

appropriate for this situation? Why or why not? If not, can you solve the problem another way?

3. In the cookie factory of problem 2, how long will it take to fill a truck if 6 assembly lines are used? (If you get stuck here, move on to the next problem and come back.)

4. Robyn used the following reasoning to solve the previous problem:

> Since 4 assembly lines fill a truck in 10 hours, 8 assembly lines should fill a truck in half that time, namely in 5 hours. Since 6 assembly lines is halfway between 4 and 8, it ought to take halfway between 10 hours and 5 hours, or $7\frac{1}{2}$ hours, to fill a truck.

Robyn's reasoning seems quite reasonable, but is it really correct? Let's look carefully.

Fill in the following table by using logical thinking about the assembly lines:

# OF ASSEMBLY LINES	# OF HOURS TO FILL A TRUCK
1	
2	
4	10 hours
8	
16	
32	

Now apply Robyn's reasoning again, but this time to 1 assembly line versus 32. Sixteen assembly lines is approximately halfway between 1 and 32. But is the number of hours it takes to fill a truck using 16 assembly lines approximately halfway between the number of hours it takes to fill a truck using 1 assembly line versus using 32 assembly lines?

What can you conclude about Robyn's reasoning?

CLASS ACTIVITY 7BB: The Consumer Price Index

Sometimes news reports compare how much was spent on items in the past and now. For example, a report in *Newsweek* magazine on December 15, 1997, published a table like the following one, listing the most expensive movies ever made:

COST IN MILLIONS			
YEAR	MOVIE	ORIGINAL	1997$
1967	*War and Peace*	$100	$482
1997	*Titanic*	200	200
1963	*Cleopatra*	37	195
1995	*Waterworld*	175	185
1997	*Speed 2: Cruise Control*	160	160
1994	*True Lies*	105	114
1962	*Mutiny on the Bounty*	21	112
1996	*Space Jam*	105	108
1996	*Eraser*	100	103
1997	*Batman & Robin*	100	100

1. What do you think "1997$" means in the table, and why are the movies ordered by that instead of by their original costs?

The following table shows the value of the CPI for some selected years:

CONSUMER PRICE INDEX (SELECTED YEARS)		
YEAR CPI	YEAR CPI	YEAR CPI
1940: 14.0	1991: 136.2	1996: 156.9
1950: 24.1	1992: 140.3	1997: 160.5
1960: 29.6	1993: 144.5	1998: 163.0
1970: 38.8	1994: 148.2	1999: 166.6
1980: 82.4	1995: 152.4	2000: 172.2
1990: 130.7		

2. What salary in the year 2000 would have had the same buying power as $20,000 did in 1950?

3. If a gallon of milk cost $3 in 2000, what should it have cost in 1940, if you use the CPI to adjust for inflation?

    Does this necessarily give you the actual cost of a gallon of milk in 1940? Why not?

4. In 1967 the CPI was 33.4; in 1997 it was 160.5. Use the CPI to put the $100 million cost of the 1967 movie *War and Peace* into 1997 dollars. Does your answer agree with *Newsweek*'s, at least approximately? Why might your answer and *Newsweek*'s not be in exact agreement?

5. If a certain item cost $2 in 1980 and $3.50 in 2000, would it be at all reasonable to argue that its price had gone down from 1980 to 2000? How so?

Chapter 8

Geometry

8.1 Visualization

CLASS ACTIVITY 8A: Visualizing Lines and Planes

1. Visualize a line in a plane. The line divides the plane into two disjoint pieces—visualize these two pieces as well. Visualize a line in space. Does a line in space divide space into disjoint pieces? The word **disjoint** means *distinct and not meeting*.

2. Visualize *two* lines in a plane. How many disjoint pieces do the two lines divide the plane into? The answer depends on how the lines are positioned relative to each other—explain. Draw pictures to aid your explanation, but be sure to also "see" this in your "mind's eye."

3. Visualize *three* lines in a plane. How many disjoint pieces do the three lines divide the plane into? Again, the answer depends on how the lines are positioned relative to each other. Try to *visualize* the distinct configurations. Then draw pictures to help you show all the different types of configurations and to see how many disjoint pieces there are in each case.

4. Visualize a plane in space. A single plane in (3-dimensional) space divides space into two disjoint regions. If the plane you are thinking of is horizontal, then these two regions are the region above the plane and the region below the plane. Visualize a nonhorizontal plane and the two distinct regions into which it divides space.

5. Visualize *two* planes in space. Into how many disjoint regions do two planes divide space? The answer depends on how the planes are arranged relative to each other—explain. Use two pieces of paper to help you, but be sure to try to see the planes in your mind's eye.

6. Visualize *three* planes in space. Into how many disjoint regions do three planes divide space? As always, the answer depends on how the planes are arranged in space. Describe all the different types of configurations and make paper models to help you. (You will probably want to cut the paper and use tape for this.) Be sure to also *visualize* all these different types of configurations. How can you tell whether you've found all the different possibilities for disjoint regions there can be?

CLASS ACTIVITY 8B: Parts of a Pyramid

You will need paper, scissors, and tape for part 1 of this activity. You will need modeling dough or modeling clay and dental floss for part 3.

The following picture shows a pyramid (like an Egyptian pyramid):

1. What shapes would you need to make the outer surface of the pyramid out of paper?

    Make a paper model of the pyramid, including the bottom. Be willing to "get messy," make mistakes, and modify your initial ideas until you find shapes that you can cut out and tape together to make a pyramid.

2. Now visualize a plane slicing through the pyramid. The places where the plane passes through the pyramid form a shape in the plane. Describe all possible shapes in the plane that can be made this way, by slicing the pyramid. Use your model to help you, but also visualize each case *without* using your model.

3. Use modeling dough or modeling clay to make a pyramid. Slice straight through your pyramid with dental floss, as if you were slicing the pyramid with a plane. The place where the dental floss cut through the pyramid should make a plane shape. What plane shape did you get this way? Put the pyramid back together and try slicing it in a different way. Now what shape do you get? Find as many different plane shapes as you can.

CLASS ACTIVITY 8C: Slicing Through a Board

You will need modeling clay or modeling dough and dental floss for this activity. Suppose you have an ordinary 2″-by-4″ board, as pictured here:

If you saw through the board with a straight cut, the place where the board was cut makes a shape in a plane.

1. Is it possible to saw the board with a straight cut in such a way that the shape formed by the cut is a square? Try to visualize if this is or isn't possible.

2. Is it possible to saw the board with a straight cut in such a way that the shape formed by the cut is *not* a rectangle? (A square *is* a kind of rectangle.) Try to visualize if this is or isn't possible. If the answer is yes, what kind of shape other than a rectangle can you get?

3. Use modeling dough to make a model of a 2″-by-4″ board. Make a straight slice through your model with dental floss. Describe the plane shape that the cut made. Now restore your model of the board to its original shape and make a different slice through your model. Keep trying different ways to slice your model. Describe all the different shapes you get where the model was cut.

CLASS ACTIVITY 8D: What Shapes Do These Patterns Make?

You will need scissors and tape for this activity.

The next picture shows small versions of patterns for shapes. Figure A.2 on page 533 has large versions of these patterns that can be cut out, folded, and taped to make closed, solid shapes.

Before you cut, fold, and tape the large patterns on page 533, *visualize* the folding process in order to help you visualize the final shapes. Be patient and make several attempts. Remember that the goal of this section is to improve your visualization skills. Discuss and debate your ideas with some of your classmates. Then cut out the large patterns on page 533 along the solid lines, fold down along the dotted lines (or fold up—but be consistent), and tape sides with matching labels together.

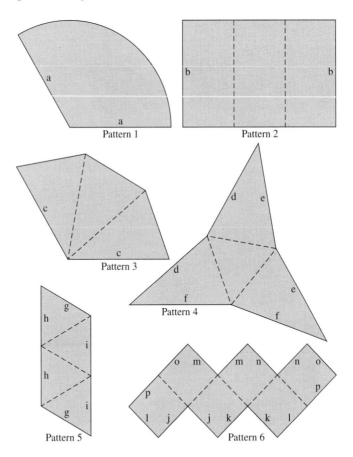

CLASS ACTIVITY 8E: Remember Those Shapes

You can use a set of blocks in this activity.

Work with a partner. Take turns being a "builder" and a "copier." The builder should build a structure out of blocks, keeping the structure hidden from the copier. When the structure is done, the copier gets a quick look at the structure and should then try to reproduce it without looking back at the original.

If blocks are not available, or as a variation, the builder can draw a picture using circles, squares, rectangles, triangles, and other geometric shapes instead of building a structure.

CLASS ACTIVITY 8F: Time Zones

A table-tennis ball and a flashlight would be useful for part 2. If these are not available, a larger ball such as a basketball, or better yet, a globe, can be used to demonstrate to the whole class.

The surface of the Earth is divided into different time zones. For example, the continental U.S. has four time zones: Eastern, Central, Mountain, and Pacific. This activity will help you explain why it makes sense to have different time zones and how times vary as you move about the world.

1. Visualize the Earth in space, rotating about the axis through the North and South Poles. The Earth completes a full rotation about its axis every 24 hours (approximately). Visualize the Sun, far away, sending light rays to illuminate the portion of the Earth that is facing the Sun. Figures 8.1 and 8.2 may help.

2. If available, a flashlight and a table-tennis ball can be used to simulate the Sun and Earth. Hold the table-tennis ball between two fingers, more or less vertically, at points representing the North and South Poles. Shine the flashlight on the side of the ball. On your table-tennis ball, where is it about noon? Where is it about midnight? Where is it sunrise? Where is it sunset? Explain your answers. Use the fact that the Sun rises in the east to distinguish sunrise from sunset.

   Now rotate the ball to simulate the Earth's rotation throughout the day. Given that the Sun rises in the east, which way should you rotate the table-tennis ball?

FIGURE 8.1

The Earth

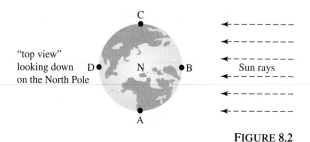

FIGURE 8.2

The Earth, Seen from above the North Pole

3. Given that the Sun rises in the east, approximately what time of day is it at locations A, B, C, and D in Figure 8.2, in which the Earth is pictured as seen from above the North Pole?

4. Explain why it makes sense that the time on the east coast of the U.S. should be different from the time on the west coast of the U.S. Is it earlier on the west coast than on the east coast, or is it later? Explain why, using the fact that the Sun rises in the east.

CLASS ACTIVITY 8G: Explaining the Phases of the Moon

Every month the Moon goes through phases, waxing from a new moon to a full moon and then waning from a full moon back to a new moon, as shown in the following diagram:

new moon ——————————→ full moon ——————————→ new moon
(invisible)   waxing   (fully visible)   waning

The phases of the Moon are caused by its rotation about the Earth every month. The Moon gives off no light of its own, so we can only see it because light from the Sun reflects off the Moon. Therefore, *we only see that portion of the Moon which faces both toward the Sun and toward us on the Earth.* As the Moon rotates about the Earth, different portions of the Moon become visible to people on Earth, depending on the positions of the Earth, Moon, and Sun.

1. Imagine floating far above the Earth and Moon in outer space, looking straight down at the plane of the path of the Moon around the Earth, as in Figure 8.3, parts A and B. Explain why the shaded portion of the Moon shown in part B represents the part of the Moon that is visible from the Earth. Use the dashed lines to help you.

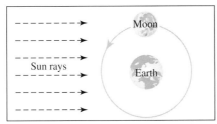

A: the Earth, Moon, and Sun rays, not to scale

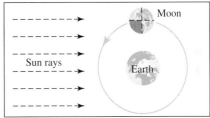

B: the portion of the Moon visible from Earth

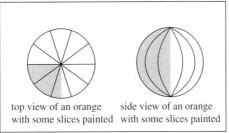

top view of an orange   side view of an orange
with some slices painted   with some slices painted

C: using an orange to represent the reflection of the Sun's rays from the Moon

FIGURE 8.3

In What Phase Is the Moon?

2. Describe how the Moon appears to a person on the Earth when the Earth, Moon, and Sun's rays are positioned as shown in Figure 8.3, parts A and B. To help you, use the idea of looking down on the top of an orange and at the side of an orange, as indicated in part C.

3. Describe how the Moon appears to a person on the Earth in each of the diagrams in Figure 8.4. In each case, explain why the Moon appears that way. Parts A – D are not to scale, but part E shows the Earth and Moon, and the distance between them, to scale.

4. Determine the phase of the Moon in Figure 8.3 (A) on page 217, and in Figure 8.4 (A – D) below. In which diagram is the Moon new? In which is it full? In which is is waxing? In which is it waning? Explain your answers.

Sun rays are not in the plane of the page; they come from slightly above this plane.

A   B

C   D

E: the Earth and Moon shown to scale

FIGURE 8.4

In What Phase Is the Moon?

You might be wondering why there aren't eclipses at every new Moon and full Moon. A solar eclipse occurs when the Moon passes right in front of the Sun, as observed from Earth, temporarily obscuring our view of the Sun. A lunar eclipse occurs when the Earth is directly between the Sun and Moon and casts a shadow on the Moon. At a new Moon, the Moon is between the Sun and the Earth. At a full Moon, the Earth is between the Sun and the Moon. So why isn't there a solar eclipse at every new Moon and lunar eclipse at every full Moon? The reason is that the Sun is not in the plane in which the Moon revolves around the Earth, so that the Earth, Moon, and Sun rarely lie in a straight line. You should think of the Sun rays shown in Figure 8.4 as coming from slightly *above* (or below) the plane formed by the page.

CLASS ACTIVITY 8H: More Patterns for Shapes

You will need scissors and tape for this activity.

The next picture shows small versions of patterns for shapes. Figures A.3 and A.4 on pages 535 and 537 have large versions of these patterns that can be cut out, folded, and taped to make closed, solid shapes.

Before you cut, fold, and tape the large patterns on pages 535 and 537, *visualize* the folding process in order to help you visualize the final shapes. Be patient and make several attempts. Discuss and debate your ideas with some of your classmates. Then cut out the patterns along the solid lines, fold down along the dotted lines (or fold up—but be consistent), and tape sides with matching labels together.

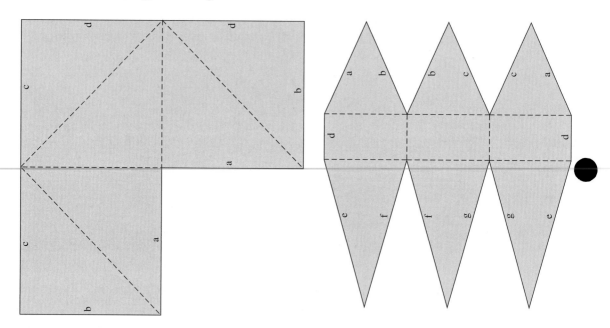

8.2 Angles

CLASS ACTIVITY 81: Angle Explorers

1. An "angle explorer" is made by fastening two cardboard strips with a brass fastener, as shown in the next figure. Discuss how to use an angle explorer to relate the two ways of describing an angle: as an "amount of turning" or as "two rays (or line segments) meeting."

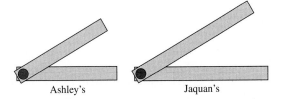

Ashley's   Jaquan's

2. Ashley and Jaquan make "angle explorers," as shown in the preceding figure, but Ashley uses shorter cardboard strips than Jaquan. Ashley says that her angle explorer shows a smaller angle than Jaquan's. What is Ashley's misconception, and how could you help her correct it?

CLASS ACTIVITY 8J: Creating Angles by Folding Paper

You will need blank paper and a ruler for this activity.

1. Draw a line anywhere on a blank piece of paper. Let A be a point somewhere
    on your line (but not at the edge of your paper). Follow the instructions in
    the next figure to create a fold line making a 90° angle (right angle) with
    the line you drew at the point A.

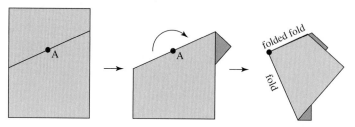

Fold along your line.   Fold the fold onto itself at the
                            point A.

When you unfold your paper, you should have a fold line that makes a
right angle with the line you drew.

2. Explain why the folding instructions in part (a) of the figure must necessarily
    create a right angle. Without measuring the resulting angle, how do you
    know that it couldn't be less than 90° or more than 90° — how do you know
    that it must be exactly 90°?

3. Now continue to fold your piece of paper from part (a) to create a 45° angle
    with your line at the point A. Explain how you know that your folding
    creates a 45° angle.

CLASS ACTIVITY 8K: Angles Formed by Two Lines

1. The next figure shows three pairs of lines meeting (or you may wish to think of this as showing one pair of lines in three situations, when the lines are moved to different positions). In each case, how do angles *a* and *c* appear to be related, and how do angles *b* and *d* appear to be related?

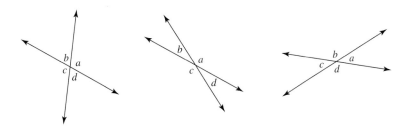

2. Do you think the same phenomenon you observed in problem 1 will hold for *any* pair of lines meeting at a point? Do you have a convincing reason why?

3. Explain *why* what you observed in problem 1 must always be true by using the fact that an angle formed by a straight line is 180°. Use this fact to tell you something about several pairs of angles.

CLASS ACTIVITY 8L: Describing Routes Using Distances and Angles

You will need a protractor and a ruler for this activity.

1. The map in the next figure shows a route along which Dave, who is blind-folded, is to walk. On the map, 1 inch represents 5 of Dave's paces. Dave starts at point A, facing the route, so that he is ready to start walking along it. Use a protractor to help you tell Dave how to get to point H. For example, here's what Dave should do to get from point A to point C:

   Starting at A, go 5 paces to B. At B, turn clockwise (to your right) 60°. Go another 10 paces to C.

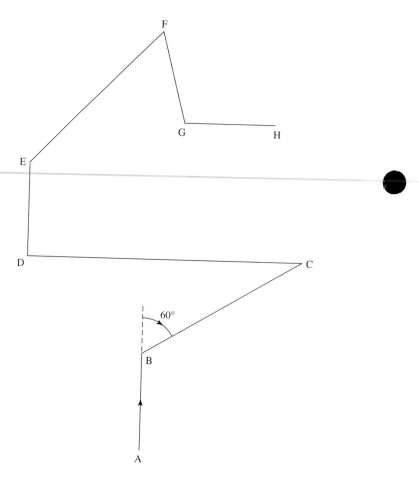

2. For each of the routes in the next figure, tell Dave, who is blindfolded, how to walk around the route. One inch on the map represents 5 of Dave's paces. In each case, Dave will start at the point labeled A, facing the route, so that he is ready to start walking along it.

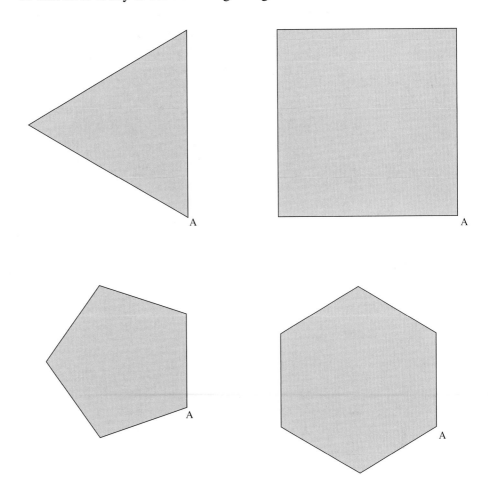

3. For each route in problem 2, determine Dave's total amount of turning along the route if he returns to point A and *turns to face the same direction in which he started*.

CLASS ACTIVITY 8M: Angles in Vision

You will need 3 straws or sticks and a lump of clay with which to join them for part 2.

1. The angles at the corners of an ordinary, rectangular piece of paper are right angles, but depending on how you hold the piece of paper, the angles may not appear as right angles in your field of vision.

   Hold a rectangular piece of paper so that it is not parallel to your face. Even though the angles at the corners are right angles, how do these angles appear to you? Do the angles appear to be right angles or not? If not, which angles are greater than 90° (obtuse) and which are less than 90° (acute)? Try to draw the angles as they appear to you. Now hold the piece of paper with a different orientation, but again not parallel to your face, and answer the previous questions once more.

   How do artists use angles?

2. Join three straws or sticks with a lump of clay such that they simulate a corner in a room where two walls and a ceiling meet. Each straw should be perpendicular to the other two straws.

   Hold your "corner" so that you can imagine you are looking at the corner of a room. (One of the straws should be vertical, simulating the edge where two walls meet.) Draw your corner, as it appears in your field of vision. Even though the angle formed by each pair of straws is a right angle, do these angles appear as right angles in your drawing?

   Now hold your corner up higher, simulating that the room you are in has a higher ceiling than before. Again, draw your corner, as it appears in your field of vision. In what way is your drawing different than before?

CLASS ACTIVITY 8N: Angles of Sun Rays

1. How are the following related?
   a. The height of the Sun in the sky

   b. The length of the shadows of telephone poles (or other objects)

   c. The angle that the Sun's rays make with horizontal ground
   Draw diagrams to help you describe and explain the relationships.

2. Because the Sun is so far away, light rays coming from the Sun form virtually parallel straight lines near the Earth. When light rays from the Sun strike a location on the Earth, they form an angle with the horizontal ground. Figure 8.5 shows a diagram of a portion of the Earth seen from above the North Pole, marked N, and Sun rays traveling toward the Earth. Assume these Sun rays are parallel to the page.
   a. At each location A, B, C, and D in Figure 8.5, show the angle that a Sun ray makes with the horizontal ground there.

   b. At each location A, B, C, and D in Figure 8.5, describe how the Sun would appear to a person standing there. Is the Sun high in the sky or low in the sky? is the Sun in the east, in the west, or directly overhead?

   c. At each location A, B, C, and D in Figure 8.5, describe how long the shadow of a telephone pole would be. Is the shadow of a telephone pole long or short compared to the other locations? How can you tell?

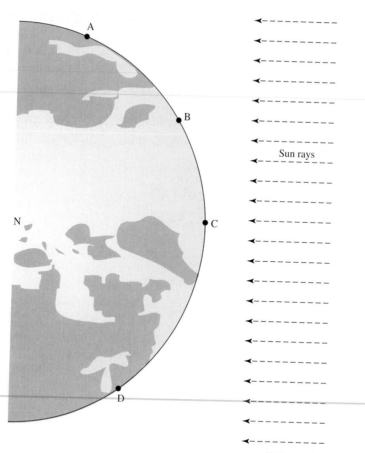

FIGURE 8.5
Parallel Sun Rays Traveling toward the Earth

CLASS ACTIVITY 80: How the Tilt of the Earth Causes Seasons

If available, a globe or a ball with labels representing the North and South Poles would be useful for this activity.

What causes the seasons? Some people mistakenly believe that the seasons are caused by the Earth's varying distance from the Sun. In fact, the distance from the Earth to the Sun varies only a little during the year. The seasons are caused by the tilt of the Earth's axis.

1. Visualize the Earth rotating around the Sun over the course of a year. As the Earth travels around the Sun, the axis between the North and South Poles of the Earth remains parallel to itself in space, in other words, the tilt of the Earth's axis does not change. The Earth's axis is tilted 23.5° from the perpendicular to the plane in which the Earth rotates about the Sun, as shown in the following diagram:

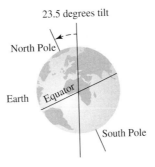

Simulate the Earth's yearly journey around the Sun either with a globe or as follows: Make a fist around a pencil. The pencil represents the Earth's axis (through the North and South Poles) and your fist represents the Earth. Imagine the Sun in front of you. Move your fist around your imagined Sun, keeping your pencil tilted to represent the tilt of the Earth. *Keep the pencil parallel to its original position* as you move your "Earth" around the "Sun." Notice that as the Earth travels around the Sun, the North Pole is sometimes tilted toward the Sun and sometimes tilted away from the Sun.

2. The following diagram shows the Earth at two different times of year. In diagram 1, the North Pole is tilted directly toward the Sun. In diagram 2, the South Pole is tilted directly toward the Sun and the North Pole is tilted directly away from the Sun. In both diagrams, assume that the Sun rays are parallel to the page. To picture other times of year, visualize the Sun's rays coming from outside of the plane of the page.

   a. Points A and B in diagrams 1 and 2 are both shown at around noon. In diagram 1, is the Sun higher in the sky at point A or point B? In diagram 2, is the Sun higher in the sky at point A or point B?

   b. During the day, the Earth rotates on its axis. In both diagrams 1 and 2, visualize how the locations of points A and B will change throughout the day. Which of the points, A or B, will receive more sunlight over the course of a day in diagram 1? Which of the points, A or B, will receive more sunlight over the course of a day in diagram 2?

   c. What season is it in the northern hemisphere in diagram 1? What season is it in the northern hemisphere in diagram 2? Why?

Diagram 1

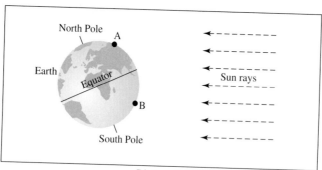

Diagram 2

FIGURE 8.6
The Earth's Position around the Sun at Different Times of Year

CLASS ACTIVITY 8P: Looking in a Mirror

We can use the laws of reflection to determine what a person looking in a mirror will see at various points.

Figure 8.7 shows a side view of a person looking into a mirror. Using the laws of reflection, determine what the person will see at each of the points A, B, and C. We see objects by seeing the light that travels from the object to our eyes. So a person looking at a particular point sees the light that travels in a straight line from that point to the person's eye. To determine what a person sees at a point in a mirror, you must determine where the light at that point came from. For this you will need the laws of reflection.

CLASS ACTIVITY 8Q: How Big Is the Reflection of Your Face in a Mirror?

You will need a mirror and a ruler for this activity.

How big is the reflection of your face in a mirror? Is it the same size as your face or is it larger or smaller, and if so, how much? The answers to these questions may surprise you.

1. Use a ruler to measure the length of your face from the top of your forehead to your chin. Now hold a mirror *parallel* to your face and measure the length of your face's reflection in the mirror, from the top of the forehead to the chin. Measure carefully!

    Hold the mirror closer to your face or farther away (but always *parallel* to your face) and repeat the measuring processes just described. The *position* of your reflection will probably change, but does the *size* of your reflection change or not? The answer may surprise you.

    Compare the length of your face and the length of your reflected face in the mirror. How do these lengths appear to be related?

2. Use the reflection laws to show where the person looking into the mirror in Figure 8.8 will see the top of her forehead and where she will see the bottom of her chin. Measure the length of the person's face and the length of her reflected face in the mirror. How do these lengths appear to be related? Your result should fit with what you discovered in part 1.

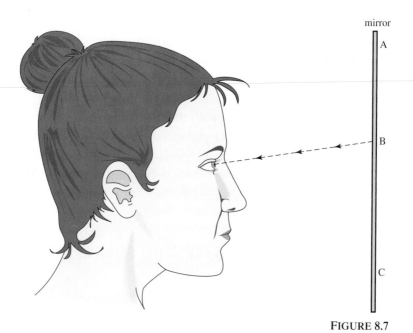

mirror

A

B

C

FIGURE 8.7

Looking into a Mirror

mirror

FIGURE 8.8

Where Is the Person's Reflection in the Mirror?

CLASS ACTIVITY 8R: Why Do Spoons Reflect Upside Down?

A large, reflective spoon would be helpful for this activity.

When you look at your reflection in the bowl of a spoon, you will notice that (in addition to looking quite distorted) your image will appear upside down. Have you ever wondered why? We will explore this now.

Figure 8.9 is a diagram of a person looking into the bowl of a (very large) spoon. Only a cross section of the spoon is shown. The lines shown are the *normal lines* to the spoon at the points A, B, and C. Use these normal lines and the laws of reflection to determine what the person sees when she looks at points A, B, and C. (Assume that the person sees light that enters the center of her eye.)

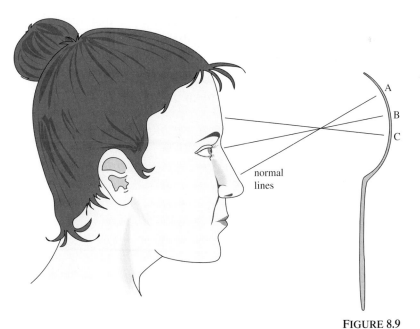

FIGURE 8.9

Looking into a Spoon

CLASS ACTIVITY 8S: The Special Shape of Satellite Dishes

Satellite dishes are shaped in a special way so as to capture efficiently incoming radio waves broadcast from a satellite. The top diagram of Figure 8.10 shows the cross section of a satellite dish. The curve formed by this cross section is called a **parabola**.

1. Verify that all incoming radio waves hitting a parabolic satellite dish (top diagram of Figure 8.10) reflect onto the receiver. The receiver is shown as a small circle inside and above the center of the satellite dish. (Actual satellite dishes usually do not extend above their receiver, as this one does, but this exaggerated diagram will be easier to work with.)

2. The cross section of a cone-shaped satellite dish forms a v-shaped curve, as shown in the bottom diagram of Figure 8.10. What kind of receiver would a cone-shaped satellite dish need in order to capture all the incoming radio waves reflected from the inside of the satellite dish? Could the receiver be as small as the one for a typical parabolic satellite dish? Explain.

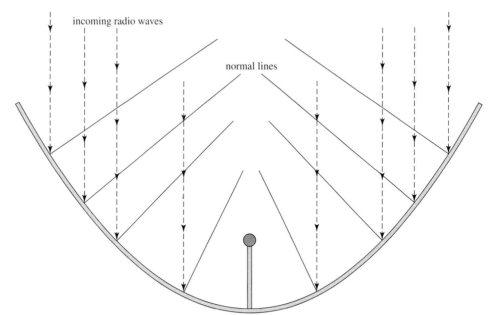

incoming radio waves

normal lines

cross section of a parabolic satellite dish

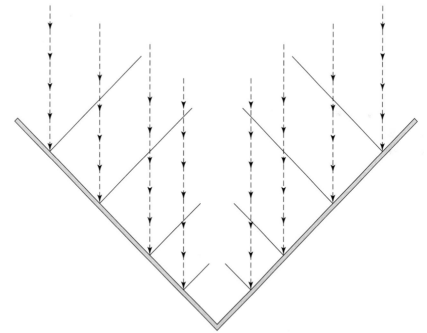

cross section of a hypothetical cone-shaped satellite dish

FIGURE 8.10

Cross Sections of Satellite Dishes

8.3 Circles and Spheres

CLASS ACTIVITY 8T: Points That Are a Fixed Distance from a Given Point

You will need a ruler for this activity.

1. Use a ruler to draw 5 different points that are 1 inch away from the point P:

•
P

Now draw 5 more points that are 1 inch away from the point P. If you could keep drawing more and more points that are 1 inch away from point P, what shape would this collection of points begin to look like?

2. Have one person point to a particular point in space, call that point P. Using a ruler, find several other locations in space that are one ruler-length away from point P. (A ruler-length might be 12 inches or 6 inches, depending on your ruler.) Try to visualize all the points in space that are one ruler-length away from your point P. What shape do you see?

CLASS ACTIVITY 8U: Circle Curiosities

You will need various coins for part 1 and a compass for part 2.

1. How many pennies can you place around a single penny, each touching the inner penny? Try it and see. Do the pennies fit snugly around the inner penny or not?

    Now try placing as many pennies as you can around a single nickel so that each penny touches the inner nickel. Do the pennies fit snugly around the inner nickel or not?

    How many nickels can you place around a single nickel, each touching the inner nickel? Do the nickels fit snugly around the inner nickel or not?

2. Although the design below looks complex, it is surprisingly easy to make. Use a compass to draw a design like the one below. Explain how to draw the design. If you look closely, you will also see the phenomenon you discovered about arranging pennies in part 1.

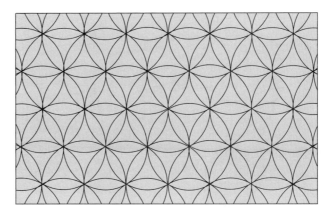

CLASS ACTIVITY 8V: Using Circles

You will need a compass for this activity. Some string would also be useful.

1. Use the definition of a circle to explain why a compass draws a circle. How is the radius of the circle related to the compass?

2. Explain how to use a piece of string and a pencil to draw a circle. Use the definition of a circle to explain why your method will draw a circle.

3. Suppose that, 1 hour and 45 minutes ago, a prisoner escaped from a prison located at point P, shown on the map that follows. Due to the terrain and the fact that no vehicles have left the area, police estimate that the prisoner can go no faster than 4 miles per hour. Show all places on the map where the prisoner might be at this moment. Explain.

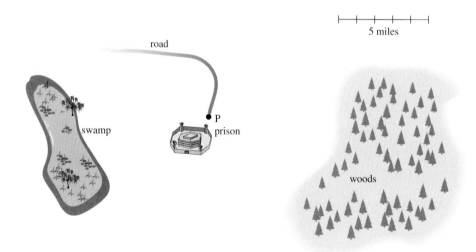

4. The treasure map for this exercise shows an X and an O marking two spots. The treasure is described as buried under a spot that is 30 feet from X and 50 feet from O. Use this information to help you show where the treasure might be buried. Is the information enough to tell you *exactly* where the treasure is buried? Explain.

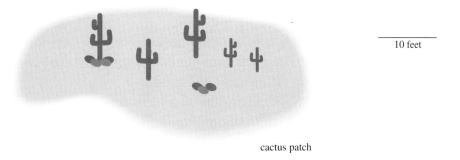

cactus patch

—————
10 feet

X   O

snake pit

CLASS ACTIVITY 8W: The Global Positioning System (GPS)

You will need string for this activity.

The Global Positioning System (GPS) is a navigation system designed and maintained by the U.S. Department of Defense for military use, but is also available for civilian use. With a hand-held GPS unit, it is possible to determine your location on the Earth, accurate to within about 10 meters. The GPS system uses a network of 24 satellites that orbit the Earth. Figure 8.11 shows a GPS satellite. A GPS unit receives information on its distance from each satellite within its range. The GPS unit can then figure its location by using those distances, based on the geometry of spheres.

Suppose a GPS unit learns that it is a certain distance from satellite 1 and another certain distance from satellite 2. The following activity will help you describe all possible locations for the GPS unit by simulating the situation with people and string:

1. Pick two people to represent satellites 1 and 2, and pick a third person who will show all possible locations of the GPS unit. The GPS person should stand in between satellites 1 and 2.

2. Cut two pieces of string, representing the distances from satellites 1 and 2 to the GPS unit.

FIGURE 8.11
A GPS Satellite

3. Satellites 1 and 2 should each hold one end of their piece of string, and the GPS person should hold the other ends of the two pieces of string in one hand, pulling the strings tight. (Everyone may have to adjust positions so that it is possible to do this. Once suitable positions are found, everyone should stay fixed in his or her position.)

4. The designated GPS person will now be able to show all possible locations of the GPS unit by moving the strings, while keeping them pulled tight and held in one hand (and while satellites 1 and 2 remain fixed in their positions). See Figures 8.12 and 8.13.

5. Describe the shape of all possible locations of the GPS unit. How is this related to the intersection of two spheres?

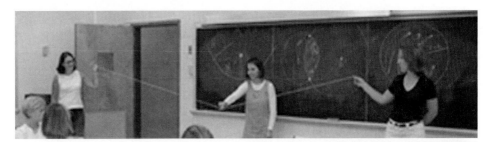

FIGURE 8.12
Showing a Position of a GPS Unit

FIGURE 8.13
Showing Another Position of a GPS Unit

6. Now suppose that there is also a third satellite beaming information to the GPS unit. Pick a person to represent sallelite 3 and cut a piece of string to represent the distance of satellite 3 to the GPS unit.

7. Satellite 3 should hold one end of her or his string while the GPS person holds the other end in the same hand with the strings from satellites 1 and 2. By pulling all three strings tight, the GPS person can show all possible locations of the GPS unit. In general, there will be two such locations. See Figures 8.14 and 8.15.

FIGURE 8.14

One Position of a GPS Unit, Given Information from 3 Satellites

FIGURE 8.15

Another Position of a GPS Unit, Given Information from 3 Satellites

How is this exercise related to the intersection of three spheres?

As you've seen, with information from three satellites, a GPS unit can narrow its location to one of two points. If one of those two locations can be recognized as being in outer space, and not on the surface of the Earth, then the GPS unit can report its location on the Earth. This is the idea behind the GPS system.

8.4 Triangles

CLASS ACTIVITY 8X: Making Right Triangles, Isosceles Triangles, and Equilateral Triangles

You will need paper, scissors, a compass, and a ruler for this activity.

How can you make examples of special triangles to show your class? This activity will show you some easy methods and will help you think about why the methods work.

1. Take three ordinary sheets of paper that have right angles at each corner. On each sheet, draw a single straight line in such a way that when you cut along these lines, you will create three different right triangles.

2. To make an isosceles triangle, start by drawing a point; let's call the point A, as shown in the next diagram. Using a ruler, draw two line segments of the same length that have A as one of their endpoints. Connect the other two end points with a line segment.

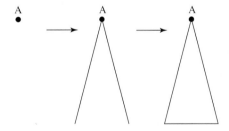

3. Before you look at the next problem, try to draw an equilateral triangle on paper using only a ruler and pencil. Why does this not work so well?

4. To make an equilateral triangle, follow the steps outlined in the next figure. Notice that you really only need to draw the top portions of the circles. If desired, cut out the resulting equilateral triangle. Use this method to make examples of several different equilateral triangles.

Explain *why* this method must always produce an equilateral triangle.

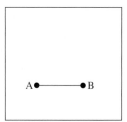

Step 1: Start with any line segment AB.

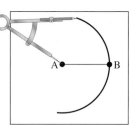

Step 2: Draw a circle centered at A, passing through B.

Step 3: Draw a circle centered at B, passing through A.

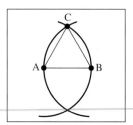

Step 4: Label one of the two points where the circles meet C. Connect A, B, and C with line segments.

CLASS ACTIVITY 8Y: Constructing Triangles of Specified Side Lengths

You will need a ruler, a compass, and a blank piece of paper for this activity.

1. The line segment AB shown in the next figure is 4 inches long. Use a ruler and compass to construct a triangle that has AB as one of its sides, has a side that is 3 inches long and has another side that is 2 inches long. Describe how you constructed your triangle and explain why your construction must produce the desired triangle. Hint: Modify the construction of an equilateral triangle shown in part 4 of Activity 8X by drawing circles of different radii.

2. Take a blank piece of paper. Use a ruler and compass to construct a triangle that has one side of length 6 inches, one side of length 5 inches, and one side of length 3 inches.

3. Is it possible to make a triangle that has one side of length 6 inches, one side of length 3 inches, and one side of length 2 inches? Explain.

CLASS ACTIVITY 8Z: Seeing That the Angles in a Triangle Add to 180°

You will need a ruler and scissors for this activity.

Work with a group of people. Each person in your group should do the following:

1. Using a ruler, draw a large triangle that looks different from the other group members' triangles.

2. Cut out your triangle.

3. As indicated below, fold the corner that is opposite the longest side (or a longest side) of your triangle down to meet the longest side. Do this in such a way that the fold line is parallel to the longest side of the triangle.

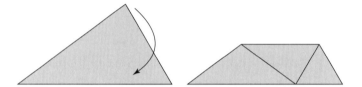

4. Fold the other two corners of the triangle in to meet the corner that is now along the longest side of the triangle.

5. What does this way of folding the triangle show you about the angles of the triangle? Do the other people in your group reach the same conclusion, even though they started with different triangles?

   (This is a neat way to see that the angles in a triangle add to 180°, but it is not so easy to explain *why* it must always work.)

CLASS ACTIVITY 8AA: Using Parallel Lines to Explain Why the Angles in a Triangle Add to 180°

This activity will show you a way to understand why the angles in a triangle add to 180°.

1. Each of the pictures in the diagram that follows shows a pair of parallel lines and third line that crosses the parallel lines. In each case, how do the angles labeled a and b appear to be related?

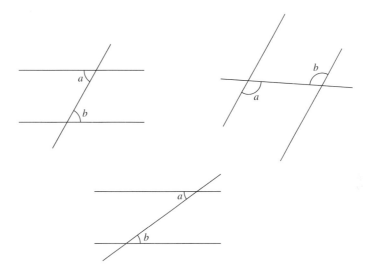

    (Pairs of angles like the angles a and b in each of the preceding pictures, which are inside a pair of parallel lines and which are on opposite sides of a line that meets the two parallel lines, are called **alternate interior angles**. In plane geometry, we can take as a *basic starting assumption* that alternate interior angles are equal. In other words we simply accept as a basic fact that alternate interior angles are equal. This is one version of what is known as the **parallel postulate**.)

2. Given any triangle with corner points A, B, and C, let *a*, *b*, and *c* be the angles of the triangle at A, B, and C, respectively. Consider the line through A parallel to the side BC that is opposite A.

    Based on what you discovered in 1, what can you say about the three adjacent angles at A that are formed by the triangle and the line through A?

    What can you conclude about the sum of the angles in the triangle?

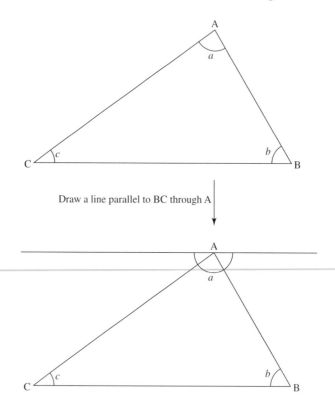

Draw a line parallel to BC through A

CLASS ACTIVITY 8BB: Explaining Why the Angles in a Triangle Add to 180° by Walking and Turning

You will need sticky notes and, if available, masking tape.

This activity will show you a way to understand why the angles in a triangle add to 180°.

1. Put three "dots" labeled A, B, and C on the floor to create the corners of a triangle. If possible, connect them with masking tape to make a triangle you can see. Label a point P on the line segment between A and B.

2. Work with a group. Pick two people from your group, one to be a *walker* and one to be a *turner*. The rest are *observers*.

   The walker's job: Stand at point P, facing point B. Walk all the way around the triangle returning to point P.

   The turner's job: Stand at one fixed spot and face the same direction that the walker faces at all times. This means that when the walker turns at a corner, you should turn in the same way.

   The observer's job: Observe the walker and the turner and make sure that they really are facing the same direction at all times.

   Repeat the walking and turning described above until everyone in your group can confidently answer the following questions:

   a. Let's say that the walker and turner were facing north when the walker began walking around the triangle. Which directions did the turner face during the experiment? Were any directions left out? Were any directions repeated?

   b. What was the full angle of rotation of the turner when the walker walked once all the way around the triangle, returning to point P?

3. On the next diagram, show which angles the walker turned through at the corners of the triangle. Label these angles d, e, and f.

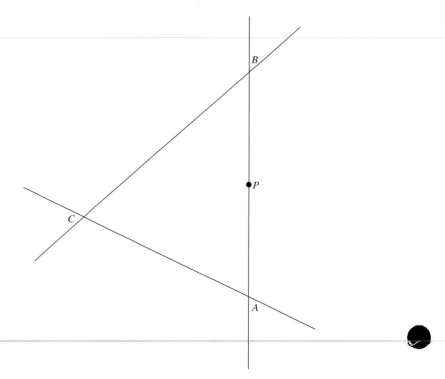

4. Based on your answer to exercise 2(b), what can you say about the value of $d + e + f$?

5. Check your answer to the previous problem by using a protractor to find the angles d, e, f and then adding them.

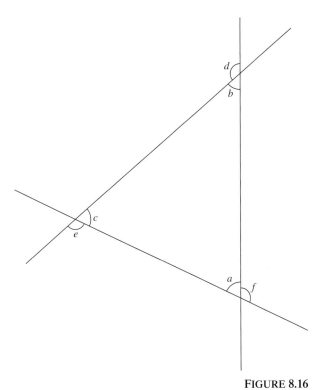

FIGURE 8.16

The Exterior Angles of a Triangle Add to 360°

6. You should have just found that

the sum of the **exterior angles** of a triangle is 360°

In other words, $d + e + f = 360°$, where d, e, and f are the exterior angles, as shown in Figure 8.16.

Use the formula $d + e + f = 360°$ to explain why the sum of the **interior angles** in a triangle is equal to 180°. In other words, show that $a + b + c = 180°$, where a, b, and c are the interior angles of a triangle, as shown in Figure 8.16.

Hint: What do you notice about $a + f$, $b + d$, and $c + e$? Can you use this somehow?

CLASS ACTIVITY 8CC: Angles and Shapes inside Shapes

1. Harry has learned that the angles in a triangle add to 180° and that there
    are 360° in a circle. Harry wonders about the next diagram, "Shouldn't the
    circle be less than 180° because it is inside the triangle?" What could you
    say to Harry?

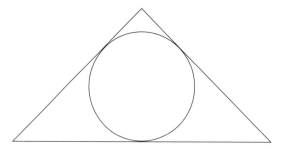

2. The next picture shows a large triangle subdivided into three smaller trian-
    gles. If the angles in each of the three smaller triangles add to 180°, then
    why don't the angles in the larger triangle add to

$$180° + 180° + 180° = 540°$$

    instead of 180°? Relate the 540° to the sum of the angles in the large
    triangle.

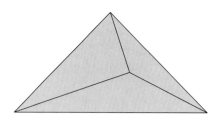

8.5 Quadrilaterals and Other Polygons

CLASS ACTIVITY 8DD: Constructing Quadrilaterals by Folding and Cutting Paper

This activity will show you some ways to fold and cut paper to create some of the special quadrilaterals. You will need paper and scissors.

1. To create a rhombus, follow the next set of instructions.

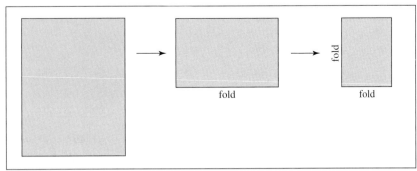

Step 1: Fold a rectangular piece of paper in half and then in half again, creating perpendicular fold lines.

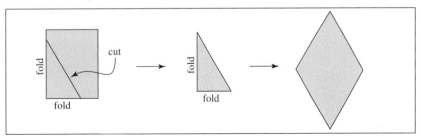

Step 2: Draw a line from anywhere on one fold to anywhere on the perpendicular fold. Cut along the line you drew. When you unfold you will have a rhombus.

By referring to the definition of rhombus, explain *why* the method described must always create a rhombus.

2. An ordinary rectangular piece of paper is one example of a rectangle. You can create other rectangles out of an ordinary piece of paper as follows: Fold the paper so that one edge of the paper folds directly onto itself. The opposite edge will automatically fold onto itself as well. Now unfold the paper and fold the paper again, this time so that the other two edges fold onto themselves. When you unfold, you can cut along the fold lines to create 4 rectangles.

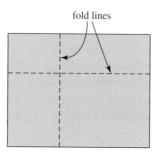

fold lines

    By referring to the definition of a rectangle, explain why the method just described must always create rectangles.

3. To create a square, start with a rectangular piece of paper of any size. (See part 2 to find out how to make rectangles of different sizes.) Fold the paper diagonally so that a short edge folds onto an edge that is perpendicular to it, as shown in the next diagram. Cut off the portion of the paper where there isn't a double thickness. When you unfold, you will have a square.

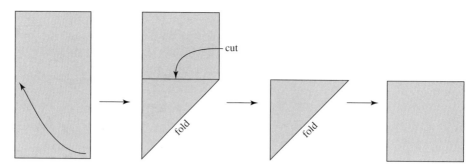

cut

fold

fold

4. Show how to create a trapezoid by starting with a rectangular piece of paper of any size. (See part 2 to find out how to make rectangles of different sizes.)

5. To create a parallelogram, start with a rectangular piece of paper of any size. (See part 2 to find out how to make rectangles of different sizes.) Follow the next set of steps.

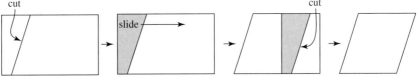

Draw a line segment connecting two opposite sides of a rectangle. Cut along the line segment. Put the piece back (shown shaded) and slide it over as shown. Mark and cut at the leading edge of the slid-over piece.

CLASS ACTIVITY 8EE: More Ways to Make Rhombuses

You will need a ruler and compass for part 3 of this activity. You might want to have string, straws, cardboard, and brass fasteners for parts 1 and 2.

1. Describe how 4 children could use 4 pieces of string to show a variety of different rhombuses.

2. Describe how you could show a variety of different rhombuses by threading straws onto string or by fastening sturdy strips of cardboard with brass fasteners.

3. In the next picture, the line segments AB and AC have the same length. Use a ruler and compass to draw a rhombus that has AB and AC as two of its sides. (You may wish to try drawing the rhombus without a compass first. Notice that it is difficult and clumsy to do so.)

   Hint: to create the rhombus you will need to construct a fourth point, D, such that the distance from D to B is equal to the distance from D to C, and such that these two distances are also equal to the common distance from A to B and A to C. Think about the *definition of circles* in order to help you figure out how to construct the point D.

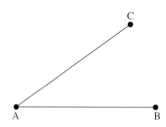

CLASS ACTIVITY 8FF: Constructing Quadrilaterals with Geometer's Sketchpad

In this activity, you will construct various kinds of quadrilaterals. Save your sketches for use in a subsequent activity.

To do this activity, you must be able to do the following in Geometer's Sketchpad:

- Construct points and line segments with the construction tools.

- Use the *Construct* menu to construct a line segment between two given points.

- Use the *Construct* menu to construct a line that is parallel to another line and goes through a given point.

- Use the *Construct* menu to construct a line that is perpendicular to another line and goes through a given point.

- Use the *Construct* menu to construct a circle that goes through a given point and has a radius of the same length as a given line segment.

- Hide objects using the *Display* menu.

1. Construct a "general" quadrilateral. You should be able to move the corner points so as to vary the quadrilateral and show (theoretically) all possible quadrilaterals (if your computer screen was infinitely large).

2. Construct a "general" trapezoid. Use the definition of trapezoid so that your construction is guaranteed to be a trapezoid, even when you move the corner points. This means that you will need to use the *construct* menu to construct a parallel line to a given line segment. By moving the corner points of your trapezoid you should be able to show (theoretically) all possible trapezoids (if your computer screen was infinitely large).

3. Construct a "general" parallelogram. Use the definition of parallelogram so that your construction is guaranteed to be a parallelogram, even when you move the corner points. By moving the corner points of your parallelogram you should be able to show (theoretically) all possible parallelograms (if your computer screen was infinitely large).

4. Construct a "general" rectangle. Use the definition of rectangle so that your construction is guaranteed to be a rectangle, even when you move the corner points. By moving the corner points of your rectangle you should be able to show (theoretically) all possible rectangles (if your computer screen was infinitely large).

5. Construct a "general" square. Use the definition of square so that your construction is guaranteed to be a square, even when you move the corner points. To do this construction, it will help you to remember the definition of a circle. By moving the corner points of your square you should be able to show (theoretically) all possible squares (if your computer screen was infinitely large).

6. Construct a "general" rhombus. Use the definition of rhombus so that your construction is guaranteed to be a rhombus, even when you move the corner points. To do this construction, it will help you to remember the definition of a circle. By moving the corner points of your rhombus you should be able to show (theoretically) all possible rhombuses (if your computer screen was infinitely large).

CLASS ACTIVITY 8GG: Relating the Kinds of Quadrilaterals

1. In each of parts (a) – (d), describe the relationships among the given kinds of shapes. In each case, write as many sentences as you can of the following forms:

    Every _____ is a _____.
    There are _____ that are not _____.

    a. Describe the relationship between squares and rectangles.

    b. Describe the relationship between squares and rhombuses.

    c. Describe the relationship between rectangles and trapezoids.

    d. Describe the relationship between rhombuses and parallelograms.

2. a. Explain why squares and rectangles are related the way they are.

    b. Explain why squares and rhombuses are related the way they are.

    c. When you relate rectangles and trapezoids, are you relying *only* on information that is stated directly in the definitions of these shapes, or are you relying on information that is not stated directly in the definitions, such as visual information?

    d. When you relate rhombuses and parallelograms, are you relying *only* on information that is stated directly in the definitions of these shapes, or are you relying on information that is not stated directly in the definitions, such as visual information?

CLASS ACTIVITY 8HH: Venn Diagrams Relating Quadrilaterals

1. Draw a Venn diagram relating the set of squares and the set of rectangles.

2. Draw a Venn diagram relating the set of rhombuses, the set of squares, and the set of rectangles.

3. Draw a Venn diagram relating the set of parallelograms and the set of trapezoids.

4. Our definition of trapezoid is a quadrilateral with *at least one* pair of parallel sides. Some books define trapezoid as a quadrilateral with *exactly one* pair of parallel sides. How would the Venn diagram relating parallegrams and trapezoids be different if we used this other definition of trapezoid?

CLASS ACTIVITY 8II: Investigating Diagonals of Quadrilaterals with Geometer's Sketchpad

You will need sketches for a general quadrilateral, rectangle, and rhombus from Class Activity 8FF for this activity.

To do this activity, you will need to be able to measure angles and lengths of line segments. Both of these can be done with the *Measure* menu. To measure an angle you will need to select three points *in the following order*: a point on one line segment, the point where the line segments meet, and a point on the other line segment.

Construct the two diagonals in each of your sketches of a general quadrilateral, rectangle, and rhombus. Now move the corner points in your sketches around in different ways so as to see many different quadrilaterals, rectangles, and rhombuses. As you move the corner points, observe the diagonals and do the following:

- Measure the angles that the diagonals make with each other.

- Find where the diagonals meet—where is this point located on the diagonals?

- Compare the lengths of the two diagonals.

What do the diagonals of rectangles all have in common? What do the diagonals of rhombuses all have in common? What about diagonals of general quadrilaterals?

CLASS ACTIVITY 8JJ: Investigating Diagonals of Quadrilaterals (Alternate)

Figure 8.17 shows examples of different kinds of quadrilaterals and their diagonals. Look carefully at the diagonals and do the following:

- Observe and (if possible) measure the angles that the diagonals make with each other.

- Observe where the diagonals meet—where is this point located on the diagonals?

- Compare the lengths of the two diagonals.

What do the diagonals of rectangles all have in common? What do the diagonals of rhombuses all have in common? What about diagonals of general quadrilaterals?

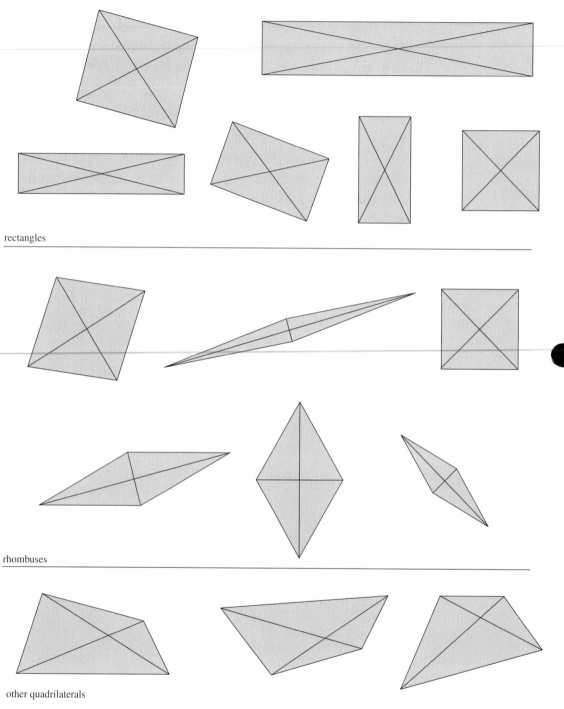

rectangles

rhombuses

other quadrilaterals

FIGURE 8.17
Some Quadrilaterials and Their Diagonals

CLASS ACTIVITY 8KK: Investigating the Angle Formed by a Diagonal of a Quadrilateral with Geometer's Sketchpad

You will need Geometer's Sketchpad sketches for a general quadrilateral and general rhombus from Class Activity 8FF for this activity.

To do this activity, you will need to be able to measure angles. (See Class Activity 8II.)

Choose a corner point of your general quadrilateral. Construct a diagonal of the quadrilateral that has your chosen point on it. The diagonal splits the angle at your chosen point into two angles. Measure these two angles and compare them. Observe how these two angles change as you move various corner points of the quadrilateral around to make different quadrilaterals.

Now choose a corner point of your general rhombus. Construct a diagonal of the rhombus that has your chosen point on it. As before, the diagonal splits the angle at your chosen point into two angles. Measure these two angles and compare them. Observe how these two angles change as you move various corner points of the rhombus around to make different rhombuses.

Compare what you observed for the quadrilateral with what you observed for the rhombus.

CLASS ACTIVITY 8LL: Investigating the Angle Formed by a Diagonal of a Quadrilateral (Alternate)

Shown in the next figure are some rhombuses and other quadrilaterals with one of the two diagonals drawn in. The two angles created by the diagonal are labeled *a* and *b*. In each case, compare angle *a* with angle *b*. Compare what you observed for quadrilaterals with what you observed for rhombuses.

rhombuses

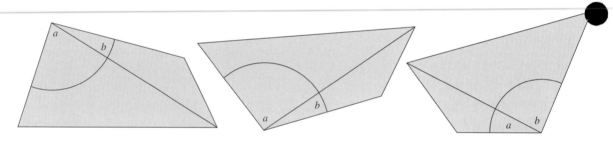

other quadrilaterals

8.6 Constructions with Straightedge and Compass

CLASS ACTIVITY 8MM: Constructing a Square and an Octagon with Straightedge and Compass

Use a straightedge and compass to do the following constructions:

1. Using a straightedge and compass, construct a line that is perpendicular to the line segment AB shown in the next figure and that passes through point A (*not* through the midpoint of AB!). Hint: First extend the line segment AB.

    Now use a straightedge and compass to construct a square that has AB as one side.

A •————————————————————• B

2. Using a straightedge and compass, construct an octagon whose corner points all lie on the circle in the next figure and whose sides all have the same length.

CLASS ACTIVITY 8NN: Relating the Constructions to Properties of Rhombuses

1. The next picture shows the result of using a straightedge and compass to construct a line that is perpendicular to a line segment AB and that divides AB in half. There are two circles of the same radius, one centered at A and one centered at B. Draw the rhombus that arises naturally from this construction. Use the definition of rhombus to explain *why* the quadrilateral that you identify as a rhombus really must be a rhombus.

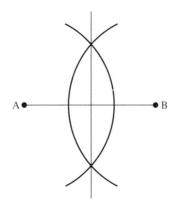

2. Which special properties of rhombuses are related to the construction of a line that is perpendicular to a line segment and divides the line segment in half? Explain.

3. The next picture shows the result of using a straightedge and compass to construct a ray that divides an angle in half. There are three circles of the same radius, one centered at P, one centered at Q, and one centered at R. Draw the rhombus that arises naturally from this construction. Use the definition of rhombus to explain *why* the quadrilateral that you identify as a rhombus really must be a rhombus.

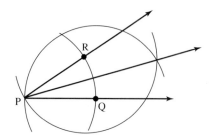

4. Which special properties of rhombuses are related to the construction of a ray that divides an angle in half? Explain.

8.7   Polyhedra and Other Solid Shapes

CLASS ACTIVITY 8OO: Patterns for Prisms, Cylinders, Pyramids, and Cones

You will need scissors, tape, a compass, a straightedge, graph paper, and blank paper for this activity.

1. Examine the patterns in the next set of figures. Try to visualize what whould happen if you were to cut these patterns out on the heavy lines, fold them on the dotted lines, and tape various sides together. What kinds of polyhedra would they make? Which parts of the patterns would make the bases?

    Now cut out the large versions of these patterns on pages 539, 541, 543, and 545 on the heavy lines, fold them on the dotted lines, and tape (or hold) the sides together to form various polyhedra. Were your predictions correct?

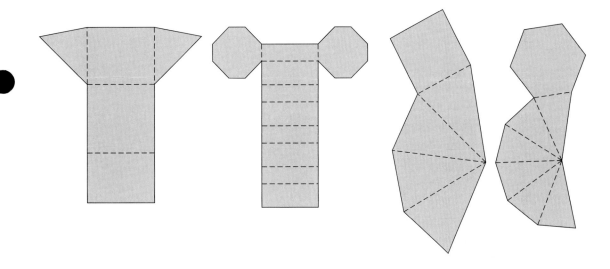

2. Make a pattern for a cylinder with a circular base. Construct your pattern so that when you cut it out you will not need to overlap any paper to make your cylinder. You may leave the bases off your pattern. Cut out your pattern and see if it works.

3. Use graph paper to make a pattern for a prism whose base is a rectangle that is not a square. Include the bases in your pattern. Cut out your pattern and see if it works.

4. Make a pattern for a cone with a circular base. Construct your pattern so that when you cut it out you will not need to overlap any paper to make your cone. You may leave the base off your pattern. Cut out your pattern and see if it works.

5. Use a straightedge and compass to make a pattern for a pentagon-based pyramid. You may leave the pentagon base off your pattern. Cut out your pattern and see if it works.

CLASS ACTIVITY 8PP: Making Prisms, Cylinders, Pyramids, and Cones

You will need either toothpicks and miniature marshmallows or modeling clay, or straws and regular-size marshmallows or modeling clay for this activity. If available, you could also use soap bubble liquid.

As in the photograph, stick toothpicks into miniature marshmallows or into small balls of modeling clay to make the the shapes listed. To make larger shapes, stick straws into balls of clay or into regular-size marshmallows. In each case, visualize the shape first and predict how many toothpicks and marshmallows you will need for the following:

1. a rectangular prism

2. a triangular prism

3. a pyramid with a triangle base

4. a pyramid with a square base

Some teachers like to dip these shapes into a soap bubble solution to show the faces of the shapes.

CLASS ACTIVITY 8QQ: Analyzing Prisms, Cylinders, and Cones

1. Answer the next group of questions *without* using a model. Use your visualization skills and look back at other models. (When you are done, verify with a model, if available.)

    How many faces does a pentagonal prism have? Why? Describe the faces of a pentagonal prism. What kinds of shapes are they? How many of each kind of shape are there?

    How many edges and how many vertices does a pentagonal prism have? Explain.

2. Answer the next group of questions *without* using a model. Use your visualization skills and look back at other models. (When you are done, verify with a model, if available.)

    How many faces does a pyramid with a hexagonal base have, assuming that you count the base? Why? Describe the faces of a pyramid with a hexagonal base. What kinds of shapes are they? How many of each kind of shape are there?

    How many edges and how many vertices does a pyramid with a hexagonal base have? Explain.

CLASS ACTIVITY 8RR: What's Inside the Magic 8 Ball?

You will need a Magic 8 Ball for this activity. (One or more can be shared by a class.) Magic 8 Balls are typically available where popular children's toys are sold. You will also need scissors and tape or snap-together plastic triangles.

1. Play with a Magic 8 Ball for a little while. Generally speaking, how does the Magic 8 Ball work? What sorts of things are inside it? Why do we see different "answers" at different times?

2. Other than breaking the Magic 8 Ball, how might you determine the shape that is inside the Magic 8 Ball?

3. Describe some properties that you think the shape inside the Magic 8 Ball should have.

4. Use snap-together plastic triangles, or use the paper triangles on page 547 to create various closed 3-dimensional shapes. Which of these shapes could possibly be the shape inside the Magic 8 Ball?

CLASS ACTIVITY 8SS: Making Platonic Solids with Toothpicks and Marshmallows

You will need toothpicks and either miniature marshmallows or modeling clay for this activity.

Make all five Platonic solids by sticking toothpicks into miniature marshmallows or small balls of clay. (Your dodecahedron may sag a little, especially if you use marshmallows.) Refer to the following descriptions of the Platonic solids:

Tetrahedron is made of 4 equilateral triangles, with 3 triangles coming together at each vertex.

Cube is made of 6 squares, with 3 squares coming together at each vertex.

Octahedron is made of 8 equilateral triangles, with 4 triangles coming together at each vertex.

Dodecahedron is made of 12 regular pentagons, with 3 pentagons coming together at each vertex.

Icosahedron is made of 20 equilateral triangles, with 5 triangles coming together at each vertex.

Use your models to fill in the following table:

SHAPE	# AND TYPE OF FACES	# OF EDGES	# OF VERTICES
Tetrahedron	4 equilateral triangles		
Cube	6 squares		
Octahedron	8 equilateral triangles		
Dodecahedron	12 regular pentagons		
Icosahedron	20 equilateral triangles		

CLASS ACTIVITY 8TT: Why Are There No Other Platonic Solids?

You will need scissors and tape for this activity. Snap-together plastic triangles, squares, and pentagons could also be helpful.

1. Each vertex of a tetrahedron has 3 equilateral triangles coming together. Each vertex of an octahedron has 4 equilateral triangles coming together. Each vertex of an icosahedron has 5 equilateral triangles coming together. Can there be a convex polyhedron whose faces are equilateral triangles and for which 6 equilateral triangles come together at each vertex? Investigate this by working with paper or plastic equilateral triangles. (Page 547 has triangles you can cut out.) Explain your conclusion.

2. What if there were a polyhedron for which 7 or more equilateral triangles came together at each vertex? Could such a polyhedron be convex? Investigate this by working with paper or plastic equilateral triangles. Explain your conclusion.

3. At each vertex of a cube there are 3 squares coming together. Can there be a convex polyhedron whose faces are squares and for which 4 squares come together at each vertex? Is it possible to make a convex polyhedron in such a way that 5 or more squares come together at each vertex? Investigate these questions by working with paper or plastic squares. (Page 549 has squares you can cut out.) Explain your conclusions.

4. At each vertex of a dodecahedron there are 3 regular pentagons coming together. Is it possible to make a convex polyhedron in such a way that 4 or more regular pentagons come together at each vertex? Investigate this by working with paper or plastic regular pentagons. (Page 549 has pentagons you can cut out.) Explain your conclusions.

5. Can there be a convex polyhedron whose faces are all regular hexagons and for which 3 hexagons come together at each vertex? Investigate this by working with paper or plastic regular hexagons. (Page 551 has hexagons you can cut out.) Explain your conclusion.

6. Is it possible to make a convex polyhedron whose faces are all regular hexagons? Consider the same question for regular 7-gons, 8-gons, etc. (Page 551 has hexagons, 7-gons, and octagons that you can cut out.)

hexagon   7-gon   8-gon

CLASS ACTIVITY 8UU: Relating the Numbers of Faces, Edges, and Vertices of Polyhedra

To do this activity, you will need to have made a polyhedron, either out of paper, or out of plastic, snap-together triangles, squares, or pentagons, or a combination of these polygons.

1. Count the number of faces, edges, and vertices of your polyhedron. Following is a table of numbers of faces, edges, and vertices of shapes that other students have made in the past. Record your data and the data of some of your classmates in the blank spaces.

	# FACES	# EDGES	# VERTICES
yours			
partner			
partner			
partner			
partner			
partner			
shape 1	14	21	9
shape 2	10	15	7
shape 3	24	36	14
shape 4	4	6	4
shape 5	8	12	6
shape 6	20	30	12

2. There is an interesting relationship between the numbers of faces, edges, and vertices. Can you find it?

    The previously recorded data (for shapes 1–6) are from polyhedra made only out of triangles. For polyhedra made only out of triangles there is a special relationship between the number of faces and the number of edges that other polyhedra do not share. Can you find it? Challenge: explain why this relationship must hold.

Chapter 9

Geometry of Motion and Change

9.1 Reflections, Translations, and Rotations

CLASS ACTIVITY 9A: Exploring Reflections with Geometer's Sketchpad

For this activity you will need to use the drawing tools for drawing circles, line segments, lines, rays, and points in Geometer's Sketchpad. You will also need to select objects with the selection tool.

1. Draw a shape or design that is not symmetrical, such as the one shown in the next figure. Then, separately, draw a line, a line segment, or a ray. Select the line, line segment, or ray, and then choose *Mark Mirror* from the *Transform* menu.

2. Your next step will be to reflect your shape across your line. Before you continue, try to visualize the location and orientation of the reflected shape.

3. Select your shape, and then choose *Reflect* from the *Transform* menu. Geometer's Sketchpad shows you both the initial location of your shape and its final location after reflecting across your marked line.

4. Move your original shape and your marked line around on the screen and observe the new locations and orientations of the reflected shape. Be sure to change the direction of your marked line, too. Why does the final position of your shape turn out the way it does? Before you move your original shape or your marked line, try to visualize how the location and orientation of the reflected shape will change.

CLASS ACTIVITY 9B: Exploring Translations with Geometer's Sketchpad

For this activity you will need to use the drawing tools for drawing circles, line segments, lines, rays, and points in Geometer's Sketchpad. You will also need to select objects with the selection tool.

1. Draw a shape or design that is not symmetrical, such as the one shown in the next figure. Then, separately, draw a line segment. Select the two endpoints of this line segment and choose *Mark Vector* from the *Transform* menu.

2. Your next step will be to translate your shape with the direction and distance specified by your line segment. Before you continue, try to visualize the location and orientation of the translated shape.

3. Select your shape, and then choose *Translate* from the *Transform* menu. Geometer's Sketchpad shows you both the initial location of your shape and its final location after translating by the distance and direction determined by your line segment.

4. Move your original shape around on the screen and change the length and direction of your line segment. Why does the final position of your shape turn out the way it does? Before you move your original shape or your line segment, try to visualize how the location of the translated shape will change.

CLASS ACTIVITY 9C: Exploring Rotations with Geometer's Sketchpad

For this activity, you will need to use the tools for drawing circles, line segments, lines, rays, and points in Geometer's Sketchpad. You will also need to select objects with the selection tool.

EXPLORING ROTATIONS BY A FIXED ANGLE:

1. Draw a shape or design that is not symmetrical, such as the one shown in the next figure. Then, separately, draw a single point. Select that point, and then choose *Mark Center* from the *Transform* menu.

2. Your next step will be to rotate your shape about your chosen point by an angle that you will specify. Before you continue, try to visualize the location and orientation of your shape after rotation.

3. Select your shape and choose *Rotate* from the *Transform* menu. A dialog box will appear. Select *By fixed angle* and enter any angle you wish in the appropriate place. (If the dialog box indicates that angles are being measured in radians, then choose *Preferences* from the *Display* menu and change the angle unit to degrees using the "pull-down" menu.) Geometer's Sketchpad shows you both the initial location of your shape and its final location after rotating about the point you marked as center, by the angle you selected.

4. Move your original shape, and move the point that you marked as center around your screen. Observe the location and orientation of your rotated shape. Why does the final position of your shape turn out the way it does? Before you move your original shape or your marked center, try to visualize how the location and orientation of the rotated shape will change.

EXPLORING ROTATIONS BY A MARKED ANGLE:

1. Draw a shape or design that is not symmetrical, such as the one shown in the next figure. Then, separately, draw a single point. Select that point, then choose *Mark Center* from the *Transform* menu.

2. Make an angle by drawing two line segments that share an endpoint. Select the three endpoints so that the second point you select is the shared endpoint. Choose *Mark Angle* from the *Transform* menu.

3. Your next step will be to rotate your shape about your marked point, by your marked angle. Before you continue, try to visualize the location and orientation of your rotated shape.

4. Select your shape and choose *Rotate* from the *Transform* menu. Geometer's Sketchpad shows you both the initial location of your shape and its final location after rotating about your marked point, by your marked angle.

5. Move your original shape and your marked center point around the screen. Why does the final position of your shape turn out the way it does? Before you move your original shape or your marked center, try to visualize how the location and orientation of your rotated shape will change.

6. Now move one of the endpoints of your marked angle. Why does the final position of your shape move the way it does? Before you move your marked angle, try to visualize how the location and orientation of the rotated shape will change.

CLASS ACTIVITY 9D: Exploring Rotations (Alternate)

You will need scissors for this activity.

1. Cut out the large circle and the two copies of a shape on page 553.

2. Place one copy of the shape on one side of your circle. You will be rotating your circle by 180° (a half turn) about its center. But before you rotate your circle, try to visualize the final position and orientation of your shape. Place the second copy of the shape on the circle to show how you think the first shape will be oriented after you rotate the circle 180°.

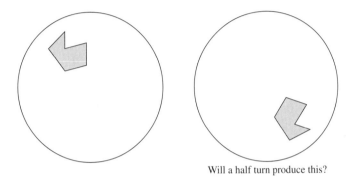

Will a half turn produce this?

3. Leave the first shape on the circle. Without changing the orientation of the second shape, move it to the side of the circle. Hold the center of the circle down with the tip of a pencil and rotate the circle 180° about its center. Did you correctly predict the final orientation of your shape? If so, the first and second shapes will be oriented in the same way.

4. Repeat the previous steps, but this time with your shape in a different orientation or in a different location on the circle. Keep repeating until you can accurately predict the final orientation of the shape after the circle is rotated.

5. Repeat the previous steps, but this time with a 90° rotation (a quarter turn), either clockwise or counterclockwise, instead of a 180° rotation.

CLASS ACTIVITY 9E: Exploring Reflections (Alternate)

You will need scissors and reusable adhesive clay or paper clips for this activity.

1. Cut out the large circle and the two copies of a shape on page 553. You may want to shade the backs of the shapes so that they look the same (more or less) on the front and back. Fold your circle in half to form a crease line that goes through the center of the circle.

2. Place one copy of the shape somewhere on the circle. You will be reflecting the shape across the crease line in the circle. But before you reflect the shape, try to visualize its final position and orientation. Place the second copy of the shape on the circle to show where you think the first shape will be located and how you think the first shape will be oriented after you reflect it across the line. Attach the second shape to the circle with adhesive clay.

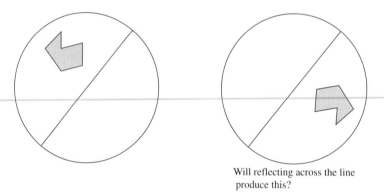

Will reflecting across the line
produce this?

3. Now reflect your first shape across the line by holding the shape in place, folding the circle along the line (with the shapes on the inside), and transferring the shape to the other side of the circle. Did you correctly predict the final position and orientation of your shape? If so, the two shapes will match one another exactly.

4. Repeat the above steps, but this time with your shape in a different orientation or in a different location. Also, change the orientation of the crease line: make it horizontal, vertical, and diagonal.

CLASS ACTIVITY 9F: Reflections, Rotations, and Translations on a Grid

1. Draw the result of reflecting the shaded shapes in the next figure across the heavy line. Explain how you know where to draw your reflected shapes.

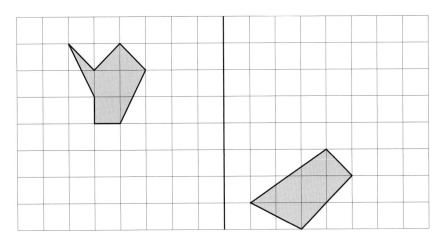

2. Draw the result of translating the shaded shapes in the next figure according to the direction and the distance given by the arrow. Explain how you know where to draw your translated shapes.

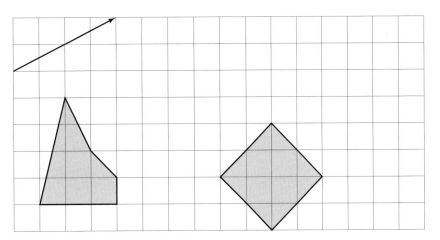

3. Draw the result of rotating the shaded shapes in the next figure by 180° around the point where the two heavy lines meet. Explain how you know where to draw your rotated shapes.

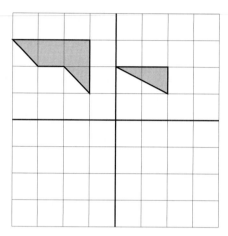

4. Draw the result of rotating the shaded shapes in the next figure by 90° counterclockwise around the point where the two heavy lines meet. Explain how you know where to draw your rotated shapes.

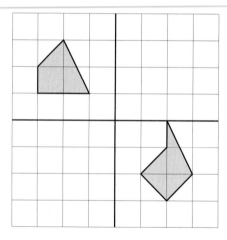

9.2 Symmetry

CLASS ACTIVITY 9G: Checking for Symmetry

You will need scissors and a toothpick or paperclip for this activity.

Five small designs are shown in the next set of diagrams. Cut out two copies of each of these designs on pages 555 and 557. For each design, determine if the design has reflection symmetry, and if so, what the lines of symmetry are; determine if the design has rotation symmetry, and if so, whether it has 2-fold, 3-fold, 4-fold, or other rotation symmetry; and determine if the design has translation symmetry.

To determine whether a design has reflection symmetry, see if there is a line such that when you fold the paper along the line, the portions of the design on either side of the fold line match one another.

To determine whether a design has rotation symmetry, put one copy of the design on top of another copy, so that when you hold the two pieces of paper up to a light, you see that the designs match one another. Poke a toothpick or paperclip through the two copies of the design. Then rotate the top copy of the design while keeping the bottom copy fixed. If you can rotate less than 360° and the designs match again, then the design has rotation symmetry. If you can rotate by that same amount n times in a row and the top design then moves back into its starting position, then the design has n-fold rotation symmetry.

To determine whether a design has translation symmetry, put one copy of the design on top of another copy, so that when you hold the two pieces of paper up to a light, you see that the designs match one another. Slide one copy of the design over the other copy. If the two copies of the design match again, then the design has translation symmetry. True translation symmetry can only occur with designs that are infinitely long, so you may need to imagine the design continuing on forever.

CLASS ACTIVITY 9H: Frieze Patterns

You will need scissors for this activity.

Seven different frieze patterns are shown below. Cut out two copies of each of these seven frieze patterns on pages 559, 561, 563, and 565 by cutting along the gray lines. Picture each of the seven frieze patterns repeating on an infinitely long strip of paper, continuing forever, forward and backward.

Show that each frieze pattern has translation symmetry. For each frieze pattern, determine whether the pattern has reflection symmetry and, if so, what the lines of symmetry are; determine whether the pattern has rotation symmetry and, if so, whether it has 2-fold, 3-fold, 4-fold, or other rotation symmetry; and determine whether the pattern has glide-reflection symmetry.

See the text or see Class Activity 9G to learn how to check for translation, rotation, and reflection symmetry.

To check for glide-reflection symmetry, put one copy of the pattern on top of another copy, so that when you hold the two pieces of paper up to a light, you see that the patterns match one another. Flip the top copy over, so that the two patterns are face to face. Slide one copy of the pattern over the other copy. If the two copies of the pattern can be made to match one another again, then the pattern has glide-reflection symmetry. As with translation symmetry, true glide-reflection symmetry can only occur with patterns that are infinitely long, so you will need to imagine the pattern continuing on forever.

CLASS ACTIVITY 9I: Creating Symmetrical Designs with Geometer's Sketchpad

To do this activity, you need to rotate, reflect, and translate objects in Geometer's Sketchpad.

1. Start by making a shape that *does not* have symmetry, such as the following:

2. Create a design that uses your shape and that has reflection symmetry.

3. Create a finite portion of an infinite design that uses your shape and that has translation symmetry.

4. Create a design that uses your shape and has 6-fold rotation symmetry.

5. Now create a design that uses your shape and that has *both* 3-fold rotation symmetry *and* reflection symmetry. The design as a whole must have both types of symmetry. Describe how you created your design.

6. Create a finite portion of an infinite design that uses your shape and that has glide-reflection symmetry.

CLASS ACTIVITY 9J: Creating Symmetrical Designs (Alternate)

You will need scissors and colored paper for this activity. Adhesive clay for attaching paper would also be useful.

1. Cut out the 24 copies of the following triangle that are on page 567:

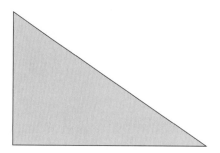

2. By placing some of the triangles on colored paper, create a design that has reflection symmetry.

3. By placing some of the triangles on colored paper, create a finite portion of an infinite design that has translation symmetry.

4. By placing some of the triangles on colored paper, create a design that has 6-fold rotation symmetry.

5. By placing some of the triangles on colored paper, create a design that has *both* 3-fold rotation symmetry *and* reflection symmetry. The design as a whole must have both types of symmetry simultaneously. Describe how you created your design.

6. By placing some of the triangles on colored paper, create a finite portion of an infinite design that has glide-reflection symmetry.

CLASS ACTIVITY 9K: Creating Escher-Type Designs with Geometer's Sketchpad (for Fun)

To do this activity you must rotate and translate objects in Geometer's Sketchpad.

Follow the instructions in Figure 9.1 to create your own Escher-type design. Be sure to select the points, and not just the line segments, when you rotate and translate the various portions of the design. You will need some of those points in order to specify subsequent rotations or translations.

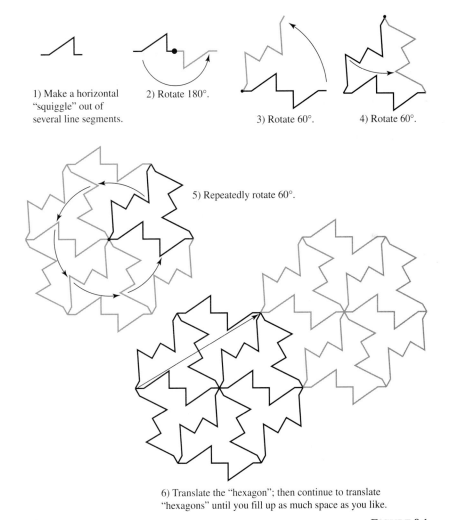

1) Make a horizontal "squiggle" out of several line segments.

2) Rotate 180°.

3) Rotate 60°.

4) Rotate 60°.

5) Repeatedly rotate 60°.

6) Translate the "hexagon"; then continue to translate "hexagons" until you fill up as much space as you like.

FIGURE 9.1

How to Make an Escher-Type Design

CLASS ACTIVITY 9L: Analyzing Designs

1. Describe one or more ways to create the design in Figure 9.3 by starting with the basic square design in Figure 9.2 and using reflections, rotations, and translations.

2. Cut out the (enlarged) copies on page 569 of the basic square design of Figure 9.2 and its reflection. Use some or all of your cut-out copies to create your own design. Describe how you used rotation, reflection, and translation on your basic shape to achieve your final design.

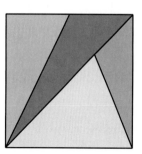

FIGURE 9.2

A Square Design

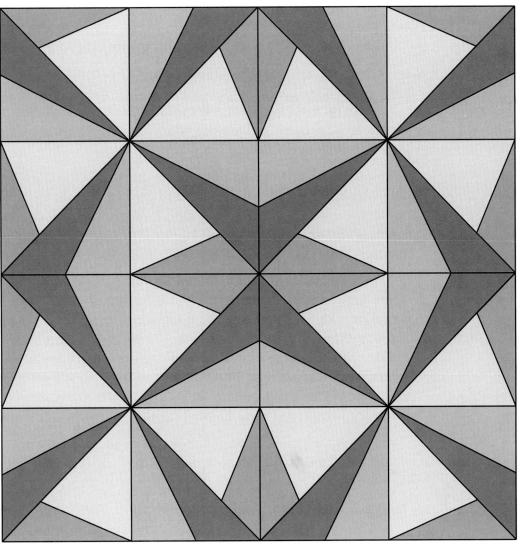

FIGURE 9.3
A Design

9.3 Congruence

CLASS ACTIVITY 9M: Triangles of Specified Side Lengths

You will need blank paper, a ruler, and a compass for this activity.

This activity will help you answer the following question: how many different triangles are there that have one side of length 6 inches, one side of length 4 inches, and one side of length 3 inches?

1. Work with one or more partners. Each partner should use a compass to draw on his or her own blank piece of paper a triangle that has one side of length 6 inches, one side of length 4 inches, and one side of length 3 inches. Try to make your triangle look different from the triangles that your partners draw. Draw your triangle with heavy lines so as to make it easily visible.

2. Compare your triangle to the triangles your partners drew. Place one piece of paper with a triangle on it over another piece of paper with a triangle on it and hold the two pieces of paper to the light. Then try to slide and rotate one piece of paper over the other to see if you can superimpose the two triangles. If not, flip one piece of paper over (so that the two triangles are "face to face") and try again to slide and rotate one piece of paper over the other in order to match the two triangles.

3. What do you conclude about your triangle versus your partners' triangles? Make a statement using the term *congruent*.

CLASS ACTIVITY 9N: Triangles and Quadrilaterals of Specified Side Lengths

You will need scissors, several straws, and some string for this activity.

1. Cut a 3-inch, a 4-inch, and a 5-inch piece of straw, and thread all three straw pieces onto a piece of string. Tie a knot so as to form a triangle from the three pieces of straw.

2. Now cut two 3-inch pieces of straw and two 4-inch pieces of straw, and thread all four straw pieces onto another piece of string in the following order: 3-inch, 4-inch, 3-inch, 4-inch. Tie a knot so as to form a quadrilateral from the four pieces of straw.

3. Compare your straw triangle and your straw quadrilateral. What is an obvious difference between them (other than the fact that the triangle is made of three pieces and the quadrilateral is made of four)?

4. When you made your triangle, if you had strung your three pieces of straw on in a different order would your triangle be different, or not?

CLASS ACTIVITY 90: Triangles with an Angle, a Side, and an Angle Specified

You will need a protractor and one or two straightedges or rulers for this activity.

1. Create a triangle that has AB (in the next figure) as one side, a 30° angle at A, and a 45° angle at B. Is there more than one way to do this? If so, compare the different triangles.

A ——————————————————————— B

2. Create a triangle that has AB (in the next figure) as one side, a 100° angle at A, and a 30° angle at B. Is there more than one way to do this? If so, compare the different triangles.

A ——————————————————————————— B

3. Make up a problem like the previous two, but with different angles. Can you use any pair of angles, or is there some restriction on which pairs of angles you can specify at A and B in order to form a triangle? Explain.

A ——————————————————————————— B

9.4 Similarity

CLASS ACTIVITY 9P: A First Look at Solving Scaling Problems

1. You have a poster that is 2 feet wide and 4 feet long. The poster has a simple design on it that you'd like to scale up and draw onto a larger poster. The larger poster is to be 6 feet wide. How long should the poster be?

    Find as many different ways as you can to solve this poster-scaling problem. In each case, explain your reasoning.

2. A large American flag can be 5 feet tall by 9 feet 6 inches wide. Suppose you want to make a scaled-down version of the flag. If the smaller flag is to be 2 feet tall, then how long should this smaller flag be? Give your answer in feet and inches. Use one of the methods you developed for part 1 to solve this problem.

CLASS ACTIVITY 9Q: A Common Misconception about Scaling

Johnny is working on the following problem:

The picture on a poster that is 4 feet wide and 6 feet long is to be scaled down and drawn onto a small poster that is 1 foot wide. How long should the small poster be?

Johnny solves the problem this way:

One foot is 3 feet less than 4 feet, so the length of the small poster should also be 3 feet less than the length of the big poster. This means the small poster should be $6 - 3 = 3$ feet long.

Is Johnny's reasoning valid? Why or why not? If not, how might you convince Johnny that his reasoning is not correct? What would be a correct way to solve the problem in that case?

CLASS ACTIVITY 9R: Enlarging and Reducing

1. Suppose that you have a postcard with an attractive picture on it and that you'd like to scale up this picture and draw it onto paper that you can cut from a roll. The roll of paper is 24 inches wide, and you can cut the paper to virtually any length. If the postcard picture is 5 inches wide and 7 inches long, then how long should you cut the 24-inch-wide paper? Assume that the 5-inch side will become 24 inches long.

    Use three different methods to solve the postcard problem: the *scale factor* method, the *relative sizes* method, and the *set up a proportion* method. In each case explain why the method makes sense. Explain the first two methods in as concrete a way as you can, as if you were teaching 5th graders who know about multiplication and division (but who do not know about setting up proportions).

2. A museum wants to put a scaled copy of one of its paintings onto a 3-inch-by-5-inch card. The painting is 42 inches by 65 inches. Explain why the copy of the painting can't fill the whole card without leaving blank spaces (i.e., explain why there will have to be a border). Recommend to the museum a size for the copy of the painting that will fit on a $3'' \times 5''$ card. Show your recommendation below in the $3'' \times 5''$ rectangle.

3. Decide whether the following problem is easier to solve with the scale factor method or with the relative sizes method. Explain your answer.

   A stuffed animal company wants to produce an enlarged version of a popular stuffed bunny. The original bunny is 6 inches wide and 11 inches tall. The enlarged bunny is to be 33 inches tall. How wide should the enlarged bunny be?

4. Decide whether the following problem is easier to solve with the scale factor method or with the relative sizes method. Explain your answer.

   A toy company wants to produce a scale model of a car. The actual car is 6 feet wide and 15 feet long. The scale model of the car is to be $2\frac{1}{2}$ inches wide. How long should the scale model of the car be?

CLASS ACTIVITY 9S: Using Scaling to Understand Astronomical Distances

Ms. Frizzle's class has been studying planets and stars. Ms. Frizzle wants to help the children get a better sense of astronomical distances by scaling down these distances. The table that follows shows the distances in kilometers from the Sun to the Earth, the Sun to Pluto, and the Sun to Alpha Centauri. Alpha Centauri is one of the closest stars to the Sun.

HEAVENLY BODY	APPROXIMATE DISTANCE FROM SUN
Earth	150 million km
Pluto	5.9 billion km
Alpha Centauri	38 trillion km

If Ms. Frizzle represents the distance from the Earth to the Sun as 10 centimeters (about the width of a hand), then how should she represent the distance from the Pluto to the Sun? How should she represent the distance from Alpha Centauri to the Sun? Explain your reasoning in such a way that 5th graders who understand multiplication and division but who do not know about setting up proportions might be able to understand.

Will Ms. Frizzle be able to show these distances in her classroom? (Recall that 100 centimeters = 1 meter, and 1 meter is about 1 yard. One thousand meters is 1 kilometer, and 1 kilometer is about $\frac{6}{10}$ of a mile, so a little over half a mile.)

CLASS ACTIVITY 9T: Measuring Distances by "Surveying"

To do this activity, you will need your own ruler and one or more yard sticks and tape measures that can be shared by the class.

This activity will help you understand how the theory of similar triangles is used in finding distances by surveying.

1. Stand a yard stick on end against a wall, or tape the yard stick vertically to the wall.

2. Stand back, away from the yard stick, in a location where you can see the yard stick. Your goal is to find your distance to the yard stick. Guess or estimate this distance before you continue.

   Your guess of how far away the yard stick is:

3. Hold your ruler in front of you with an outstretched arm. Make the ruler vertical, so that it is parallel to the yard stick. Close one eye and with your open eye, "sight" from the ruler to the yard stick. Use the ruler to determine how big the yard stick appears to be from your location.

   Record the apparent size of the yard stick here:

4. With your arm still stretched out in front of you, have a classmate measure the distance from your sighting eye to the ruler.

   Record the distance from your sighting eye to the ruler here:

5. Use the theory of similar triangles to determine your distance to the yard stick. Sketch your eye, the ruler, and the yardstick, showing the relevant similar triangles. (Your sketch does not need to be to scale.) Explain why the triangles are similar.

   Is your calculated distance close to your estimated distance? If not, which one seems to be faulty, and why?

6. Now move to a new location and find your distance to the yard stick again with the same technique.

CLASS ACTIVITY 9U: Determining the Height of a Tree

This activity requires several tape measures that can be shared by the class.

How could you find the height of a tree, for example, without measuring it directly? This class activity provides two ways to do this with similar triangles.

First Method: Go outside and find a tree whose height you will measure. Before you continue, guess or estimate the height of the tree.

This method will work only if your tree is on level ground and casts a fully visible shadow. (So you need a sunny day.)

1. Measure the length of the shadow of the tree (from the base of the tree to the shadow of the tip of the tree).

2. Measure the height of a classmate and measure the length of that person's shadow.

3. Sketch the two similar triangles in this situation. Explain why the triangles are similar. Use your similar triangles to find the height of the tree.

    Is your calculated height fairly close to your estimated height of the tree? If not, which one do you think is faulty? Why?

Second Method: Go outside and find a tree whose height you will measure. Before you continue, guess or estimate the height of the tree.

As long as you can go outside and have tape measures that are long enough, this method will work. (If you can't go outside, you can use this method to measure the height of your room.)

1. Stand away from the tree, hold one arm out straight, close one eye, and raise your arm until you see the top of the tree aligned with your fingertips. Have a classmate measure the height from your fingertips straight down to the ground (while you are sighting the top of the tree) as well as the distance from your feet (directly below your eyes) to where the tape measure touches the ground. Also have a classmate measure the height of your eyes. Then find your distance to the base of the tree. (You can do this either by measuring directly or by "pacing off" the distance and measuring your stride length.)

    Record the following measurements:

    a. Height of fingertips above the ground:

    b. Distance *along the ground* from directly below your eyes to where the tape measure measuring the height of your fingertips hits the ground:

    c. Height of eyes:

    d. Distance to tree:

2. Now draw a diagram showing the relationships between the height of the tree, your arm, and your eyes, and showing all the various measurements you took. (Your drawing does not have to be to scale.) Find the height of the tree. (Look for similar triangles.)

    Is your calculated height close to your estimated height of the tree? If not, which number seems to be faulty? Why?

Chapter 10

Measurement

10.1 The Concept of Measurement

CLASS ACTIVITY 10A: Misconceptions about Measurement

1. Children sometimes try to measure the length of an object by placing one end of the object at the 1 marking instead of the 0 marking, as shown on the centimeter ruler in the figure. How might you help a child understand why the strip below is not 5 cm long even though the end of the strip is at 5?

2. Some children might report that the strip measured by the inch ruler shown is 2.3 inches long. Why is this not correct? What is a correct way to report the length of the strip?

CLASS ACTIVITY 10B: Becoming Familiar with Centimeters and Meters

You will need either a tape measure or scissors and tape with which to cut out and tape together the tape measure on page 571.

1. Measure the following, both in centimeters and in inches:

OBJECT	CENTIMETERS	INCHES
index finger length		
hand length		
hand width		
length of arm		
your height		

2. Find ten different objects around you (e.g., desk, blackboard, book, etc.). Without looking at a tape measure or ruler, estimate their lengths, widths, or heights in centimeters or meters. Then check the actual length in centimeters or meters.

OBJECT	ESTIMATE IN CENTIMETERS/METERS	ACTUAL IN CENTIMETERS/METERS

CLASS ACTIVITY 10C: Becoming Familiar with Units of Area

If available, square tiles that are 1-inch-by-1-inch and 1-centimeter-by-1-centimeter, as well as 1-foot-by-1-foot squares, would be helpful for this activity.

1. Discuss the following as clearly and concretely as you can, as if you were teaching children:

    a. What does it mean to say that a shape has an area of 6 square inches? Illustrate concretely with tiles, if available, or use the graph paper in Figure 10.1.

    b. What does it mean to say that a shape has an area of 12 square centimeters? Illustrate concretely with tiles, if available, or use the graph paper in Figure 10.2.

    c. What does it mean to say that a rug has an area of 20 square feet?

    d. What does it mean to say that the floor of a room has an area of 30 square meters?

2. If we weren't thinking carefully, we might try to illustrate 6 square inches by drawing a square that is 6 inches wide and 6 inches long. Why is it easy to think that such a square has area 6 square inches, and why is this *not correct*?

3. People sometimes say, "Area is length times width." Why is it not correct to characterize area this way?

FIGURE 10.1
Inch Graph Paper

FIGURE 10.2

Centimeter Graph Paper

CLASS ACTIVITY 10D: Becoming Familiar with Units of Volume

If available, cubes that are 1-inch-by-1-inch-by-1-inch and 1-centimeter-by-1-centimeter-by-1-centimeter, as well as an example of a 1-foot-by-1-foot-by-1-foot cube, would be helpful for this activity.

1. Discuss the following as clearly and concretely as you can, as if you were teaching children:

   a. What does it mean to say that an object has a volume of 6 cubic inches? Illustrate concretely with cubes, if available.

   b. What does it mean to say that an object has a volume of 12 cubic centimeters? Illustrate concretely with cubes, if available.

   c. What does it mean to say that a room has a volume of 1200 cubic feet?

   d. What does it mean to say that tank has a volume of 150 cubic meters?

2. If we weren't thinking carefully, we might try to illustrate 6 cubic inches by making a cube that is 6 inches wide, 6 inches deep, and 6 inches high. Why is it easy to think that such a cube has a volume of 6 cubic inches, and why is this *not correct*?

3. People sometimes say, "Volume is height times width times depth." Why is it not correct to characterize volume this way?

10.2 Error and Accuracy in Measurements

CLASS ACTIVITY 10E: Reporting and Interpreting Measurements

1. The following picture shows two rulers measuring identical shaded strips:

   a. How should you report the length of the strip using the first ruler? Explain.

   b. How should you report the length of the strip using the second ruler? Explain.

kilograms

2. The long shaded line on the dial above indicates the weight of a person in kilograms. Which of the following should you report as the weight of the person, and why?

   51 kg,   51.3 kg,   51.4 kg,   51.5 kg,   51.37 kg,   51.38 kg

3. As abstract numbers, $4 = 4.0$, but does it mean the same thing to say that an object weighs 4 kg as to say that it weighs 4.0 kg? If not, what is the difference?

4. One source says that the average distance from the Earth to the Sun is 93,000,000 miles, and another source says that the average distance from the Earth to the Sun is 92,960,000 miles. Can both of these descriptions be correct or must at least one of them be wrong? Explain.

10.3   Length, Area, Volume, and Dimension

CLASS ACTIVITY 10F: Dimension and Size

You will need scissors and tape for part (2) of this activity.

1. In the book *Captain Underpants and the Attack of the Talking Toilets* [9, p. 30], the character Melvin describes a machine called the PATSY 2000 that he has invented:

    "The PATSY 2000 can take any one-dimensional image and create a living, breathing, three-dimensional copy of that image. For example, take this ordinary photograph of a mouse."

    Are the terms *one-dimensional* and *three-dimensional* used properly here? Discuss.

2. Use the centimeter graph paper on page 573 to make a pattern for a closed box. The box should have six sides, and when you cut out and fold the pattern, there should be no overlapping pieces of paper. Describe one-dimensional, two-dimensional, and three-dimensional parts or aspects of your box. In each case, give the size of the part or aspect of the box using an appropriate unit.

3. Imagine a lake. Describe one-dimensional, two-dimensional, and three-dimensional parts or aspects of the lake. In each case, state how you would measure the size of that part or aspect of the lake—by length, by area, or by volume—and name an appropriate U.S. customary unit and an appropriate metric unit for measuring or describing the size of that part or aspect of the lake. What are practical reasons for wanting to know the sizes of these parts or aspects of the lake?

4. Imagine a house. Describe one-dimensional, two-dimensional, and three-dimensional parts or aspects of the house. In each case, state how you would measure the size of that part or aspect of the house—by length, by area, or by volume—and name an appropriate U.S. customary unit and an appropriate metric unit for measuring or describing the size of that part or aspect of the house. What are practical reasons for wanting to know the sizes of these parts or aspects of the house?

10.4 Calculating Perimeters of Polygons, Areas of Rectangles, and Volumes of Boxes

CLASS ACTIVITY 10G: Explaining Why We Add to Calculate Perimeters of Polygons

If available, string will be helpful for this activity.

Imagine you are working with elementary school children. Tell the children what we mean by the term "perimeter." You may wish to use the string to help you.

If you didn't have string, how would you calculate the perimeter of the polygon in the next figure? Why does it make sense that we can calculate the perimeter by adding? The grid lines are 1 cm apart.

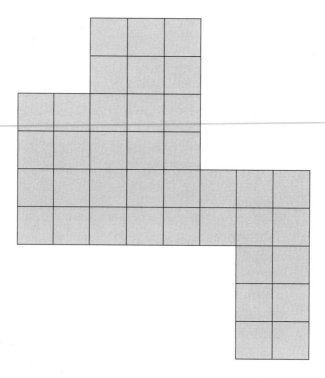

CLASS ACTIVITY 10H: Perimeter Misconceptions

You will need a centimeter ruler for part 2.

1. Johnny wants to calculate the perimeter of the shaded shape in Figure (a). Johnny's method is to shade the squares along the border of the shape, as shown in Figure (b), and to count these border squares. Therefore Johnny says the perimeter of the shape is 24 cm. Is Johnny's method valid? If not, why not? How might you help Johnny better understand what perimeter is?

(a)

(b)

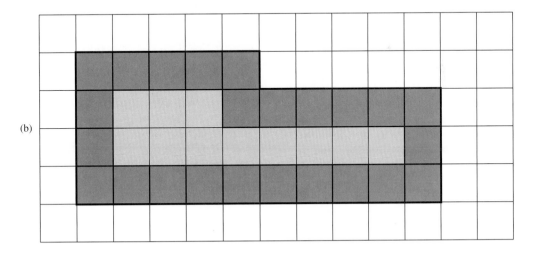

2. When Susie was asked to draw a shape with perimeter 15 cm, she drew a shape like the shaded one shown in the next figure on centimeter grid paper.

    a. Carefully measure the diagonal line segment in the shaded shape with a centimeter ruler. Then explain why the shape does not have perimeter 15 cm.

    b. Draw a shape that has perimeter 15 cm on the graph paper below. (The corners of your shape do not have to be located where grid lines meet.)

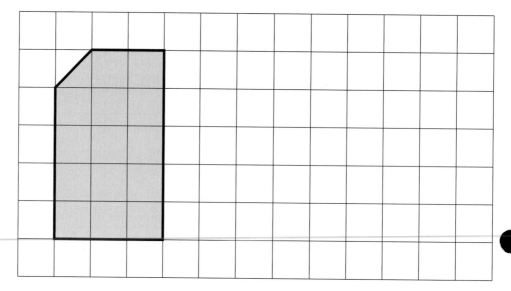

CLASS ACTIVITY 101: Explaining Why We Multiply to Determine Areas of Rectangles

If available, a set of 1-inch-by-1-inch square tiles would be helpful; if they are not available, then you will need scissors for this activity.

1. If square tiles are not available, cut out the small 1-inch-by-1-inch squares on page 575. Use the rectangle on page 575 and either the paper squares or a set of 1-inch-by-1-inch tiles to help you explain why we can determine the area of a rectangle by multiplying its length by its width. Your explanation should rely on the interpretation of multiplication in terms of grouping and on the meaning of area.

2. Explain how to see the area of the following large rectangle as consisting of $3\frac{1}{2}$ groups with $4\frac{1}{2}$ cm^2 in each group, thereby explaining why it makes sense to multiply

$$3\frac{1}{2} \times 4\frac{1}{2}$$

to determine the area of the rectangle in square centimeters:

1 cm^2

    Then calculate $3\frac{1}{2} \times 4\frac{1}{2}$ and verify that this calculation has the same answer as when you determine the area of the rectangle by counting full 1-cm-by-1-cm squares and combining partial squares.

CLASS ACTIVITY 10J: Explaining Why We Multiply to Determine Volumes of Boxes

You will need scissors and tape for this activity. If available, a set of 1-inch-by-1-inch-by-1-inch cubes would be helpful.

Cut out the pattern on page 577, fold it, and tape it to make an open-top box. If a set of cubes is not available, then cut out the patterns for cubes on page 579 and fold and tape them to make 1-inch-by-1-inch-by-1-inch cubes. Use the box and the 1-inch-by-1-inch-by-1-inch cubes to help you explain why we can multiply the length times the width times the depth of the box to determine the volume of the box. Your explanation should rely on the interpretation of multiplication in terms of grouping and on the meaning of volume.

10.5 Comparing Sizes of Objects

CLASS ACTIVITY 10K: The Biggest Tree in the World

Listed next are several different trees that could perhaps qualify as the biggest tree in the world. Compare these trees. Why can reasonable people differ about which tree is biggest?

Tree # 1: "General Sherman" is a giant sequoia located in Sequoia National Park in California. (See Figure 10.3.) According to the National Park Service, General Sherman is 275 feet tall, has a circumference (at its base) of 103 feet, and has a volume of 52,500 cubic feet.

Tree # 2: "General Grant" is a giant sequoia located in Sequoia National Park in California. According to the National Park Service, General Grant is 268 feet tall, has a circumference (at its base) of 108 feet, and has a volume of 46,600 cubic feet.

Tree #3: "Mendocino Tree" is a redwood tree in Montgomery Redwoods State Reserve near Ukiah, California. It is 368 feet tall and has a diameter of 10.4 feet, which means that its circumference should be about 33 feet.

Tree #4: A Banyan tree in Calcutta, India, has a circumference of 1,350 feet (meaning the circumference of the whole tree, not just the trunk) and covers three acres.

Tree #5: A tree in Santa Maria del Tule near Oaxaca, Mexico, is 130 feet tall and is described as requiring 40 people holding hands to encircle it.

Some websites have photos of these large trees. See

www.aw-bc.com/beckmann

FIGURE 10.3
Is "General Sherman" the Biggest Tree in the World?

CLASS ACTIVITY 10L: Comparing Sizes of Boxes

You will need scissors and tape for this activity.

1. Figures A.26 and A.27 on pages 581 and 583 have patterns for boxes drawn on centimeter graph paper. (Adjacent grid lines are 1 cm apart.) Cut out the box patterns on the heavy outer lines. Fold the patterns along the inner heavy lines and tape them to make boxes that look like the following:

2. Determine the surface areas and volumes of the boxes. Be sure to use appropriate units in each case.

3. Explain why either of the two boxes can be considered the larger of the two.

10.6 Converting from One Unit of Measurement to Another

CLASS ACTIVITY 10M: Conversions: When Do We Multiply? When Do We Divide?

1. Julie is confused about why we *multiply* by 3 to convert 6 yards to feet. She thinks we should *divide* by 3 because feet are smaller than yards.

   a. Draw a picture to show Julie how yards and feet are related. Use your picture and the meaning of multiplication to explain to Julie why we multiply by 3 to convert 6 yards to feet.

   b. Julie knows that if she measures the length of a table in yards she will get a smaller number than if she measures the length of the table in feet. Given this, how might you help Julie understand why we multiply by 3 to convert 6 yards to feet?

   c. Try to think of other ways to help Julie better understand conversions. What problems or questions could you pose to Julie?

2. Nate is confused about why we *divide* by 100 to convert 200 centimeters to meters. He thinks we should *multiply* by 100 because meters are bigger than centimeters. What are some ways you could help Nate better understand conversions?

3. Shaquila is 57 inches tall. How tall is Shaquila in feet?

   a. Solve this conversion problem in a simple fashion and explain why your method of solution makes sense in a way that children could understand.

   b. Describe a number of different correct ways to write the answer to the conversion problem. Explain briefly why these different ways of writing the answer mean the same thing.

4. Suppose that the children in your class want to have a party at which they will serve punch to drink. The punch that the children want to serve is sold in half-gallon containers. If 25 people attend the party, and if each person drinks 8 fluid ounces of punch, then how many containers of punch will you need? Describe several different ways that children could correctly solve this problem. For each method of solving the problem, explain simply and clearly why the method makes sense.

CLASS ACTIVITY 10N: Converting Measurements With and Without Dimensional Analysis

1. If a woman is 165 centimeters tall, how tall is she in feet and inches? First estimate your answer. Then use the fact that 1 inch = 2.54 cm to determine the woman's height in feet and inches in the following two different ways:
   a. using logical thinking about multiplication and division

   b. using dimensional analysis

2. Convert 1 mile to kilometers using the fact that 1 inch = 2.54 cm. Calculate your answer in the following two different ways:
   a. using logical thinking about multiplication and division

   b. using dimensional analysis

CLASS ACTIVITY 10O: Area and Volume Conversions: Which Are Correct and Which Are Not?

1. Analyze the calculations that follow, which are intended to convert 25 square meters to square feet. Which use legitimate methods and are correct, and which are not? Explain.

   a.

   $$25 \text{ m}^2 = 25 \text{ m} \ \times \ \frac{100 \text{ cm}}{1 \text{ m}} \times \frac{1 \text{ in}}{2.54 \text{ cm}} \times \frac{1 \text{ ft}}{12 \text{ in}} = 82 \text{ ft}^2$$

   b.

   $$25 \text{ m}^2 = 25 \text{ m}^2 \times \frac{100 \times 100 \text{ cm}^2}{1 \text{ m}^2} \times \frac{1 \text{ in}^2}{2.54 \times 2.54 \text{ cm}^2} \times \frac{1 \text{ ft}^2}{12 \times 12 \text{ in}^2} = 269 \text{ ft}^2$$

   c.

   $$25 \text{ m} = 25 \text{ m} \times \frac{100 \text{ cm}}{1 \text{ m}} \times \frac{1 \text{ in}}{2.54 \text{ cm}} \times \frac{1 \text{ ft}}{12 \text{ in}} = 82 \text{ ft}$$

   Therefore,

   $$25 \text{ m}^2 = 82^2 \text{ ft}^2 = 6727 \text{ ft}^2$$

   d. 25 square meters is the area of a square that is 5 meters wide and 5 meters long, so

   $$5 \text{ m} = 5 \text{ m} \ \times \ \frac{100 \text{ cm}}{1 \text{ m}} \times \frac{1 \text{ in}}{2.54 \text{ cm}} \times \frac{1 \text{ ft}}{12 \text{ in}} = 16.404 \text{ ft}$$

   Therefore,

   $$25 \text{ m}^2 = 16.404 \times 16.404 \text{ ft}^2 = 269 \text{ ft}^2$$

2. Use the fact that 1 inch = 2.54 cm to convert 27 cubic feet to cubic meters in at least two different ways.

Chapter 11

More about Area and Volume

11.1 The Moving and Combining Principles about Area

CLASS ACTIVITY 11A: Different Shapes with the Same Area

You will need scissors and tape for this activity.

Cut out the four 10-cm-by-15-cm rectangles on pages 587 and 589.

1. Cut one of the two rectangles on page 587 diagonally in half, creating two identical triangles, as shown in the middle of the next figure. Use the moving and combining principles to determine the area of each triangle.

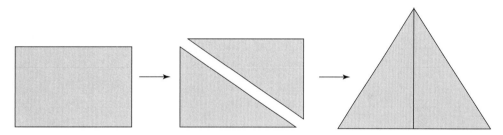

Rearrange the two triangles and tape them together, without overlapping, to create a single large triangle, as shown on the right in the previous figure. Use the moving and combining principles to determine the area of this new, large triangle.

2. Cut the other rectangle on page 587 diagonally in half, creating two triangles. Rearrange the two triangles and tape them together, without overlapping, to create a single large triangle that is different from the triangle you created in part (a). Use the moving and combining principles to determine the area of this new, large triangle.

3. Cut one of the two rectangles on page 589 diagonally in half, creating two triangles. Rearrange the two triangles and tape them together, without overlapping, to create a parallelogram that is not a rectangle. (There are two different ways you can do this.) Use the moving and combining principles to determine the area of the parallelogram.

4. Cut the other rectangle on page 589 into pieces of any size or shape you like. Rearrange those pieces and tape them together, without overlapping, to create a new shape, such as the one in the figure. You can even make a shape that is not flat, if you like. Use the moving and combining principles to determine the area of your new shape.

5. Now compare all four shapes that you created in parts (a), (b), (c), and (d). What do all the shapes have in common, and what is different about the shapes? Do all the shapes have the same perimeter? Do all the shapes have the same length?

CLASS ACTIVITY 11B: Using the Moving and Combining Principles

You will need blank paper, scissors, and a ruler for part 2 of this activity.

1. The grid lines in the next figure are 1 cm apart. Use the moving and combining principles about areas to help you determine the area of each of the three triangles shown (in square centimeters). Explain why your answers are correct. *Do not* use a formula for areas of triangles.

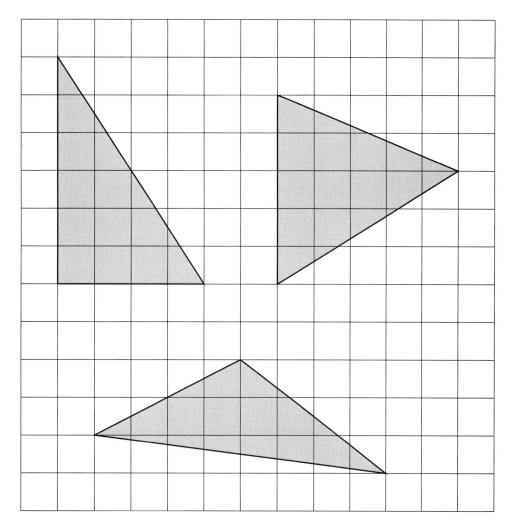

2. Take a piece of paper and fold it into fourths by folding it in half and then in half again, as shown in the next diagram. While the paper is still folded, cut off the "open" corner—so that you cut off four triangles, as indicated on the right. When you unfold the paper you will have either an octagon, a hexagon, or a rhombus, depending on how you cut. (Can you see how to make each of these shapes?)

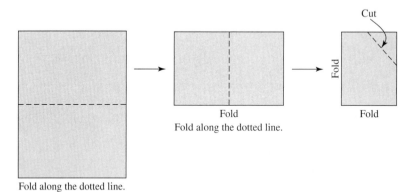

Fold along the dotted line.

Fold along the dotted line.

Determine the area of your octagon, hexagon, or rhombus. Use only the moving and combining principles, actual measurements, and the formula for areas of rectangles to determine the area. Do not use any other formulas.

CLASS ACTIVITY 11C: Using the Moving and Combining Principles to Determine Surface Area

You will need blank paper, scissors, and tape for this activity.

1. Take a standard 8.5-in-by-11-in piece of paper, roll it up, and tape it, without overlapping the paper, to make a cylinder without bases, as shown in the next figure. What is the surface area of the cylinder? Why?

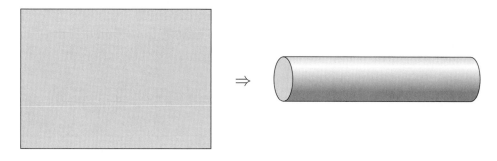

2. The 8 triangles on the centimeter graph paper on page 585 can be cut out and taped together, without overlapping, to form an octahedron. Use the moving and combining principles to determine the surface area of the octahedron. Do not use any formula for the area of a triangle.

11.2   Using the Moving and Combining Principles to Prove the Pythagorean Theorem

CLASS ACTIVITY 11D: Using the Pythagorean Theorem

You will need a calculator for part 2 of this activity.

1. What, if anything, does the Pythagorean theorem say about the three triangles in the next figure? The letters a, b, c, d, e, f, x, y, and z represent the lengths of the indicated sides (all measured in the same units).

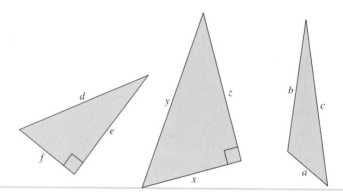

2. Tyler and Sarah measured the distance between two trees and found it to be 18 feet. But when they measured this distance, Tyler held up his end of the tape measure 8 inches higher than Sarah's end. If Sarah and Tyler had measured the distance between the trees by holding the tape measure horizontally, would they get an appreciably different result? Explain.

CLASS ACTIVITY 11E: Can We Prove the Pythagorean Theorem by Checking Examples?

You will need a ruler with $\frac{1}{4}$-inch markings (or finer) for this activity.

1. For each of the right triangles, measure the lengths of the sides and check that the Pythagorean theorem really is valid in each case. In other words, check that the sum of the squares of the lengths of the two shorter sides really is equal to the square of the length of the hypotenuse.

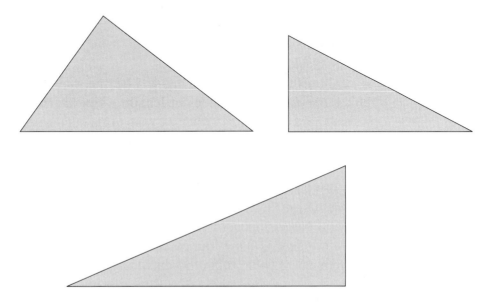

2. Would it be possible to prove that the Pythagorean theorem is true by checking many right triangles, continuing what you did in part (a)? Explain.

CLASS ACTIVITY 11F: A Proof of the Pythagorean Theorem

Start with any arbitrary right triangle. Let a and b be the lengths of the short sides, and let c be the length of the hypotenuse. (See Figure 11.1). To prove the Pythagorean theorem we must explain why $a^2 + b^2 = c^2$ is true. Even though we will be working with copies of the *particular* triangle shown in Figure 11.1, our explanation for why the Pythagorean theorem is true will be *general* because it would work in the same way for *any* right triangle.

1. Figure 11.2 shows some triangles and some squares. All the triangles shown are copies of our original right triangle with sides of lengths a, b, and c. The square shapes have all four sides the same length and four angles right angles, making them true squares.

    Follow the instructions in Figure 11.2 and show two different ways of filling a square that has sides of length $a + b$ with triangles and squares without gaps or overlaps. You may wish to cut out the squares and triangles on page 591 and use these to help you figure out how to fill in the squares of side length $a + b$.

2. Now use part 1 and the moving and combining principles about areas to explain why $a^2 + b^2 = c^2$. There are several different ways to do this.

    Hint: Notice that *both* of the two ways of filling a square of side length $a + b$ in Figure 11.2 use four copies of the original right triangle.

    Summarize your proof of Pythagoras's theorem.

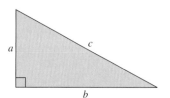

FIGURE 11.1

A Right Triangle

Draw the triangles and squares above into the square below so that they fill it without gaps or overlaps.

Draw the triangles and square above into the square below so that they fill it without gaps or overlaps.

FIGURE 11.2

Two Ways to Fill a Square of Side Length $a + b$

3. Here is a subtle point in the proof of the Pythagorean theorem: In both of the squares of side length $a + b$ in Figure 11.2, there are places along the edges where three figures (two triangles and a square) meet at a point. How do we know that the edge formed there really is a straight line and doesn't actually have a small bend in it, such as pictured in the next figure? We need to know that the edge there really is straight in order to know that the assembled shapes really do create large *squares*, and not *octagons*. Explain why these edges really are straight. (Hint: Consider the angles at the points where a square and two triangles meet.)

11.3 Approximating Areas of Irregular Shapes

CLASS ACTIVITY 11G: Determining the Area of an Irregular Shape

1. Think about several different ways that you might determine (at least approximately) the surface area of Lake Lalovely shown on the map in Figure 11.3. Suppose that you have the following items on hand:

   • many 1-inch-by-1-inch paper or plastic squares

   • graph paper (adjacent lines separated by 1/4 inch)

   • a scale for weighing (such as one used to determine postage)

   • string

   • modeling dough or clay

   Which of these items could help you to determine approximately the surface area of the lake. How?

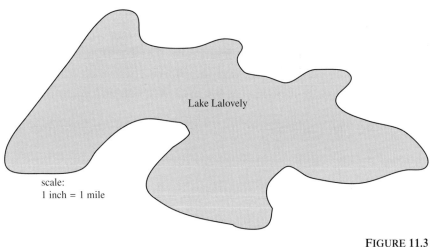

Lake Lalovely

scale:
1 inch = 1 mile

FIGURE 11.3
Lake Lalovely

2. Suppose that you have a map with a scale of 1 inch = 100 miles. You trace a state on the map onto $\frac{1}{4}$-inch graph paper (the grid lines are spaced $\frac{1}{4}$ inch apart). You count that the state takes up about 100 squares of graph paper. Approximately what is the area of the state? Explain.

3. Suppose that you have a map with a scale of 1 inch = 15 miles. You cover a county on the map with a $\frac{1}{8}$-inch-thick layer of modeling dough. Then you reform this piece of modeling dough into a $\frac{1}{8}$-inch-thick rectangle. The rectangle is $2\frac{1}{2}$ inches by $3\frac{3}{4}$ inches. Approximately what is the area of the county? Explain.

4. Suppose that you have a map with a scale of 1 inch = 50 miles. You trace a state on the map, cut out your tracing, and draw this tracing onto card stock. Using a scale, you determine that a full $8\frac{1}{2}$-inch-by-11-inch sheet of card stock weighs 10 grams. Then you cut out the tracing of the state that is on card stock and weigh this card-stock tracing. It weighs 6 grams. Approximately what is the area of the state? Explain.

11.4 Cavalieri's Principle about Shearing and Area

CLASS ACTIVITY 11H: Shearing a Toothpick Rectangle to Make a Parallelogram

For this activity you will need enough toothpicks to form a rectangle, as shown in the next figure.

1. Stack your toothpicks to form a rectangle, as shown, and determine the area of this rectangle.

2. Now push on the ends of the toothpicks so as to shear your rectangle, forming a parallelogram as shown in the following figure:

3. What happens to the area of the rectangle when it is sheared into the shape of a parallelogram? What is the area of the parallelogram formed by your toothpicks?

4. If a classmate shears her rectangle more than you shear yours, so that her parallelogram is more elongated than yours, will the area of your classmate's parallelogram differ from the area of your parallelogram? Explain.

CLASS ACTIVITY 11I: Is This Shearing?

The next figure shows a rectangle made of toothpicks being sheared into a parallelogram. During the process of shearing, which of the following change and which remain the same?

- the area

- the lengths of the sides

- the height of the stack of toothpicks

The next figure shows a rectangle made with pieces of drinking straws tied with a string being "squashed" into a parallelogram. During the process of "squashing," which of the following change and which remain the same?

- the area

- the lengths of the sides

- the "vertical height" of the straw figure

Is the process of "squashing" the same as shearing? Why or why not?

CLASS ACTIVITY 11J: Shearing Parallelograms

1. Imagine shearing parallelogram ABCD so that side AB remains fixed. Draw the path that the line segment CD could move along during shearing. How is this path related to the line segment AB?

2. Determine the area of the next parallelogram by shearing it into a rectangle. Explain your reasoning. Adjacent dots are 1 cm apart.

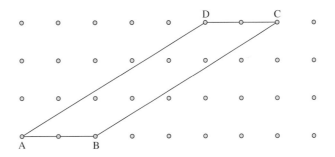

3. Determine the area of the next parallelogram by shearing it into a rectangle. Explain your reasoning. Adjacent dots are 1 cm apart. Note: Shearing does not have to be horizontal.

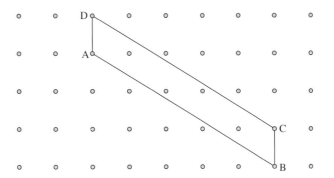

CLASS ACTIVITY 11K: Shearing Triangles

You will need scissors for this activity.

1. Cut out the large triangle on page 593 and cut it into strips along the dotted lines. On a flat surface, put the paper strips back together to make the original triangle. Now give your paper strips a push from the side, simulating shearing, as indicated in the next figure. When you shear your paper triangle you can form new shapes that are basically triangles except that the edges are jagged. (If your paper strips were infinitesimally thin, then the edges would not be jagged.)

   By shearing your paper triangle, form various different (jagged) triangles, including a right triangle.

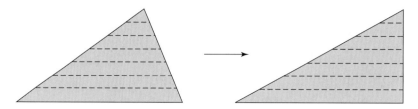

   Determine which of the following change during shearing and which remain the same:

   • the area

   • the lengths of the sides

   • the height of the "stack" of paper strips

2. Imagine shearing the triangle ABC so that side AB remains fixed. Draw all the locations to which point C could move during shearing. Describe the nature of these locations, in particular; how are they related to the line segment AB?

3. Determine the area of the next triangle by first shearing the triangle into a right triangle and then using the moving and combining principles to determine the area of the right triangle. Explain why you can determine the area of the original triangle by this method. Adjacent dots are 1 cm apart.

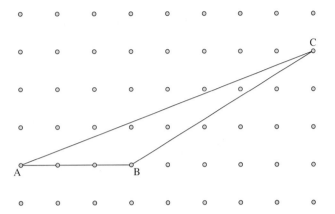

4. Determine the area of the next triangle by first shearing the triangle into a right triangle and then using the moving and combining principles to determine the area of the right triangle. Explain why you can determine the area of the original triangle by this method. Note: Shearing does not have to be horizontal.

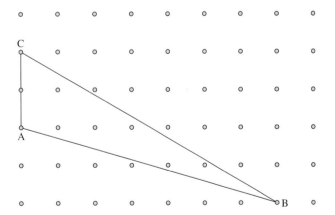

11.5 Areas of Triangles

CLASS ACTIVITY 11L: Choosing the Base and Height of Triangles

Show the three different ways to choose the base and height of the triangles shown in the next figure. Once you have chosen a base, the right angle formed by the corner of a piece of paper may help you determine where to draw the height, which must be perpendicular to the base.

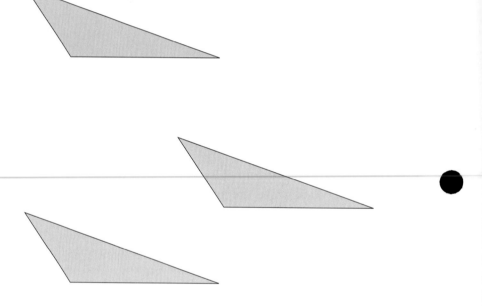

CLASS ACTIVITY 11M: Explaining Why the Area Formula for Triangles Is Valid

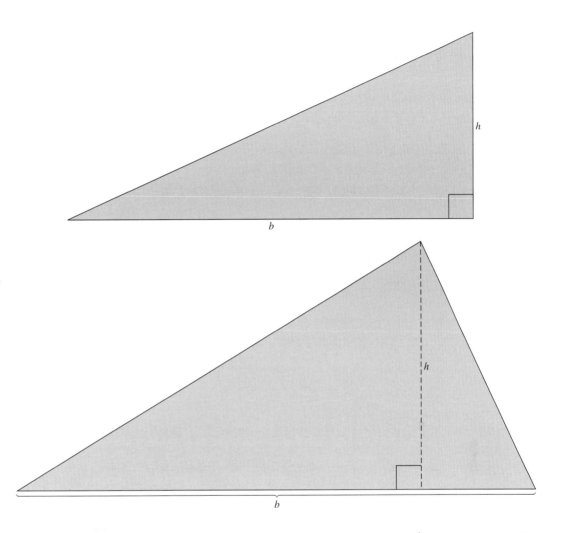

1. Explain why each of the preceding triangles has area $\frac{1}{2}b \times h$ square units for the given choices of b and h.

   Depending on your explanation, the formula $\frac{1}{2}(b \times h)$, the formula $(\frac{1}{2}b) \times h$, or the formula $b \times (\frac{1}{2}h)$ may be most suitable for describing the area of the triangle. Why is it valid to describe the area with any one of these three formulas?

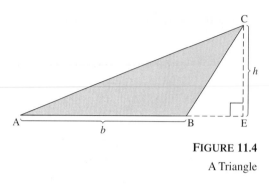

FIGURE 11.4

A Triangle

2. The area of the triangle in Figure 11.4 is still $\frac{1}{2}b \times h$ square units for the given choices of b and h. What is wrong with the following reasoning that claims to show that the area of the triangle ABC is $\frac{1}{2}b \times h$ square units?

> Draw a rectangle around the triangle ABC, as shown in Figure 11.5. The area of this rectangle is $b \times h$ square units. The line AC cuts the rectangle in half, so the area of the triangle ABC is half of $b \times h$ square units, in other words $\frac{1}{2}b \times h$ square units.

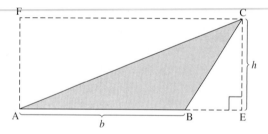

FIGURE 11.5

Can You Find the Area This Way?

3. What is a valid way to explain why the triangle in part 2 has area $\frac{1}{2}b \times h$ square units for the given choice of b and h?

11.6 Areas of Parallelograms

CLASS ACTIVITY 11N: Do Side Lengths Determine the Area of a Parallelogram?

1. A rectangle is a special kind of parallelogram. We can calculate the area of a rectangle in terms of the lengths of the sides of the rectangle. Does this mean we can therefore calculate the area of a parallelogram in terms of the lengths of the sides of the parallelogram? Investigate this question as follows:

    The three parallelograms in Figure 11.6 (the first of which is also a rectangle) all have two sides that are 3 cm long and two sides that are 7 cm long. The small squares in the grid are 1 cm by 1 cm.

    a. Use the moving and combining principles to determine the areas of the three parallelograms in Figure 11.6.

    b. Can there be a formula for areas of parallelograms that is only in terms of the lengths of the sides? Explain why or why not.

2. There is no formula for areas of parallelograms that is expressed solely in terms of the lengths of the *sides* of the parallelogram. However, there *is* a formula for areas of parallelograms. Try to find a formula *in terms of lengths of parts of the parallelogram.* Use the following parallelogram to help you explain your formula:

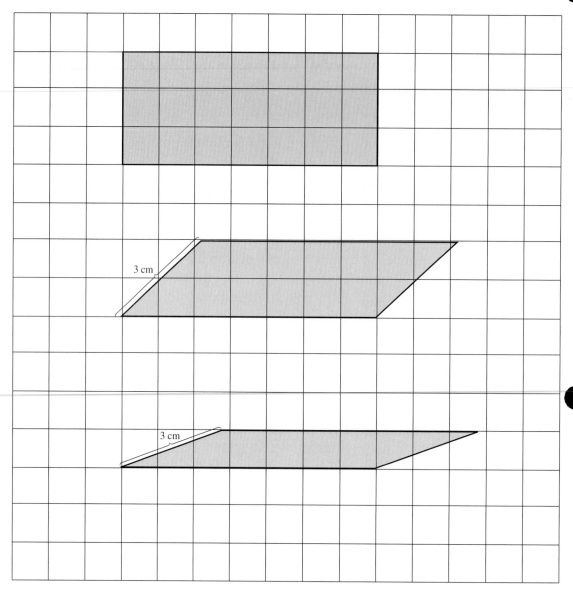

FIGURE 11.6

Three Parallelograms

11.7 Areas of Circles and the Number Pi

CLASS ACTIVITY 110: How Big Is the Number π?

Suppose that the only thing you know about the number π is that it is the circumference of a circle of diameter 1. Explain how you can use the picture below to give information about the size of the number π. (Based on the picture, you should be able to say that π lies between two numbers. Which two numbers?)

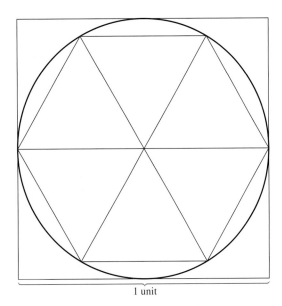

1 unit

CLASS ACTIVITY 11P: Over- and Underestimates for the Area of a Circle

Scissors might be helpful for this activity.

Use the next picture to explain why the area of a circle that has radius r units is less than $4r^2$ square units and greater than $2r^2$ square units. In other words, explain why

$$2r^2 \text{ units}^2 < \text{area of circle} < 4r^2 \text{ units}^2$$

In order to explain why the area of the circle is greater than $2r^2$ square units, it may help you to trace, cut out, and rearrange the triangles inside the circle.

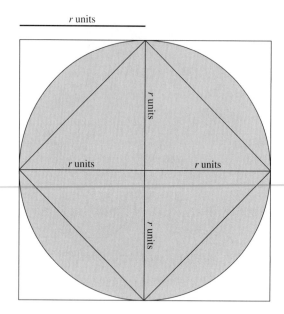

CLASS ACTIVITY 11Q: Why the Area Formula for Circles Makes Sense

You will need scissors for this activity.

1. Trace the given circle and cut your traced circle into 8 pie pieces. Arrange the 8 pie pieces as shown at the top of Figure 11.7.

2. Now cut your traced circle into 16 pie pieces. Arrange the 16 pie pieces as shown in the middle of Figure 11.7.

3. Imagine cutting a circle into more and more smaller and smaller pie pieces, and rearrange them as in Figure 11.7.
   What shape would your rearranged circle become more and more like?
   What would the lengths of the sides of this shape be?
   What would the area of this shape be?

4. Using your answers to part (3), explain why it makes sense that a circle of radius r units has area πr^2 square units.

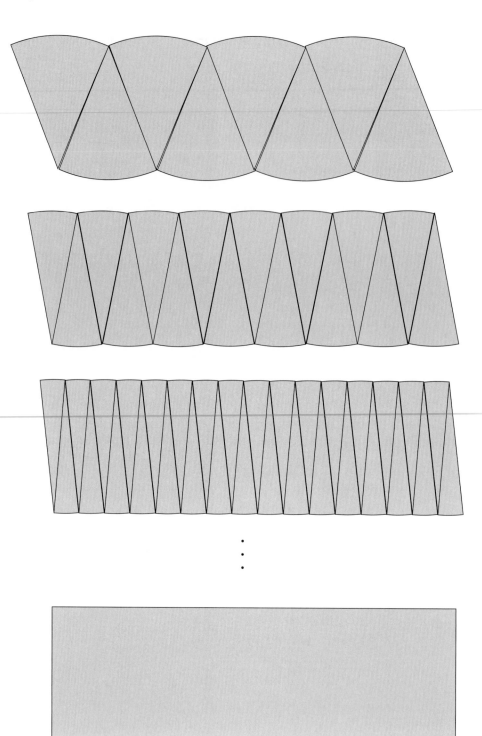

FIGURE 11.7
Rearranging a Circle

CLASS ACTIVITY 11R: Using the Circle Circumference and Area Formulas

You will need paper, a compass, and a protractor for parts 3 and 4.

1. A company wants to manufacture tin cans that are 3 inches in diameter and 4 inches tall. Describe the shape and dimensions of the paper label the company will need to wrap around the curved portion of each can. Explain your reasoning.

2. A reflecting pool will be made in the shape of the shaded region shown in the next figure. The curves shown are $\frac{1}{4}$ circles. What is the surface area of the pool? Explain your reasoning.

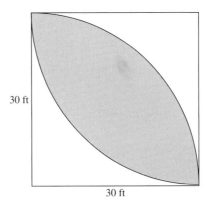

30 ft

30 ft

3. Make a pattern for a cone such that the base is a circle of radius 2 inches and the slanted portion is made from a half-circle. Determine the total surface area of your cone.

4. Make a pattern for a cone such that the base is a circle of radius 2 inches and the slanted portion is made from part of a circle of radius 6 inches. What fraction of the 6-inch circle will you need to use? Determine the total surface area of your cone.

11.8   Relating the Perimeter and Area of a Shape

CLASS ACTIVITY 11S: How Are Perimeter and Area Related?

If available, string would be useful for this activity.

1. Suppose surveyors have determined that a forest on flat terrain has a perimeter of 200 miles. What is the area of the forest? Can you answer this question without additional information, or is more than one answer possible? Draw pictures, experiment, discuss, and debate this question for a few minutes. If available, use a loop of string to help you think about the question.

    Now suppose that you learn that the forest is in the shape of a rectangle. Can you determine the area now, or is more than one answer possible?

2. Figure 11.8 shows centimeter graph paper. Draw at least 5 different rectangles of perimeter 20 cm on this graph paper. Include some rectangles that have sides whose lengths *aren't whole numbers* of centimeters.

3. Determine the areas of the rectangles you just drew. In the next table, list the areas of your rectangles in decreasing order. Below each area, draw a small sketch showing the approximate shape of the corresponding rectangle.

    How are the larger area rectangles qualitatively different in shape from the smaller area ones?

area						
shape						

4. Show how two people can use a loop of string and 4 fingers to represent all rectangles of a certain fixed perimeter.

    Now consider all the rectangles of perimeter 20 cm, *including those whose side lengths aren't whole numbers of centimeters*. What are all the theoretical possibilities for the areas of rectangles of perimeter 20 cm? What is the largest possible area, what is the smallest possible area (if there is one)?

5. Suppose that a forest on flat terrain is shaped like a rectangle and has perimeter 200 miles. What can you say about the forest's area? Give the most informative answer that you can.

6. Now suppose that a forest on flat terrain has perimeter 200 miles, but there is no information on the shape of the forest. Now what can you say about the forest's area? Use a loop of string to help you think about this question.

FIGURE 11.8
Centimeter Graph Paper

CLASS ACTIVITY 11T: Can We Determine Area by Measuring Perimeter?

Nick wants to find the area of an irregular shape. Nick cuts a piece of string so that it goes all the way around the outside of the shape. Then Nick forms his piece of string into a square on top of graph paper. Using the graph paper, Nick gets a good estimate for the area of his string square. Nick then uses the square's area as his estimate for the area of the original irregular shape.

Discuss whether or not Nick's method is a legitimate way to estimate areas of irregular shapes.

11.9   Principles for Determining Volumes

CLASS ACTIVITY 11U: Determining a Volume by Submersing in Water

For this activity you will need a milliliter measuring cup, water, a centimeter ruler, and a good sized lump of clay that still fits comfortably in your measuring cup. Use synthetic clay that does not dissolve in water (modeling dough dissolves in water).

1. Form your lump of clay into a rectangular prism and determine the volume of the clay in cubic centimeters by measuring the height, width, and depth of the rectangular prism.

2. Pour water into your measuring cup and note the volume of water in milliliters. Submerse your clay prism in the water and determine the volume of your clay prism in milliliters. Explain why your method for determining the volume of the prism makes sense.

3. Reconcile the volume you calculated in problem 1 with the volume you calculated in problem 2. In particular, how can you relate a volume described in cubic centimeters with a volume described in milliliters?

4. Remove your clay prism from the water and subdivide it into several pieces. Attach these pieces to form a new shape. Submerse this new shape in the water, and note the volume by which the water level rises. Is it the same as before? If you mold the clay into some other solid shape, will the clay still displace the same amount of water when it is submersed?

CLASS ACTIVITY 11V: Floating Versus Sinking: Archimedes' Principle

For this activity you will need a milliliter measuring cup, water, a small paper cup, and several coins or other small, heavy objects that fit inside the cup. In part 3 you will need a scale for weighing.

1. Pour water into your measuring cup and float the paper cup on the water. Note the volume of water in milliliters. Now put the coins in the cup so that the cup and coins are floating in the water. By how much did the water level rise? Does this increase in water level tell you the volume of the coins?

2. Predict what will happen to the water level when you take the coins out of the cup and submerse them in the water: will the water level go up or will the water level go down? Submerse the coins and see if your prediction was correct.

    Did the increase in water level in part 1 tell you the volume of the coins or not? Explain.

3. Exactly how much water does a floating object displace? Do the following to find out:

    a. Weigh your coins from part 1.

    b. Weigh an amount of water that weighs as much as your coins.

    c. Float your coins in the paper cup in the measuring cup and record the water level.

    d. Remove your coins from the paper cup and pour the water you measured in (b) into the measuring cup. Compare the water level now to the water level in part (c). If you did everything correctly, these two water levels should be the same.

    This experiment illustrates **Archimedes' principle**, that a floating object displaces an amount of water that weighs as much as the object.

4. Determine approximately how much a quarter weighs in grams by using Archimedes' principle. Observe how much the water level rises when you put several quarters in a cup floating in water in a measuring cup.

5. Ships usually have markings on their sides to show how low or high the ship is floating in the water. Besides showing how low or high the ship is floating, what other information could the captain of the ship get by observing which mark is at the water line?

6. The Great Salt Lake in Utah, and the Dead Sea in Israel and Jordan are lakes that have so much salt in them that people float in the water. (See Figure 11.9.) Use Archimedes' principle to explain why people float in these lakes. What is it about this salty water that causes people to float?

FIGURE 11.9

Floating in the Dead Sea

11.10 Volumes of Prisms, Cylinders, Pyramids, and Cones

CLASS ACTIVITY 11W: Why the Volume Formula for Prisms and Cylinders Makes Sense

1. The simplest kind of prism is a right rectangular prism, which is just a box shape. We have already seen that a box that is H units high, D units deep, and W units wide has volume

$$H \times D \times W$$

cubic units. Explain why the volume of such a box can be expressed as

(height) × (area of base)

cubic units.

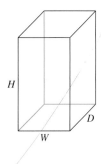

2. Use the result of part (1) and Cavalieri's principle to explain why the

(height) × (area of base)

gives the correct volume for an *oblique* rectangular prism that is H units high, D units deep, and W units wide. Explain why the height should be measured perpendicular to the bases, and not "on the slant."

3. Using only the volume formula for *rectangular* prisms and the moving and combining principles about volumes, explain why the

$$(\text{height}) \times (\text{area of base})$$

formula gives the correct volume for the triangular prism in the next figure. You may wish to cut out the patterns on page 595 to make two models of the triangular prism.

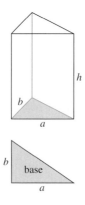

4. To explain why the

$$(\text{height}) \times (\text{area of base})$$

formula gives the correct volume for all prisms and cylinders, imagine building a prism or cylinder with 1-unit-by-1-unit-by-1-unit clay cubes (or other cubes that could be cut into pieces). Think about building the shape in layers. The first layer should cover the base with a single layer of cubes. (Note that the cubes might need to be cut apart and re-formed in order to cover the base.) By considering the number of layers you will need and the number of cubes in each layer, explain why the volume of the prism or cylinder is

$$(\text{height}) \times (\text{area of base})$$

cubic units.

5. Using only the volume formula for *rectangular* prisms and the moving and combining principles about volumes, determine the volume of the *parallelogram-base* prism on the left in the next figure in terms of *a*, *b*, and *h*. You may wish to cut out the patterns on pages 597 and 599 to make models of the three prisms shown.

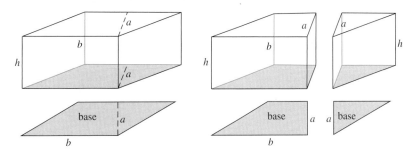

6. Explain how to use the idea of Class Activity 11Q to "rearrange" a right cylinder to form a rectangular prism, as indicated in the next figure. Use this idea to determine the volume of the cylinder in terms of *r* and *h*.

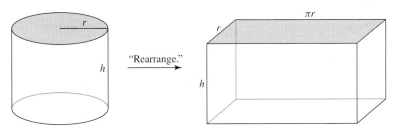

CLASS ACTIVITY 11X: Using Volume Formulas

For this activity, you will need several drink containers that show how much they hold in milliliters or liters. You will also need either a tape measure or scissors and tape.

1. If you don't already have a centimeter tape measure, cut out Figure A.36 on page 601, and tape it together to make a centimeter tape measure.

2. Use a centimeter tape measure to measure the lengths of various parts of your drink containers. Use these measurements to calculate the approximate volume of liquid in your (full) drink containers in cubic centimeters.

3. Compare your calculated volumes of the drink containers to the capacities (in milliliters or liters) shown on the containers. In each case, do the two agree? Remember that one cubic centimeter holds one milliliter of liquid.

CLASS ACTIVITY 11Y: Filling Boxes and Jars

1. How many plastic 2-cm-by-2-cm-by-2-cm cubes can be stacked neatly in an 8-cm-by-10-cm-by-12-cm box? Explain.

2. How many plastic 2-cm-by-2-cm-by-2-cm cubes can be stacked neatly in an 8-cm-by-9-cm-by-12-cm box? Explain.

3. A BerryBombs cereal box is 10 inches tall, $7\frac{1}{2}$ inches wide, and $2\frac{1}{2}$ inches deep. Give the length, width, and depth of a cardboard box that could hold exactly 12 BerryBombs cereal boxes leaving no extra space. Now find the dimensions of another box that could hold 12 BerryBombs cereal boxes with no extra space.

4. A 9-inch-by-9-inch-by-12-inch jar in the shape of a rectangular prism is completely filled with gum balls of diameter $\frac{3}{4}$ inches. Estimate the number of gum balls in the jar, explaining your reasoning.

5. A jar in the shape of a 9-inch tall cylinder with a circular base of diameter 6 inches is completely filled with gum balls of diameter $\frac{3}{4}$ inches. Estimate the number of gum balls in the jar, explaining your reasoning.

CLASS ACTIVITY 11Z: Comparing the Volume of a Pyramid with the Volume of a Rectangular Prism

You will need scissors, tape, and dry beans or rice for this activity.

1. Cut out, fold, and tape the patterns on pages 603 and 605 to make an open rectangular prism and an open pyramid with a square base.

2. Verify that the prism and the pyramid have bases of the same area and have equal heights.

3. Just by looking at your shapes, make a guess: how do you think the volume of the pyramid compares with the volume of the prism?

4. Now fill the pyramid with beans and pour the beans into the prism. Keep filling and pouring until the prism is full. Based on your results, fill in the blanks in the equations that follow:

    volume of prism = ___ × volume of pyramid

    volume of pyramid = ___ × volume of prism

CLASS ACTIVITY 11AA: The $\frac{1}{3}$ in the Volume Formula for Pyramids and Cones

You will need scissors and tape for this activity.

According to the volume formula, a right pyramid that is 1 unit high and has a 1-unit-by-1-unit square base has volume

$$\frac{1}{3} \times 1 \times (1 \times 1) \text{ unit}^3 = \frac{1}{3} \text{ unit}^3$$

Now pretend that you *don't yet* know the volume formula for pyramids and cones. This class activity will help you use fundamental principles about volumes to explain where the $\frac{1}{3}$ comes from.

1. Cut out three of the four patterns on pages 607 and 609. (The fourth is a spare.) Fold these patterns along the *undashed* line segments and glue or tape them to make three *oblique* pyramids. Make sure the dashed lines appear on the outside of each oblique pyramid.

2. Fit the three oblique pyramids together to make a familiar shape. What shape is it? What is the volume of the shape formed from the three oblique pyramids? Therefore, what is the volume of one of the oblique pyramids?

3. Use your answers to parts (2) and (3) and Cavalieri's principle to explain why a *right* pyramid that is 1 unit high and has a 1-unit-by-1-unit square base has volume $\frac{1}{3}$ cubic units. (The dashed lines on the model oblique pyramids are meant to help you see how to shear the oblique pyramid. Imagine that the oblique pyramids are made out of a stack of small pieces of paper, where each dashed line going around the oblique pyramid represents a piece of paper.)

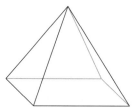

CLASS ACTIVITY 11BB: The Volume of a Rhombic Dodecahedron

1. Cut out the patterns on page 611 and use them to make 6 pyramids.

2. Cut out the pattern on the bottom of page 613 and use it to make a cube.

3. Show how to fit the 6 pyramids together to make a copy of the cube. If the cube is 1 unit wide, 1 unit deep, and 1 unit high, then what is the volume of the cube and what is the volume of each pyramid?

4. Cut out the two patterns at the top of page 613 and put them together to make a closed shape. The shape will have 12 faces, each of which is a rhombus. The shape is called a **rhombic dodecahedron**.

5. Show how to fit the cube and the 6 pyramids together to make a copy of the rhombic dodecahedron. Therefore, what is the volume of the rhombic dodecahedron?

6. One interesting property of rhombic dodecahedra is that they can be stacked and fit together to fill up space without any gaps. If you have a number of rhombic dodecahedra, try this out. Cubes can also be stacked and fit together to fill up space without any gaps, but ordinary dodecahedra (with pentagon faces) cannot.

11.11   Areas, Volumes, and Scaling

CLASS ACTIVITY 11CC: Areas and Volumes of Similar Boxes

You will need scissors and tape for this activity.

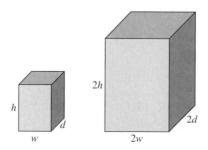

1. Cut out the patterns in Figures A.43 and A.44 on pages 615 and 617. Fold these patterns to make two boxes (rectangular prisms), but leave them untaped, so that you can still unfold them. One box will have width w, depth d, height h, and one box will have width $2w$, depth $2d$, and height $2h$. So the big box is twice as wide, twice as deep, and twice as high as the small box.

2. By working with the unfolded patterns of the two boxes, determine how the surface area of the big box compares with the surface area of the small box. Is the surface area of the big box twice as large, three times as large, etc., as the surface area of the small box? Look and think carefully—the answer may not be what you first think it is. Explain clearly why your answer is correct.

3. Now tape up the small box and tape up most of the large box. Leave an opening so that you can put the small box inside it. Determine how the volume of the big box compares to the volume of the small box. Is the volume of the big box twice as large, three times as large, etc., as the volume of the small box? Once again, think carefully, and explain why your answer is correct.

4. What if there were an even bigger box whose width, depth, and height were each three times the respective width, depth, and height of the small box. How would the surface area of the bigger box compare to the surface area of the small box? Answer this question by thinking about how to make a pattern for the bigger box and determining how the pattern of the bigger box would compare with the pattern of the small box.

   How would the volume of the bigger box compare to the volume of the small box?

5. Now imagine a variety of bigger boxes. Fill in the first two empty columns in the next table with your previous results. Continue to fill in the remaining empty columns by extrapolating from your results.

SIZE OF BIG BOX COMPARED TO SMALL BOX					
LENGTH, WIDTH, DEPTH	2 TIMES	3 TIMES	5 TIMES	2.7 TIMES	k TIMES
surface area					
volume					

CLASS ACTIVITY 11DD: Areas and Volumes of Similar Cylinders

1. Cut out the patterns for cylinders, Figures A.45 and A.46 on pages 619 and 621. Use the patterns to make two cylinders, but don't glue or tape them because you will need to unfold them. The small cylinder has radius r and height h. The big cylinder has radius $2r$ and height $2h$, so the big cylinder has twice the radius and is twice as high as the small one.

2. How does the surface area of the large cylinder compare to the surface area of the small cylinder? Is it twice as large, three times as large, etc.? Use your patterns to get a feel for what the answer should be. Then give a clear and thorough explanation of your answer. To give a thorough explanation you will have to do more than just physically compare the cylinder's patterns.

3. How does the volume of the large cylinder compare to the volume of the small cylinder? Is it twice as large, three times as large, etc.? Tape up your patterns to form cylinders, and use the cylinders to get a feel for what the answer should be. Then give a clear and thorough explanation of your answer. To give a thorough explanation you will have to do more than just physically compare the cylinders.

4. Now imagine a variety of bigger cylinders. Fill in the first empty column in the next table with your previous results. Continue to fill in the remaining empty columns by extrapolating from your results. Compare this table with the table in problem 5 of the previous class activity.

SIZE OF BIG CYLINDER COMPARED TO SMALL CYLINDER					
LENGTH, WIDTH, DEPTH	2 TIMES	3 TIMES	5 TIMES	2.7 TIMES	k TIMES
surface area					
volume					

CLASS ACTIVITY 11EE: Determining Areas and Volumes of Scaled Objects

1. Compare your tables for problem 5 of Class Activity 11CC and problem 4 of Class Activity 11DD. Extrapolate from these results to answer the following questions: If someone made a Goodyear blimp that was 1.5 times as wide, 1.5 times as deep, and 1.5 times as high as the current one, how much material would it take to make the larger blimp compared to the current blimp? How much more gas would it take to fill this bigger Goodyear blimp, compared the current one (at the same pressure)?

2. An adult alligator can be 15 feet long and weigh 475 pounds. Suppose that some excavated dinosaur bones indicate that the dinosaur was 30 feet long and was shaped roughly like an alligator. How much would you expect the dinosaur to have weighed?

alligator   dinosaur

Chapter 12

Number Theory

12.1 Factors and Multiples

CLASS ACTIVITY 12A: Factors, Multiples, and Rectangles

1. Elsie has 24 square tiles that she wants to arrange in the shape of a rectangle (in such a way that the rectangle is completely filled with tiles). How many different rectangles can Elsie make?

   Does this problem draw mainly on the concept of factors or on the concept of multiples? Why?

2. What if Elsie only has 13 tiles? Now how many rectangles can she make?

3. If Elsie has more than 24 square tiles will she necessarily be able to make more rectangles than she could in problem 1? Try some experiments.

4. John has many 1-inch-by-1-inch square tiles. John will use his tiles to make rectangles (in such a way that each rectangle is filled with tiles), each of which has a side that is 4 inches long. What are the areas of the rectangles that John can make?

   Does this problem draw mainly on the concept of factors or on the concept of multiples? Why?

CLASS ACTIVITY 12B: Problems about Factors and Multiples

1. For each of the situations listed, write a problem about the items or the scenario. In each case, solving your problem should require using either the concept of factors or the concept of multiples. Solve each problem, stating how factors or multiples are involved.

   a. The children in a class are clapping, snapping, and stomping to a steady beat in the following pattern: clap, clap, snap, stomp, clap, clap, snap, stomp, ...

   b. At the store, pencils come in packages of 12.

   c. A large package of candy contains 36 pieces.

   d. Tyrone made many towers out of snap cubes (snap-together cubes). Each tower is made of 5 snap cubes.

   e. Amy has a collection of 45 marbles.

2. For each of the situations listed, describe an activity involving the items. In each case, your activity should require using either the concept of factors or the concept of multiples. For each activity, explain how factors or multiples are used.

   a. A drum and a tambourine

   b. Beads in several different colors and string with which to make neck-laces

   c. Graph paper and markers (optional: scissors)

3. Consider the following problem:

   A rectangular garden has an area of 64 square feet. What could its length and width be?

   Why can you not solve the problem just by finding all the factors of 64? What must you add to the statement of the problem so that it *can* be solved by finding the factors of 64?

4. Write a problem about a realistic situation that you could give to children to help them understand the concept of factors. Explain how your problem involves the concept of factors and how it could help children to understand this concept. Solve your problem.

5. Write a problem about a realistic situation that you could give to children to help them understand the concept of multiples. Explain how your problem involves the concept of multiples and how it could help children to understand this concept. Solve your problem.

CLASS ACTIVITY 12C: Finding All Factors

1. Tyrese is looking for all the factors of 156. So far, Tyrese has divided 156 by all the counting numbers from 1 to 13, listing those numbers that divide 156 and listing the corresponding quotients. Here is Tyrese's work so far:

$$
\begin{array}{ll}
1,\ 156 & 1 \times 156 = 156 \\
2,\ 78 & 2 \times 78 = 156 \\
3,\ 52 & 3 \times 52 = 156 \\
4,\ 39 & 4 \times 39 = 156 \\
6,\ 26 & 6 \times 26 = 156 \\
12,\ 13 & 12 \times 13 = 156 \\
13,\ 12 & 13 \times 12 = 156 \\
\end{array}
$$

Should Tyrese keep checking to see if numbers larger than 13 divide 156, or can Tyrese stop dividing at this point? If so, why? What are all the factors of 156?

2. Find all the factors of 198 in an efficient way.

CLASS ACTIVITY 12D: Do Factors Always Come in Pairs?

Carmina noticed that factors always seem to come in pairs. For example,

$$48 = 1 \times 48, \quad \text{1 and 48 are a pair of factors of 48.}$$
$$48 = 2 \times 24, \quad \text{2 and 24 are a pair of factors of 48.}$$
$$48 = 3 \times 16, \quad \text{3 and 16 are a pair of factors of 48.}$$
$$48 = 4 \times 12, \quad \text{4 and 12 are a pair of factors of 48.}$$
$$48 = 6 \times 8, \quad \text{6 and 8 are a pair of factors of 48.}$$

The number 48 has 10 factors that come in 5 pairs. Carmina wants to know if every counting number always has an even number of factors. Investigate Carmina's question carefully. When does a counting number have an even number of factors, and when does it not?

12.2   Greatest Common Factor and Least Common Multiple

CLASS ACTIVITY 12E: Situations Involving the Least Common Multiple and the Greatest Common Factor

1. Explain how to use the following patterns to determine the least common multiple of 4 and 6:

2. Use the following strips to determine and discuss the least common multiple of 6 and 8:

3. Many teachers have snap cubes (snap-together cubes) readily available in their classroom. Describe how to use snap cubes to determine and discuss the least common multiple of 10 and 8.

4. Explain how a least common multiple is relevant to the following situation: A class is clapping and snapping to a steady beat. Half of the class uses the pattern

    snap, snap, clap, snap, snap, clap, . . .

    The other half of the class uses the pattern:

    snap, clap, snap, clap, snap, clap, . . .

5. a. Describe how to use a collection of 16 small objects to determine all the factors of 16.

    b. Describe how to use a collection of 16 small objects and another collection of 20 small objects to determine the greatest common factor of 16 and 20. Explain why your method makes sense.

6. By shading or outlining the rectangles in the next figure, show the two ways of subdividing a 12-unit-by-8-unit rectangle into squares of the same size, other than 1-unit-by-1-unit squares, such that the sides of the squares are a whole number of units long. Then use your work to determine the greatest common factor of 12 and 8, explaining your reasoning.

7. Two gears are meshed, as shown in the next figure, with the stars on each gear aligned. The large gear has 36 teeth and the small gear has 15 teeth. Each gear rotates around a pin through its center. How many revolutions will the large gear have to make and how many revolutions will the small gear make in order for the stars to be aligned again? How is this question related to GCFs or LCMs?

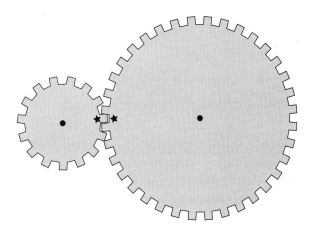

CLASS ACTIVITY 12F: Problems Involving Greatest Common Factors and Least Common Multiples

1. Pencils come in packages of 18; erasers that fit on top of these pencils come in packages of 24. What is the smallest number of pencils and erasers that you can buy so that each pencil can be matched with an eraser? How many packages of pencils will you need and how many packages of erasers? (Assume that you must buy whole packages—you can't buy partial packages.)

    Solve the problem, explaining your solution. Does this problem involve the GCF or the LCM?

2. Ko has a bag with 45 red candies and another bag with 30 green candies. Ko wants to make goody bags so that each goody bag contains the same number of red candies, each bag contains the same number of green candies (which may be different from the number of red candies), and all his candies will be used up in the goody bags. What is the largest number of goody bags that Ko can make this way? How many red candies and how many green candies will go in each goody bag?

    Solve the problem, explaining your solution. Does this problem involve the GCF or the LCM?

3. Sam has many 8-inch sticks that he is placing end to end to make a line of sticks. Becky has many 12-inch sticks that she is placing end to end to make a line of sticks. If Sam and Becky want their lines of sticks to be equally long, how long could they be? What is the shortest such length?

    Solve the problem, explaining your solution. Does this problem involve the GCF or the LCM?

CLASS ACTIVITY 12G: Relationships Between the GCF and the LCM

1. Suppose you are teaching children about least common multiples and you only use the following examples to illustrate the concept:

$$4 \quad \text{and} \quad 7$$
$$3 \quad \text{and} \quad 10$$
$$5 \quad \text{and} \quad 12$$
$$8 \quad \text{and} \quad 9$$

What misconception about the LCM might the children develop? Explain why. What other kinds of examples should the children see? Describe some examples that you think are good and explain why you think they are good.

2. By experimenting with a number of pairs of counting numbers A and B, discover one or more relationships among A, B, GCF, and LCM, where GCF stands for the greatest common factor of A and B and LCM stands for the least common multiple of A and B.

For example,

- If $A = 6$ and $B = 8$, then GCF $= 2$ and LCM $= 24$.

- If $A = 8$ and $B = 12$, then GCF $= 4$ and LCM $= 24$.

- If $A = 3$ and $B = 5$, then GCF $= 1$ and LCM $= 15$.

In these and other examples, how are A, B, GCF, and LCM related?

3. Examine the first four "flower" designs in Figure 12.1. Try to find relationships between the number of dots at the center of the flower, the number describing how the petals were made (e.g., by connecting every 8th dot or every 15th dot), and the number of petals in the flower design. These numbers are listed in the following table.

DESIGN	NUMBER OF DOTS	A PETAL CONNECTS EVERY ___TH DOT	NUMBER OF PETALS
design 1	36	8	9
design 2	36	15	12
design 3	36	16	9
design 4	30	14	15
design 5	30	4	
design 6	30	12	

4. Predict the number of petals that the 5th and 6th flower designs will have. Then complete the designs to see if your prediction was correct. (To complete the designs, you might find it easiest to count dots forward and then draw the petal backwards.)

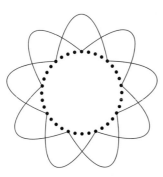

36 dots
a petal connects every 8th dot
9 petals

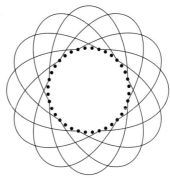

36 dots
a petal connects every 15th dot
12 petals

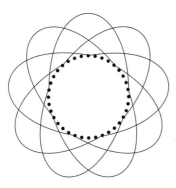

36 dots
a petal connects every 16th dot
9 petals

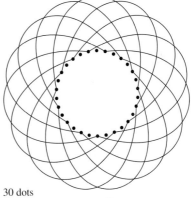

30 dots
a petal connects every 14th dot
15 petals

30 dots
a petal connects every 4th dot
____ petals

30 dots
a petal connects every 12th dot
____ petals

FIGURE 12.1

Flower Designs

CLASS ACTIVITY 12H: Using GCFs and LCMs with Fractions

1. Show how to determine the simplest form of

$$\frac{36}{90}$$

   by first finding the GCF of 36 and 90.

2. Show how to determine the simplest form of

$$\frac{36}{90}$$

   without finding the GCF of 36 and 90 first.

3. Compare your work in parts (1) and (2). Which method did you prefer? Why?

4. Show how to add

$$\frac{1}{6} + \frac{1}{10}$$

   in two ways: using the least common denominator and using the denominator which is the product of the two denominators. Which method did you prefer? Why?

5. If we use the least common denominator to add two fractions, is the resulting sum necessarily in simplest form?

12.3 Prime Numbers

CLASS ACTIVITY 12I: The Sieve of Eratosthenes

1. Use the Sieve of Eratosthenes to find all the prime numbers up to 120. Start by circling 2 and crossing off every 2nd number after 2. Then circle 3 and cross off every 3rd number (cross off a number even if it already has been crossed off). Continue in this manner, going back to the beginning of the list, circling the next number N that hasn't been crossed off, and then crossing off every Nth number until every number in the list is either circled or crossed off. The numbers that are circled at the end are the prime numbers from 2 to 120.

	2	3	4	5	6	7	8	9	10
11	12	13	14	15	16	17	18	19	20
21	22	23	24	25	26	27	28	29	30
31	32	33	34	35	36	37	38	39	40
41	42	43	44	45	46	47	48	49	50
51	52	53	54	55	56	57	58	59	60
61	62	63	64	65	66	67	68	69	70
71	72	73	74	75	76	77	78	79	80
81	82	83	84	85	86	87	88	89	90
91	92	93	94	95	96	97	98	99	100
101	102	103	104	105	106	107	108	109	110
111	112	113	114	115	116	117	118	119	120

2. Explain why the circled numbers must be prime numbers and why the numbers that are crossed off are not prime numbers.

CLASS ACTIVITY 12J: The Trial Division Method for Determining if a Number Is Prime

You will need the list of prime numbers from Class Activity 12I on the Sieve of Eratosthenes for this activity.

1. Using the trial division method and your list of primes from the Sieve of Eratosthenes, determine whether the three numbers listed are prime numbers. Record the results of your trial divisions below the number. (The first few are done for you.) You will need these results for part (3).

239   323   4001

$239 \div 2 = 119.5$ $323 \div 2 = 161.5$ $4001 \div 2 = 2000.5$

$239 \div 3 = 79.67\ldots$ $323 \div 3 = 107.67\ldots$ $4001 \div 3 = 1333.67\ldots$

2. In the trial division method, you only determine whether your number is divisible by *prime* numbers. Why is this legitimate? Why don't you also have to find out if your number is divisible by other numbers such as 4, 6, 8, 9, 10, etc.?

3. How do you know when to stop with the trial division method? To help you answer this, look at the list of divisions you did in part (1). As you go down each list, what happens to the divisor and the quotient? If your number *was* divisible by some whole number, at what point would that whole number be known?

12.4 Even and Odd

CLASS ACTIVITY 12K: Why Can We Check the Ones Digit to Determine if a Number Is Even or Odd?

Remember that a whole number is called "even" if that number of objects can be divided into groups of 2 with none left over:

Why is it valid to determine whether a number of objects can be divided into groups of 2 with none left over by checking the ones digit of the number? We will investigate this question in this class activity.

1. Recall that we can represent the expanded form of a whole number with bundled toothpicks (or other bundled or grouped objects) as in Figure 12.2. Using Figure 12.2, explain why 134 toothpicks can be divided into groups of 2 with none left over, but there will be 1 toothpick left over when 357 toothpicks are divided into groups of 2. Explain why we only have to consider the ones digit to determine if there will be a toothpick left over by describing what happens with each bundle of 100 toothpicks and each bundle of 10 toothpicks when we divide the toothpicks into groups of 2.

FIGURE 12.2

Representing 134 and 357 with Bundled Toothpicks

2. Working more generally, let ABC be a three-digit whole number with A hundreds, B tens, and C ones. Use the idea of representing ABC with bundled toothpicks to help you explain why ABC is divisible by 2 exactly when C is either 0, 2, 4, 6, or 8. What can we say about each of the B bundles of 10 toothpicks and each of the A bundles of 100 toothpicks when we divide the toothpicks into groups of 2?

CLASS ACTIVITY 12L: Problems about Even and Odd Numbers

1. Explain why an odd number can always be written in the form $2N + 1$ for some whole number N.

2. Will said that he put his homework in between pages 131 and 132 of his book. What do you think?

3. Without counting them, determine if the number of squares on a checkerboard is even or odd. Explain.

4. Without determining the number of dots in the following design, determine whether this number is even or odd.

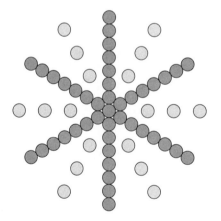

5. Give some examples of things where you can tell right away that their number is even or odd without actually counting them.

CLASS ACTIVITY 12M: Questions about Even and Odd Numbers

1. If you add an odd number and an odd number, what kind of number do you get? Investigate this question by working out examples. Then explain why your answer is always correct. Try to find several different explanations by working with the various equivalent ways of saying that a number is even or odd.

2. If you multiply an even number and an odd number, what kind of number do you get? Investigate this question by working out examples. Then explain why your answer is always correct. Try to find several different explanations by working with the various equivalent ways of saying that a number is even or odd.

3. Ask some other questions about even and odd numbers. Investigate your questions and then explain why your answers are always correct.

CLASS ACTIVITY 12N: Extending the Definitions of Even and Odd

We have defined even and odd only for counting numbers. What if we wanted to extend the definition of even and odd to other numbers?

1. If we extend the definitions of even and odd to all the integers, then what should 0 be, even or odd? What should -5 be, even or odd? Explain.

2. Give definitions of even and odd that apply to all integers, not just to the counting numbers.

3. Would it make sense to extend the definitions of even and odd to the rational numbers (fractions)? Why or why not?

12.5 Divisibility Tests

CLASS ACTIVITY 120: The Divisibility Test for 3

1. Is it possible to tell if a whole number is divisible by 3 just by checking its last digit? Investigate this question by considering a number of examples. State your conclusion.

2. The divisibility test for 3 says that you can determine whether a counting number is divisible by 3 by adding its digits and checking to see if this sum is divisible by 3. If the sum is divisible by 3, then the original number is, too; if the sum is not divisible by 3, then the original number is not either.

    For each of the numbers listed, see if the divisibility test for 3 really does accurately predict which numbers are divisible by 3. That is, for each number, check it's divisibility by 3 by using long division or a calculator, and then add the digits of the number and see if that sum is divisible by 3. The two conclusions should agree.

    Example: 1437 is divisible by 3 because $1437 \div 3 = 479$, with no remainder.

    $1 + 4 + 3 + 7 = 15$ also indicates that 1437 is divisible by 3, because $15 \div 3 = 5$, with no remainder.

    2570

    123

    14,928

    7213

    555,555

    11,111

3. In your own words, explain why the divisibility test for 3 is valid for 3-digit counting numbers. In other words, explain why you can determine whether or not a 3-digit counting number, ABC, is divisible by 3 by adding its digits, $A + B + C$, and determining if this sum is divisible by 3.

In order to develop your explanation, consider the following:

a. Think about representing 3-digit numbers with bundled toothpicks. For example, we can represent the number 247 using 2 bundles of 100 toothpicks, 4 bundles of 10 toothpicks, and 7 individual toothpicks, as shown in Figure 12.3. The number ABC is represented by A bundles of 100 toothpicks, B bundles of 10 toothpicks, and C individual toothpicks.

b. Notice that a counting number is divisible by 3 exactly when that many objects can be divided into groups of 3 with none left over.

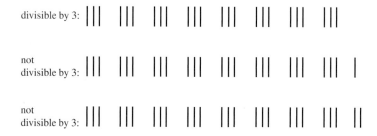

c. A counting number is divisible by 3 exactly when that number of toothpicks can be put into groups of 3 with none left over. Consider starting to divide bundled toothpicks into groups of 3 by dividing *each individual bundle* of 10 and *each individual bundle* of 100 into groups of 3. Determine how many toothpicks will be left over if you divide the bundles this way and if you do no further dividing into groups of 3.

247   2(100)   4(10)   7(1)

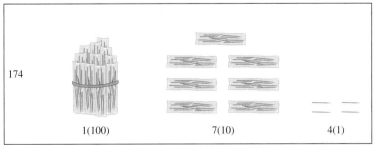

174   1(100)   7(10)   4(1)

FIGURE 12.3

Representing 247 and 174 with Bundled Toothpicks

4. Relate your explanation in part (3) to the following equations:

$$ABC = A \cdot 100 + B \cdot 10 + C$$
$$= (A \cdot 99 + B \cdot 9) + (A + B + C)$$
$$= (A \cdot 33 + B \cdot 3) \cdot 3 + (A + B + C)$$

12.6 Rational and Irrational Numbers

CLASS ACTIVITY 12P: Decimal Representations of Fractions

The decimal representations of the following fractions are shown to 16 decimal places, with no rounding:

$\frac{1}{12} = .0833333333333333$ $\frac{1}{4} = .25$

$\frac{1}{11} = .0909090909090909$ $\frac{2}{5} = .4$

$\frac{113}{33} = 3.424242424242424$ $\frac{37}{8} = 4.625$

$\frac{491}{550} = .8927272727272727$ $\frac{17}{50} = .34$

$\frac{14}{37} = .3783783783783783$ $\frac{1}{125} = .008$

$\frac{35}{101} = .3465346534653465$ $\frac{9}{20} = .45$

$\frac{1}{41} = .0243902439024390$ $\frac{19}{32} = .59375$

$\frac{5}{7} = .7142857142857142$ $\frac{1}{3200} = .0003125$

$\frac{1}{14} = .0714285714285714$ $\frac{1}{64,000} = .000015625$

$\frac{1}{21} = .0476190476190476$ $\frac{1}{625} = .0016$

1. In what way are the decimal representations in the first column similar? In what way are the decimal representations of the fractions in the second column similar?

2. Complete the next set of calculations using longhand division (not a calcu-
    lator!) to find the decimal representations of $\frac{2}{55}$ and $\frac{1}{101}$. At each step in the
    long-division process, write down the remainder you obtain.

$$
\begin{array}{r}
0.0 \\
55\overline{)2.0000000} \\
-\,0 \\
\hline
20
\end{array}
$$
remainder 2

remainder 20

remainder ____

remainder ____

remainder ____

remainder ____

remainder ____

remainder ____

$$
\begin{array}{r}
0.0 \\
10\overline{)1.0000000} \\
-\,0 \\
\hline
10
\end{array}
$$
remainder 1

remainder 10

remainder ____

remainder ____

remainder ____

remainder ____

remainder ____

remainder ____

3. Use longhand division to calculate the decimal representations of $\frac{3}{8}$ and $\frac{1}{7}$.
    As in part (2), write down the remainder you get at each step.

4. Answer the following questions for the decimal representations of the fractions in parts 2 and 3:

    - What happened to the decimal representation of the fraction when you got a remainder of 0?

    - What happened to the decimal representation of the fraction when you got a remainder that you had before?

5. Without actually carrying it out, imagine doing longhand division to find the decimal representation of $\frac{7}{31}$.

    a. What remainders could you possibly get in the longhand division process when finding $7 \div 31$? For example, could you possibly get a remainder of 45 or 73 or 32? How many different remainders are theoretically possible?

    b. If you were doing longhand division to find $7 \div 31$ and you got a remainder of 0 somewhere along the way, what would that tell you about the decimal representation of $\frac{7}{31}$?

    c. If you were doing longhand division to find $7 \div 31$ and you got a remainder you'd gotten before, what would then happen in the decimal representation of $\frac{7}{31}$?

    d. Now use your answer to parts (a), (b), and (c) to explain why the decimal representation of $\frac{7}{31}$ must either terminate or eventually repeat after at most 30 decimal places.

6. In general, suppose that $\frac{A}{B}$ is a proper fraction of whole numbers. Explain why the decimal representation of $\frac{A}{B}$ must either terminate or begin to repeat after at most $B - 1$ decimal places.

7. Could the number

$$.1010010001000010000010000001 \ldots$$

where the decimal representation continues forever with the pattern of more and more 0s in between 1s, be the decimal representation of a fraction of whole numbers? Explain your answer.

CLASS ACTIVITY 12Q: Writing Terminating and Repeating Decimals as Fractions

1. By using denominators that are suitable powers of 10, show how to write the following terminating decimals as fractions:

$$0.137 = \qquad\qquad 0.25567 =$$

$$13.89 = \qquad\qquad 329.2 =$$

2. Write the following fractions as decimals and observe the pattern:

$$\frac{1}{9} =$$

$$\frac{1}{99} =$$

$$\frac{1}{999} =$$

$$\frac{1}{9999} =$$

$$\frac{1}{99,999} =$$

3. Using the decimal representations of $\frac{1}{9}, \frac{1}{99}, \ldots$, that you found in part (2), show how to write the following decimals as fractions:

$$0.\overline{2} = 0.222222\ldots = \qquad\qquad 0.\overline{08} = 0.080808\ldots =$$

$$0.\overline{003} = 0.003003\ldots = \qquad\qquad 0.\overline{52} = 0.525252\ldots =$$

$$0.\overline{1234} = \qquad\qquad 0.\overline{123456} =$$

4. Use the fact that

$$0.\overline{49} = \frac{49}{99}$$

to write the next four repeating decimals as fractions. Hint: Shift the decimal point by dividing by suitable powers of 10.

$$0.0\overline{49} = \qquad\qquad 0.00\overline{49} =$$

$$0.000\overline{49} = \qquad\qquad 0.0000\overline{49} =$$

5. Use the results of part (4), together with the fact that

$$0.3\overline{49} = 0.3 + 0.0\overline{49} \qquad 0.12\overline{49} = 0.12 + 0.00\overline{49}$$

and other similar facts to determine how to write the following repeating decimals as fractions:

$$7.3\overline{49} = \qquad\qquad 0.12\overline{49} =$$

$$1.2\overline{49} = \qquad\qquad 0.111\overline{49} =$$

CLASS ACTIVITY 12R: What Is 0.9999...?

1. Use the fact that $\frac{1}{9} = 0.\overline{1} = 0.111111111\ldots$ to determine the decimal representations of the following fractions:

$\frac{2}{9} =$ $\qquad$ $\frac{6}{9} =$

$\frac{3}{9} =$ $\qquad$ $\frac{7}{9} =$

$\frac{4}{9} =$ $\qquad$ $\frac{8}{9} =$

$\frac{5}{9} =$ $\qquad$ $\frac{9}{9} =$

What can you conclude about $0.\overline{9}$?

2. Add longhand:

$$0.9999999999\ldots$$
$$+\; 0.1111111111\ldots$$

Note that the nines and ones repeat forever.
Now subtract longhand: $\quad -\;\; .1111111111\ldots$

Look back at what you just did: Starting with $0.\overline{9}$, you added and then subtracted $0.\overline{1}$. What does this tell you about $0.\overline{9}$?

3. Let N stand for the number $0.\overline{9} = 0.999999\ldots$:

$$N = 0.999999999\ldots$$

Write the decimal representation of $10N$:

$$10N =$$

Now subtract N from $10N$ in two ways—in terms of N and as decimal numbers:

in terms of N :   as decimals :

$$
\begin{array}{r}
10N \\
-N \\
\hline
\end{array}
\qquad
\begin{array}{r}
-0.999999999 \\
\hline
\end{array}
$$

What can you conclude about $0.\overline{9}$?

4. Given that the number 1 has two different decimal representations, namely, 1 and $0.\overline{9}$, find different decimal representations of the following numbers:

$$17 =$$

$$23.42 =$$

$$139.8 =$$

CLASS ACTIVITY 12S: The Square Root of 2

1. If the sides of a square are 1 unit long, then how long is the diagonal of the square?

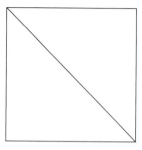

2. Use a calculator to find the decimal representation of $\sqrt{2}$. Based on your calculator's display, does it look like $\sqrt{2}$ is rational or irrational? Why? Can you tell *for sure* just by looking at your calculator's display?

3. What is the decimal representation of

$$\frac{1{,}414{,}213{,}562}{999{,}999{,}999}?$$

Is this number rational or irrational? Compare with part 2.

4. Suppose that it were somehow possible to write the square root of two as a fraction $\frac{A}{B}$ of counting numbers:

$$\sqrt{2} = \frac{A}{B}.$$

Show that, in this case, we would get the equation

$$A^2 = 2 \times B^2$$

5. Suppose A is a counting number, and imagine factoring it into a product of prime numbers. For example, if A is 30, then you factor it as

$$A = 2 \times 3 \times 5$$

Now think about factoring A^2 as a product of prime numbers. For example, if $A = 30$, then
$$A^2 = 2 \times 3 \times 5 \times 2 \times 3 \times 5$$

Could A^2 have an odd number of prime factors? Make a general qualitative statement about the number of prime factors that A^2 has.

6. Now suppose that B is a counting number, and imagine factoring the number $2 \times B^2$ into a product of prime numbers. For example, if $B = 15$, then

$$2 \times B^2 = 2 \times 3 \times 5 \times 3 \times 5$$

Could $2B^2$ have an even number of prime factors? Make a general qualitative statement about the number of prime factors that $2 \times B^2$ has.

7. Now use your answers in parts 5 and 6 to explain why a number in the form A^2 can never be equal to a number in the form $2 \times B^2$, when A and B are counting numbers.

8. What does part 7 lead you to conclude about the assumption in part 4 that it is somehow possible to write the square root of two as a fraction of counting numbers? Now what can you conclude about whether $\sqrt{2}$ is rational or irrational?

CLASS ACTIVITY 12T: Pattern Tiles and the Irrationality of the Square Root of 3

You will need a set of pattern tiles like the ones shown in the next figure for this activity. If a set of pattern tiles is not available, cut out the paper pattern tiles on pages 623, 625, and 627.

One fascinating aspect of mathematics is that there are connections between simple Kindergarten activities and much more advanced ideas that children might not encounter until high school or college math classes. This class activity will show you one such connection involving pattern tiles.

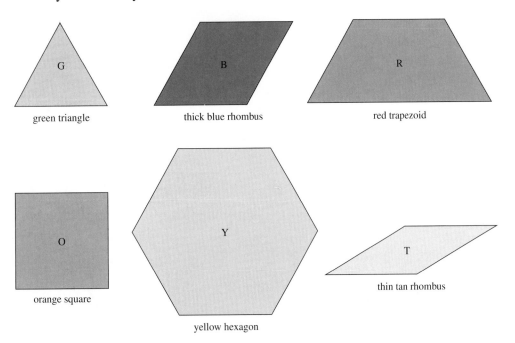

green triangle   thick blue rhombus   red trapezoid

orange square   yellow hexagon   thin tan rhombus

1. In early elementary school, children sometimes use pattern tiles to fill shapes. Find several different ways to fill each of the shapes in Figures 12.4 and 12.5 with pattern tiles.

   Even though there are many different ways to fill the shapes, can any of the shapes in Figure 12.4 be filled using one or more squares or thin rhombuses?

   Can any of the shapes in Figure 12.5 be filled without using either squares or thin rhombuses?

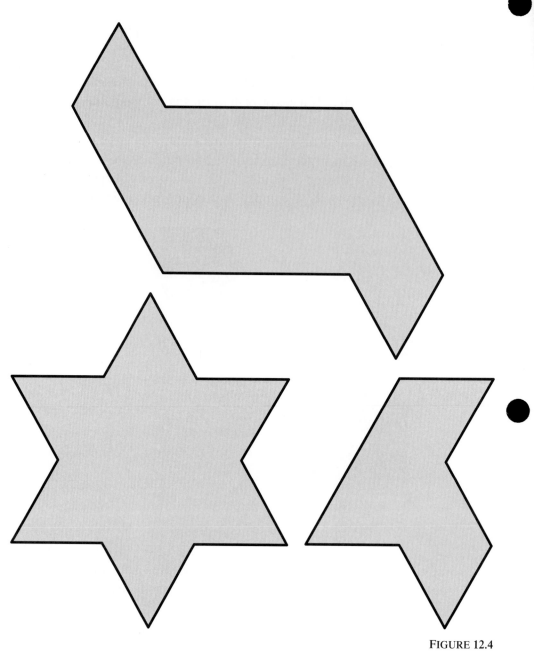

FIGURE 12.4
Fill These Shapes with Pattern Tiles

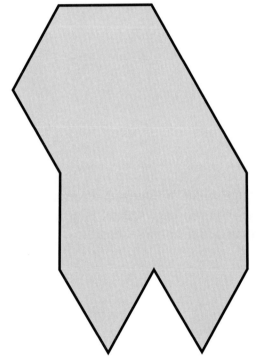

FIGURE 12.5

Fill These Shapes with Pattern Tiles

2. When children try to fill shapes with pattern tiles in different ways, they may begin to notice relationships among the different tiles. Find as many relationships among the tiles as you can. Express these relationships using the symbols G, Y, R, B, T, and O, where

    *   G stands for the area of the green triangle.

    *   Y stands for the area of the yellow hexagon.

    *   R stands for the area of the red trapezoid.

    *   B stands for the area of the thick blue rhombus.

    *   T stands for the area of the thin tan rhombus.

    *   O stands for the area of the orange square.

    For example, because two green triangles fit together to make a thick blue rhombus,

    $$2G = B$$

3. If you have not yet done so, find a relationship between T and O, the areas of the thin tan rhombus and the orange square. Hint: use triangles in addition to the thin tan rhombus and the orange square.

4. Can you find any way to relate G, Y, R and B with O, the area of the orange square?

    Can you find any way to relate G, Y, R and B with T, the area of the thin tan rhombus?

1 inch

1/2 inch

FIGURE 12.6

The Green Triangle

5. Use the Pythagorean theorem and Figure 12.6 to help you determine the area, in square inches, of the green triangle. Your answer should involve a square root of 3.

6. Using the relationships that you found in part 2, and the area of the green triangle that you found in part 5, determine Y, R, and B, the areas of the yellow hexagon, the red trapezoid, and the thick blue rhombus. All these areas will involve the square root of 3. Fill in the values for G, Y, R, and B in Figure 12.7.

7. The orange square is 1 inch wide and 1 inch long, therefore, its area is 1 square inch. Use the relationship between O and T that you found in part 3 to determine T. Fill in the values for O and T in Figure 12.7.

8. Looking at the values you wrote in Figure 12.7, how are the areas of the green triangle, the yellow hexagon, the red trapezoid, and the thick blue rhombus qualitatively different from the areas of the orange square and the thin tan rhombus? Given this, and the fact that $\sqrt{3}$ is irrational, is it surprising that you could not find a relationship between G, Y, R, B, and O or G, Y, R, B and T in part 4?

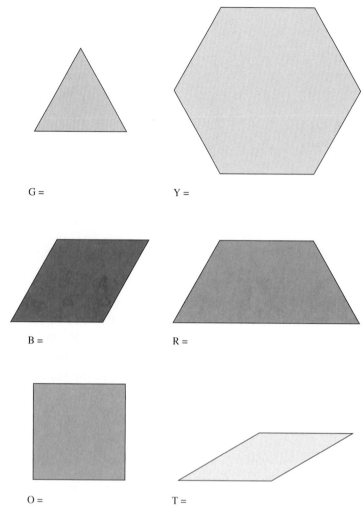

G =   Y =

B =   R =

O =   T =

FIGURE 12.7
Fill in the Areas of These Shapes

Chapter 13

Functions and Algebra

13.1 Mathematical Expressions, Formulas, and Equations

CLASS ACTIVITY 13A: Writing Expressions and a Formula for a Flower Pattern

1. Explain why the number of dots in pattern A of Figure 13.1 is equal to

$$1 + 6 \cdot 5 + 4 \cdot 3$$

2. Find an expression involving multiplication and addition, such as the expression in problem 1, that is equal to the number of dots in pattern B of Figure 13.1. Explain why your expression describes the total number of dots.

3. Find expressions involving multiplication and addition that are equal to the number of dots in patterns C and D of Figure 13.1. Explain why your expressions describe the total number of dots.

4. Fill like parts in the large flower in Figure 13.2 with the same number of dots. Then write an expression for the total number of dots in your flower pattern. Write equations in which you evaluate this expression, determining the total number of dots in your flower pattern.

5. Now consider general flower patterns like the ones in Figure 13.1 and the one you created in part 4. If M, N, and P are any counting numbers, we can imagine a flower pattern that has M dots in the center circle, N dots in each of the circles surrounding the center circle, and P dots in each of the petals of the flower. Write a formula, in terms of M, N, and P, for the number of dots in the flower pattern. Explain why your formula describes the total number of dots.

6. Create a design that illustrates the formula

$$M + 2N + 2P$$

by imagining different portions of the design filled with different numbers of dots. Explain why your design illustrates the formula $M + 2N + 2P$.

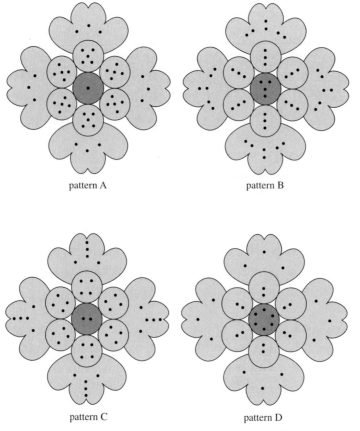

pattern A   pattern B

pattern C   pattern D

FIGURE 13.1

Write Expressions for the Total Number of Dots in Each Flower

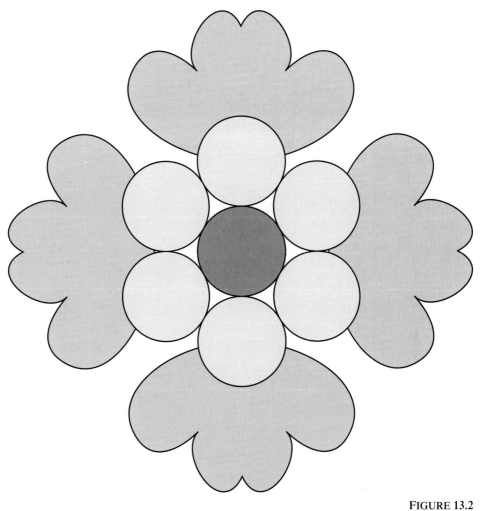

FIGURE 13.2

Fill Like Parts with Equal Numbers of Dots and Write an Expression for the Total Number of Dots

CLASS ACTIVITY 13B: Expressions and Formulas for Story Problems

1. Ben put his card collection into two different types of bags. He put 2 cards in each of 3 small bags and he put 5 cards in each of 4 large bags. Write an expression using multiplication and addition for the total number of cards in Ben's card collection.

2. Kaia put all but 3 stickers of her sticker collection into E envelopes. There are 8 stickers in each envelope.

   a. Draw pictures showing how Kaia's sticker collection is arranged if $E = 2$ and if $E = 3$.

   b. Write a formula for the total number of stickers Kaia has in terms of E. Relate your formula to your pictures in part (a).

3. Clara has pencils to give out to her 6 friends. When Clara tries to give P pencils to each friend she is 1 pencil short.

   a. Draw pictures showing how Clara distributes her pencils among her friends if $P = 3$ and if $P = 4$.

   b. Write a formula for the total number of pencils that Clara has in terms of P. Relate your formula to your pictures in part (a).

4. Write a story problem so that some quantity in the story situation can be expressed as $4x + 2$. Explain why $4x + 2$ is the appropriate formula for the quantity.

5. Write a story problem so that some quantity in the story situation can be expressed as $4x - 2$. Explain why $4x - 2$ is the appropriate formula for the quantity.

6. There are T tons of sand in a pile.

   a. Assume $\frac{1}{4}$ of the sand in the pile is removed from the pile and, after that, another $\frac{2}{3}$ of a ton of sand is dumped onto the pile. Write a formula in terms of T for the number of tons of sand that are in the pile now.

   b. Evaluate your formula from part (a) when $T = 1\frac{2}{3}$.

   c. Starting with T tons of sand, assume $\frac{2}{3}$ of a ton of sand is dumped onto the pile and, after that, $\frac{1}{4}$ of the sand in the pile is removed. Write a formula in terms of T for the number of tons of sand that are in the pile now. Is this formula the same as the formula in part (a)?

   d. Evaluate your formula from part (c) when $T = 1\frac{2}{3}$.

CLASS ACTIVITY 13C: Deriving the Formula for Temperature in Degrees Fahrenheit in Terms of Degrees Celsius

1. For each pair of numbers, determine the number that is halfway between the two numbers. In each case, explain why your answer is correct.
   a. 0 and 14

   b. 0 and 11

   c. 0 and b

   d. 2 and 14

   e. 2 and 11

   f. 2 and b

   g. a and b

2. For each pair of numbers, determine the number that is $\frac{1}{3}$ of the way between the two numbers (and closer to the first number). In each case, explain why your answer is correct.
   a. 0 and 12

   b. 0 and 11

   c. 0 and b

   d. 2 and 14

   e. 2 and 12

   f. 2 and b

   g. a and b

3. For each pair of numbers, determine the number that is 40% of the way between the two numbers (and closer to the first number). In each case, explain why your answer is correct.
   a. 0 and 120

   b. 0 and b

   c. 20 and 170

   d. 20 and b

   e. a and b

4. Water freezes at 0° Celsius, which is 32° Fahrenheit, and boils at 100° Celsius, which is 212° Fahrenheit. Given that 40° Celsius is 40% of the way between 0° Celsius and 100° Celsius, what is 40° Celsius in degrees Fahrenheit? Answer this question based on your work in part 3.

5. Based on your work in part 3, write an expression for the number that is $P\%$ between two numbers a and b. Explain why your expression fits with your work in part 3.

6. Based on your work in previous parts of this problem, write a formula for the temperature in degrees Fahrenheit of $C°$ Celsius. Your formula should be in terms of C. Explain why your formula is correct. (You may assume that C is between 0 and 100, but the correct formula will be valid for other values of C as well.)

CLASS ACTIVITY 13D: Writing Equations for Square Patterns

1. By determining the total number of small squares in the square pattern (a) in two different ways, explain why pattern (a) gives rise to the equation

$$1 + 4 \cdot 2 + 4 \cdot 4 = 5 \cdot 5$$

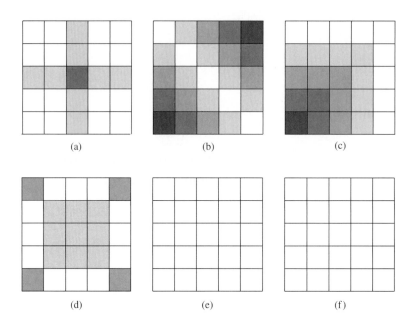

(a)   (b)   (c)

(d)   (e)   (f)

2. By determining the total number of small squares in the square pattern (b) in two different ways, explain why pattern (b) gives rise to the equation

$$1 + 2 + 3 + 4 + 5 + 4 + 3 + 2 + 1 = 5 \cdot 5$$

3. By determining the total number of small squares in the square pattern (c) in two different ways, find an equation that arises from pattern (c). Do the same for pattern (d). Do the same for (e) and (f) after you have created your own patterns in these squares.

CLASS ACTIVITY 13E: Writing Equations for Story Situations

For each of the following story situations, write the corresponding equation:

1. Markus had M dollars in his bank account. After removing $\frac{1}{5}$ of the money in the account and then putting in another $200, Markus now has $800.

2. Keisha had K dollars in her bank account. After removing $200 and then removing $\frac{1}{5}$ of the remaining money, Keisha now has $800.

3. Originally there were L liters of liquid in a container. After $\frac{2}{3}$ of the liquid was poured out, another $2\frac{1}{2}$ liters of liquid were poured into the container. When $\frac{1}{4}$ of the liquid was poured out, 4 liters remained.

4. There are 2 times as many pencils in Maya's pencil box as in David's. Draw a picture to help you explain why your equation is correct.

5. Work with a partner. You and your partner should each write your own story problem that gives rise to an equation. Don't show your partner your story problem. Write the equation associated with your story problem. Show this equation to your partner, keeping your story problems hidden from each other. Now write a story problem to go along with your partner's equation. Compare the new story problems to the originals.

CLASS ACTIVITY 13F: Evaluating Expressions with Fractions Efficiently and Correctly

1. In order to evaluate

$$\frac{8}{35} \cdot \frac{35}{61}$$

we can cancel thus:

$$\frac{8}{\cancel{35}} \cdot \frac{\cancel{35}}{61} = \frac{8}{61}$$

Discuss the following equations and explain why they demonstrate that the canceling shown previously is legitimate:

$$\frac{8}{35} \cdot \frac{35}{61} = \frac{8 \cdot 35}{35 \cdot 61} = \frac{8 \cdot 35}{61 \cdot 35} = \frac{8}{61} \cdot \frac{35}{35} = \frac{8}{61}$$

2. Write equations to demonstrate that the canceling shown in the following equations is legitimate:

$$\frac{\overset{2}{\cancel{18}}}{5} \cdot \frac{7}{\underset{11}{\cancel{99}}} = \frac{2}{5} \cdot \frac{7}{11} = \frac{14}{55}$$

3. Which of the cancelations in (a) through (d) are correct and which are incorrect? Explain your answers.

    a.

$$\frac{\overset{6}{\cancel{36}} \cdot \overset{16}{\cancel{96}}}{\underset{1}{\cancel{6}}} = \frac{6 \cdot 16}{1} = 96$$

    b.

$$\frac{\overset{6}{\cancel{36}} \cdot 96}{\underset{1}{\cancel{6}}} = \frac{6 \cdot 96}{1} = 576$$

    c.

$$\frac{\overset{6}{\cancel{36}} + \overset{16}{\cancel{96}}}{\underset{1}{\cancel{6}}} = \frac{6 + 16}{1} = 22$$

    d.

$$\frac{\overset{6}{\cancel{36}} + 96}{\underset{1}{\cancel{6}}} = \frac{6 + 96}{1} = 102$$

13.2 Solving Equations with Pictures and with Algebra

CLASS ACTIVITY 13G: Solving Equations Algebraically and with a Pan Balance

Solve $5x + 1 = 2x + 7$ in two ways, with equations and with pictures of a pan balance. Relate the two methods.

with equations:

$$5x + 1 = 2x + 7$$

with a pan balance:

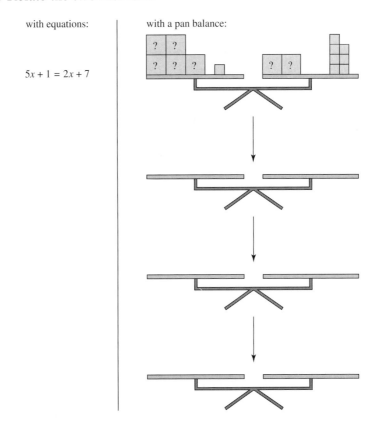

CLASS ACTIVITY 13H: Solving Story Problems with Singapore-Style Strip Diagrams and with Algebra

1. A fourth-grade problem (from [3] volume 4A part one, p. 62)[1]: Meifen and Suhua have 2000 stickers altogether. If Meifen has 600 more stickers than Suhua, how many stickers does Meifen have?

    Solve this problem in two ways: by using the strip diagram shown and with equations. Discuss how the two solution methods are related.

2. A fourth-grade problem (from [4] volume 4B, p. 62): Ailin paid $8.25 for a book and a comic. The book cost twice as much as the comic. Find the cost of the book.

    Solve this problem in two ways: by using the strip diagram shown and with equations. Discuss how the two solution methods are related.

Material throughout this activity is adapted with permission from *Primary Mathematics*, Vol. 4A, p. 40; Vol. 4B, p. 62; Vol. 5A, pp. 59, 60; Vol. 6B, pp. 64, 67; and from *Primary Mathematics Workbook*, Vol. 4A part 1, p. 62; Vol. 4B part 2, p. 59 by Ministry of Education and Times Media Private Limited.

3. A fifth-grade problem (from [4] volume 5A, p. 59. The diagram shown is similar to a diagram on that page.): Encik Hassan gave $\frac{2}{5}$ of his money to his wife and spent $\frac{1}{2}$ of the remainder. If he had $300 left, how much money did he have at first?

Solve this problem in two ways: by using the strip diagram shown and with equations. Discuss how the two solution methods are related.

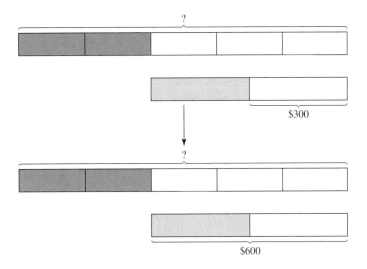

4. A fifth-grade problem (from [4] volume 5A, p. 60): $\frac{3}{7}$ of the apples in a box are red apples. The rest are green apples. There are 24 green apples. How many apples are there altogether?

Solve this problem in two ways: by using the strip diagram shown and with equations. Discuss how the two solution methods are related.

red apples   24 green apples

5. A sixth-grade problem (from [4] volume 6B, p. 67. The diagram shown is similar to a diagram on that page.): Raju had 3 times as much money as Gopal. After Raju spent $60 and Gopal spent $10, they each had an equal amount of money left. How much money did Raju have at first?

Solve this problem in two ways: by using the strip diagram shown and with equations. Discuss how the two solution methods are related.

6. A fourth-grade problem (from [4] volume 4A, p. 40): The difference between two numbers is 2184. If the bigger number is 3 times the smaller number, find the sum of the two numbers.

   Solve this problem in two ways: with the aid of a diagram and with equations. Discuss how the two solution methods are related.

7. A fourth-grade problem (from [3] volume 4B part 2, p. 59): After spending $\frac{3}{5}$ of his money on a badminton racket, Ahmad had $14 left. How much did the badminton racket cost?

   Solve this problem in two ways: with the aid of a diagram and with equations. Discuss how the two solution methods are related.

8. A fifth-grade problem (from [4] volume 5A, p. 60): Mr. Li gave $\frac{1}{4}$ of a sum of money to his wife. Then he divided the remainder equally among his 4 children. If each child received $600, find the sum of money.

   Solve this problem in two ways: with the aid of a diagram and with equations. Discuss how the two solution methods are related.

9. A sixth-grade problem (from [4] volume 6B, p. 64): When a bottle is $\frac{1}{2}$ filled with water, it weighs 2.6 kg. The bottle weighs 4 kg when it is full. Find the weight of the empty bottle.

   Solve this problem in two ways: with the aid of a diagram and with equations. Discuss how the two solution methods are related.

CLASS ACTIVITY 131: Solving Story Problems

The story problems in this activity are taken from Class Activity 13E. Solve each problem, either with the aid of a diagram or using equations. Explain your reasoning.

1. Initially, Markus had M dollars in his bank account. After removing $\frac{1}{5}$ of the money in the account and then putting in another $200, Markus now has $800. How much money did Markus have initially?

2. Keisha had K dollars in her bank account. After removing $200 and then removing $\frac{1}{5}$ of the remaining money, Keisha now has $800. How many dollars did Keisha have in her bank account before removing any money?

3. Originally there were L liters of liquid in a container. After $\frac{2}{3}$ of the liquid was poured out, another $2\frac{1}{2}$ liters of liquid were poured into the container. When $\frac{1}{4}$ of the liquid was poured out, 4 liters remained. What was the original amount of liquid in the container?

13.3 Sequences

CLASS ACTIVITY 13J: Arithmetic Sequences of Numbers Corresponding to Sequences of Figures

1. In the following sequence of figures made up of small squares, assume that the sequence continues by adding 2 shaded squares to the top of a figure in order to get the next figure in the sequence.

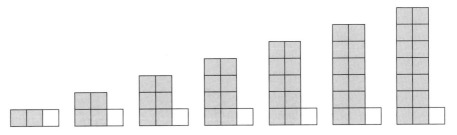

a. In the next table, write the number of small squares making up each figure.

Imagine that the sequence of figures continues forever, so that for each counting number N, there is an Nth figure. What is a formula for the number of small squares in the Nth figure? Add this information to the table.

POSITION OF FIGURE	NUMBER OF SMALL SQUARES IN FIGURE
1st	
2nd	
3rd	
4th	
5th	
6th	
7th	
⋮	⋮
Nth	

b. Relate the structure of the formula you found in part (a) to the structure of the previous figures. Explain why your formula makes sense by relating your formula to the structure of the figures.

c. How many small squares will make up the 25th figure in the sequence? How can you tell?

d. Will there be a figure in the sequence that is made of 150 small squares? If yes, which one? If no, why not? Answer these questions in two ways: with algebra and in a way that a third, fourth, or fifth grader might be able to.

e. Will there be a figure in the sequence that is made of 85 small squares? If yes, which one? If no, why not? Answer these questions in two ways: with algebra and in a way that a third, fourth, or fifth grader might be able to.

2. In the following sequence of figures made of small circles, assume that the sequence continues by adding a white circle to the end of each of the three "arms" of a figure in order to get the next figure in the sequence.

a. In the next table, write the number of small circles that the previous figures are made of.

Imagine that the sequence of figures continues forever, so that for each counting number N, there is an Nth figure. What is a formula for the number of small squares in the Nth pattern? Add this information to your table.

POSITION OF FIGURE	NUMBER OF SMALL SQUARES IN FIGURE
1st	
2nd	
3rd	
4th	
5th	
6th	
⋮	⋮
Nth	

b. Relate the structure of the formula you found in part (a) to the structure of the figures. Explain why your formula makes sense by relating your formula to the structure of the figures.

c. How many small circles will the 38th figure in the sequence be made of? How can you tell?

d. Will there be a figure in the sequence that is made of 100 small circles? If yes, which one? If no, why not? Answer these questions in two ways: with algebra and in a way that a third, fourth, or fifth grader might be able to.

e. Will there be a figure in the sequence that is made of 125 small circles? If yes, which one? If no, why not? Answer these questions in two ways: with algebra and in a way that a third, fourth, or fifth grader might be able to.

CLASS ACTIVITY 13K: Creating Sequences of Figures from Formulas

This activity concerns the following three sequences:

The first sequence is the one whose Nth entry is $2N + 3$.

The second sequence is the one whose Nth entry is $4N + 1$.

The third sequence is the one whose Nth entry is N^2.

1. Write the first 7 numbers in each of the three sequences.

2. Informally discuss the following:

    In what way are the first two sequences similar? In what way are they different? In what way are the first two sequences different from the third sequence?

    How do the first two sequences grow? In other words, how do these sequences change in going from one entry to the next? Contrast the way the first two sequences grow with the way the third sequence grows.

3. Given that 729 is one of the entries in the first sequence, can you predict the next entry without using the formula? How?

    Given that 729 is one of the entries in the second sequence, can you predict the next entry without using the formula? How?

    Given that 729 is one of the entries in the third sequence, is there an easy way to predict the next entry without using the formula? Why is this harder than for the other two sequences?

4. How is the way the first two sequences grow related to their formulas? Why does that make sense?

5. Draw a sequence of figures made of small circles so that the Nth figure in the sequence is made of $2N + 3$ small circles.

Draw another sequence of figures made of small circles so that the Nth figure in the sequence is made of $4N + 1$ small circles.

Draw another sequence of figures made of small circles or small squares so that the Nth figure in the sequence is made of N^2 small circles or small squares.

6. How is the structure of the figures you drew in part 5 related to the formulas for the number of small circles they are made of?

CLASS ACTIVITY 13L: Geometric Sequences

1. Write a formula for a sequence whose first few entries are the number of small squares in the next sequence of figures. Explain why you wrote your formula as you did.

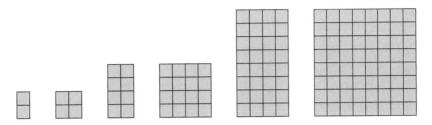

2. Write a formula for a sequence whose first few entries are the number of small squares in the next sequence of figures. Explain why you wrote your formula as you did.

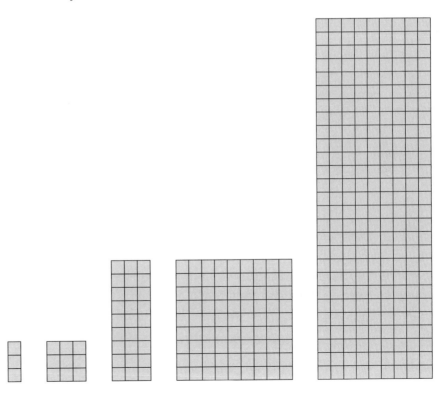

3. Suppose you owe $1000 on your credit card and that the credit card company charges you 1.4708% interest every month. That is, at the end of each month an additional 1.4708% of the amount you owe is added to the amount you owe. (This is what would happen if your credit card charged an annual percentage rate of 17.6496%.) Let's assume that you do not pay off any of this debt or the interest that is added to it. Let's also assume that you don't add any more debt other than the interest that you are charged.

   a. Fill in the next table to show how much you owe at the end of 1 month, 2 months, and so on up to 12 months. Explain why you can get each entry from the previous entry by multiplying by 1.014708.

MONTH	AMOUNT YOU OWE AT END OF MONTH		MONTH	AMOUNT YOU OWE AT END OF MONTH
1			7	
2			8	
3			9	
4			10	
5			11	
6			12	

   b. Determine how much you will owe at the end of 24 months without finding how much you will owe at the end of 13 months, 14 months, 15 months, and so on.

   c. Write a formula for the amount of money you will owe at the end of N months. Explain why your formula is valid.

   d. Use your formula from part (c) to determine how much money you will owe after 4 years.

CLASS ACTIVITY 13M: Repeating Patterns

1. Even very young children can work with repeating patterns. For example, see the activities in *Navigating through Algebra in Prekindergarten – Grade 2* by the National Council of Teachers of Mathematics [7]. The problems below are similar to some of the problems described there.

    a. Assume that the following pattern of a square followed by 3 circles and 2 triangles continues to repeat:

    What will be the 100th shape in the pattern? Explain how you can tell.

    b. How many circles will there be among the first 150 entries of the given sequence? Explain your reasoning.

2. What day of the week will it be 100 days from today? Determine the answer with math. Explain your reasoning. How is this problem related to repeating patterns?

3. What time of day will it be 100 hours from now? Determine the answer with math. Explain your reasoning. How is this problem related to repeating patterns?

4. Five friends are sitting in a circle as shown. Antrice does "eenie meenie minee moe, catch a tiger by his toe, if he hollers, let him go, y-e-s spells yes and you are it" starting with Benton and going clockwise.

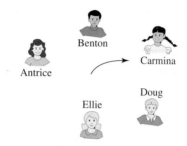

a. Who will be "it"? Explain how to predict the answer using math.

b. What if Fran comes and sits between Ellie and Antrice before Antrice does "eenie meenie minee moe…," then who will be "it"?

c. Some people use a different "eenie meenie minee moe" chant. If you know a different one, use math to determine who will be "it" with your chant.

5. What is the digit in the ones place of 2^{100}? Explain how you can tell.

CLASS ACTIVITY 13N: The Fibonacci Sequence in Nature and Art

You will need pine cones or pineapples for part 1. You will need a ruler for parts 2 and 3. You will need graph paper for part 4.

The Fibonacci sequence is

$$1, \quad 1, \quad 2, \quad 3, \quad 5, \quad 8, \quad 13, \quad 21, \quad 34, \dots$$

Each entry in the sequence is obtained by adding the previous two entries.

1. Look closely at a pine cone or pineapple. You should see two sets of "swirls." One set swirls around clockwise, the other set swirls around counterclockwise. Count the number of swirls in each set. These numbers are usually consecutive Fibonacci numbers.

2. Measure the lengths of the indicated bones in your body, rounded to the nearest inch, and record the results in the next table. Use the same finger for all finger measurements.

BONE CONNECTING	LENGTH OF BONE
shoulder and elbow	
elbow and wrist	
wrist and first knuckle	
first knuckle and second knuckle	
second knuckle and third knuckle	
third knuckle and fingertip	

Compare the lengths of your bones in inches to the Fibonacci sequence.

3. Draw a rectangle whose proportions are pleasing to your eye. Carefully measure the length and width of your rectangle. Then divide the length (the longer measurement) by the width (the shorter measurement). Is this ratio close to the ratios of the following consecutive Fibonacci numbers?

$$\frac{3}{2} = 1.5, \quad \frac{5}{3} = 1.67, \quad \frac{8}{5} = 1.6, \quad \frac{13}{8} = 1.625$$

4. The beginning of a sequence of rectangles is shown next. The sequence starts with a 1-unit-by-1-unit square. To create the next rectangle in the sequence, attach a square to the previous rectangle. Attach the square either below the rectangle or to the right of the rectangle, alternating between attaching it below and attaching it to the right.

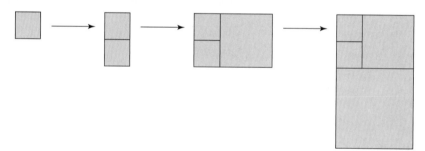

a. On graph paper draw the next two rectangles in the sequence.

b. Do you find the proportions of these rectangles pleasing to your eye?

c. What are the lengths and widths of rectangles in this sequence?

13.4 Series

CLASS ACTIVITY 130: Sums of Counting Numbers

Imagine that the next sequence of rectangular patterns is to continue indefinitely in such a way that to get the next rectangular pattern in the sequence, we add a row of white squares to the bottom and then a column of dark squares to the right.

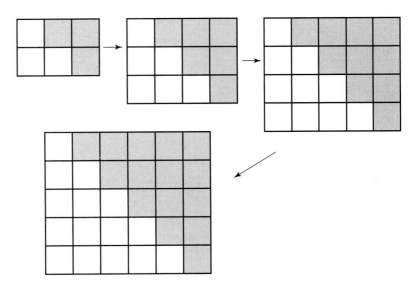

1. Discuss how the following equations are associated with the first two rectangular patterns:

$$1 + 2 = \frac{2 \cdot 3}{2}$$
$$1 + 2 + 3 = \frac{3 \cdot 4}{2}$$

2. Find equations like the ones in part (a) that are associated with the 3rd and 4th rectangular patterns in the sequence. Discuss how these equations are related to the patterns.

3. Determine the sum of the following arithmetic series, and explain your reasoning:

$$1 + 2 + 3 + 4 + \ldots + 198 + 199 + 200$$

4. Write an equation that is associated with the Nth pattern in the previous sequence of rectangles. Explain your work.

CLASS ACTIVITY 13P: Sums of Odd Numbers

Figure 13.3 shows a sequence of square patterns of increasing size. Each square pattern is made of smaller squares of different colors. To get the next square pattern in the sequence, we always add a row and column of small squares of a new color along the bottom and right. Imagine this sequence of square patterns continuing indefinitely.

1. For each square pattern shown in the sequence in Figure 13.3, find two different ways to express the total number of small squares that make up the square pattern. Write an associated equation.

2. Determine the sum of the first 100 odd numbers. Explain your reasoning.

3. Determine the sum of the arithmetic series

$$1 + 3 + 5 + \ldots + 95 + 97 + 99$$

Explain your reasoning.

4. Write an equation that is associated with the Nth square pattern in the sequence in Figure 13.3. Explain your work.

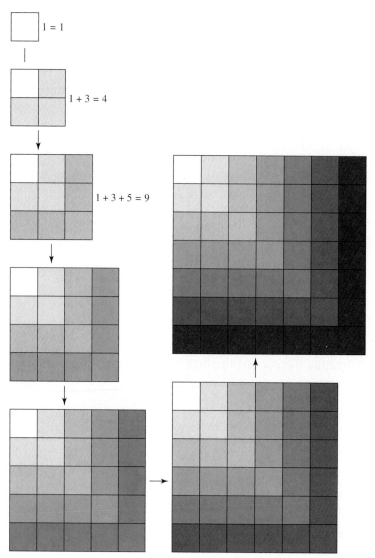

FIGURE 13.3

Sums of Odd Numbers

CLASS ACTIVITY 13Q: Sums of Squares

This activity is related to Class Activity 11AA on explaining why there is a factor of $\frac{1}{3}$ in the volume formula for pyramids and cones. In that activity, 3 oblique pyramids were put together to make a cube. In this activity, you will see that 3 oblique "step pyramids" fit together to make a rectangular prism—except that there is a gap in the prism. By describing the "step pyramids" and the "gap," you can derive a formula for a sum of squares.

Before you start this activity, you may want to review how the 3 oblique pyramids of Class Activity 11AA fit together to make a cube. Observe that the points of the 3 pyramids come together.

1. **a.** Using blocks in 3 different colors, make 3 oblique "step pyramids," as pictured in Figure 13.4, each of a different color. Your step pyramids should have 2 layers: the bottom layer made of $2^2 = 4$ blocks and the top layer made of 1 block.

FIGURE 13.4

3 Oblique Step Pyramids

b. Put your 3 step pyramids together, so that their "points" (top layers) come together (just like the three oblique pyramids in Class Activity 11AA), and so that together, they *almost* form a rectangular prism.

Observe that if you add 1 block in the middle and 2 blocks at an edge, you will get a rectangular prism that is 3 blocks wide, 3 blocks deep, and 2 blocks tall.

c. Explain how part (b) gives rise to the following equation:

$$3 \cdot (1 + 2^2) = 3 \cdot 3 \cdot 2 - (1 + 2)$$

2. a. Using blocks in 3 different colors, make 3 oblique "step pyramids," as pictured in Figure 13.5, each of a different color. This time your step pyramids should have 3 layers: the bottom layer made of $3^2 = 9$ blocks, the middle layer made of $2^2 = 4$ blocks, and the top layer made of 1 block.

FIGURE 13.5

3 Oblique Step Pyramids

b. Put your 3 step pyramids together, so that their "points" (top layers) come together (just like in part (b) above, and just like the three oblique pyramids in Class Activity 11AA), and so that together, they *almost* form a rectangular prism. It might help to secure your step pyramids with masking tape.

   Observe that if you add 1 block, and another 2 blocks in the middle, and 3 blocks on the edge, you will get a rectangular prism that is 4 blocks wide, 4 blocks deep, and 3 blocks tall.

c. Explain how part (b) gives rise to the following equation:

$$3 \cdot (1 + 2^2 + 3^2) = 4 \cdot 4 \cdot 3 - (1 + 2 + 3)$$

3. If you can, make 3 step pyramids that each have 4 layers: the bottom layer made of 4^2 blocks, and the remaining layers made of 3^2, 2^2, and 1 block(s), respectively. Put them together as before, and explain how this gives rise to the equation

$$3 \cdot (1 + 2^2 + 3^2 + 4^2) = 5 \cdot 5 \cdot 4 - (1 + 2 + 3 + 4)$$

4. Imagine that you could continue this process of putting larger and larger step pyramids together indefinitely. Use your discoveries and the fact that

$$1 + 2 + 3 + \ldots + N = \frac{N(N+1)}{2}$$

to give a formula for

$$1 + 2^2 + 3^2 + \ldots + N^2$$

In other words, write an equation for which the left-hand side is $1 + 2^2 + 3^2 + \ldots + N^2$.

5. Based on your formula in part 4, calculate

$$1 + 2^2 + 3^2 + \ldots + 100^2$$

CLASS ACTIVITY 13R: Sums of Powers of Two

1. Discuss how the following equations are associated with the sequence of figures in Figure 13.6:

$$
\begin{aligned}
1 + 2 &= 4 - 1 \\
1 + 2 + 4 &= 8 - 1 \\
1 + 2 + 4 + 8 &= 16 - 1 \\
1 + 2 + 4 + 8 + 16 &= 32 - 1
\end{aligned}
$$

2. Based on part 1, predict the sum of the following geometric sequence without adding all the terms:

$$1 + 2 + 4 + 8 + 16 + 32 + 64 + 128 + 256 + 512$$

3. Based on part 1, predict a formula in terms of N for the following geometric series (fill in the blank with an appropriate expression):

$$1 + 2 + 2^2 + 2^3 + 2^4 + \ldots + 2^N = \underline{\hspace{1cm}}$$

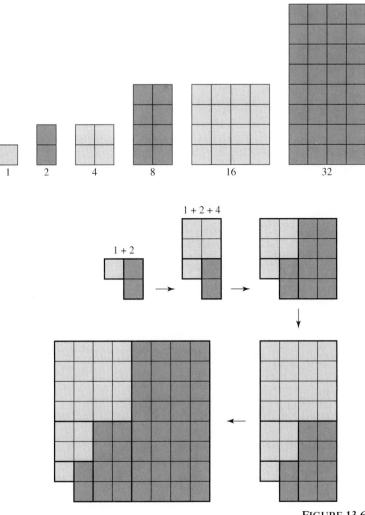

FIGURE 13.6

Sums of Powers of 2

4. Here is a way to find a formula for the sum of the geometric series in part 3: Let S be this sum, so that

$$S = 1 + 2 + 2^2 + 2^3 + 2^4 + \ldots + 2^N$$

Use the distributive property to write $2S$ as a series (fill in the blank with a series):

$$2S = 2 \cdot (1 + 2 + 2^2 + 2^3 + 2^4 + \ldots + 2^N)$$
$$= \underline{\hspace{5cm}}$$

Now calculate $2S - S$ in the following two ways, in terms of S and as a series:

$2S - S$ in terms of S: $2S - S$ as a series :

$2S$

$\underline{-S}$ $\underline{-1 - 2 - 2^2 - 2^3 - 2^4 - \ldots - 2^N}$

The two results you get must be equal, so you get an equation. Solve this equation for S.

CLASS ACTIVITY 13S: An Infinite Geometric Series

Assume that the next sequence of partially shaded squares shown continues indefinitely, in such a way that we get the next square in the sequence by shading $\frac{1}{2}$ of the unshaded part of a square.

1. Explain why the shaded portions of the 2nd, 3rd, and 4th squares in the sequence are

$$\frac{1}{2} + \left(\frac{1}{2}\right)^2$$

$$\frac{1}{2} + \left(\frac{1}{2}\right)^2 + \left(\frac{1}{2}\right)^3$$

$$\frac{1}{2} + \left(\frac{1}{2}\right)^2 + \left(\frac{1}{2}\right)^3 + \left(\frac{1}{2}\right)^4$$

2. What fraction of the square is shaded in the 2nd, 3rd, and 4th figures? Give each answer in simplest form. Based on your results, predict what fraction of the Nth square is shaded.

3. Based on your work in part 2, when would you reach a square that is at least 99.9% shaded?

4. Based on the sequence of shaded squares, what would you expect the infinite sum

$$\frac{1}{2} + \left(\frac{1}{2}\right)^2 + \left(\frac{1}{2}\right)^3 + \left(\frac{1}{2}\right)^4 + \left(\frac{1}{2}\right)^5 + \cdots$$

to be equal to?

5. Here is a way to calculate the infinite sum in part 4. Let S stand for this sum. In other words,

$$S = \frac{1}{2} + \left(\frac{1}{2}\right)^2 + \left(\frac{1}{2}\right)^3 + \left(\frac{1}{2}\right)^4 + \left(\frac{1}{2}\right)^5 + \ldots$$

Assuming that there is an "infinite distributive property," write $\frac{1}{2}S$ as an infinite sum (fill in the blank):

$$\frac{1}{2}S = \frac{1}{2} \cdot \left(\frac{1}{2} + \left(\frac{1}{2}\right)^2 + \left(\frac{1}{2}\right)^3 + \left(\frac{1}{2}\right)^4 + \ldots\right)$$

$$= \underline{\hspace{5cm}}$$

Now calculate $S - \frac{1}{2}S$ in two ways, in terms of S and as a series:

in terms of S: as a series :

$$S$$ $$\frac{1}{2} + \left(\frac{1}{2}\right)^2 + \left(\frac{1}{2}\right)^3 + \left(\frac{1}{2}\right)^4 + \left(\frac{1}{2}\right)^5 + \ldots$$

$$-\frac{1}{2}S$$ $$\underline{\hspace{6cm}}$$

The two results you get must be equal, so you get an equation. Solve this equation for S.

CLASS ACTIVITY 13T: Making Payments into an Account

You will need a calculator for this activity.

Suppose that at the beginning of every month, you make a payment of $200 into an account that earns 1% interest per month (that is, the value of the account at the end of the month is 1% higher than it was at the beginning of the month).

1. Make a guess: after making your 12th payment at the beginning of the 12th month, how much money will be in the account? (The remaining parts of this activity will help you calculate this amount exactly.)

2. Explain why the entries shown in the right-hand column in the next table are correct. Then fill in the remaining columns with series similar to those in the first three rows. (You may use "..." within your series in the last row.)

MONTH	AMOUNT AT BEGINNING OF MONTH (AFTER PAYMENT)
1	200
2	$200 + (1.01)200$
3	$200 + (1.01)200 + (1.01)^2 200$
4	
5	
6	
⋮	⋮
12	

3. Let S be the series you wrote in the last row of the right column in part 2. Use the distributive property to write $(1.01)S$ as a series.

4. Calculate $(1.01)S - S$ in two ways: in terms of S and as a series.

5. The two results you get in part 4 must be equal, so you get an equation. Solve this equation for S. Compare the result with your guess in part 1.

13.5 Functions

CLASS ACTIVITY 13U: Interpreting Graphs of Functions

1. Items (a) through (f) are hypothetical descriptions of a population of fish. Each description corresponds to a population function, for which the input is time elapsed since the fish population was first measured, and the output is the population of fish at that time. Match the descriptions of these population functions to the graphs in Figure 13.7. In each case, explain why the shape of the graph fits with the description of the function.

   a. The population of fish rose slowly at first, and then rose more and more rapidly.

   b. The population of fish rose rapidly at first, and then rose more and more slowly.

   c. The population of fish rose at a steady rate.

   d. The population of fish dropped rapidly at first, and then dropped more and more slowly.

   e. The population of fish dropped slowly at first, and then dropped more and more rapidly.

   f. The population of fish dropped at a steady rate.

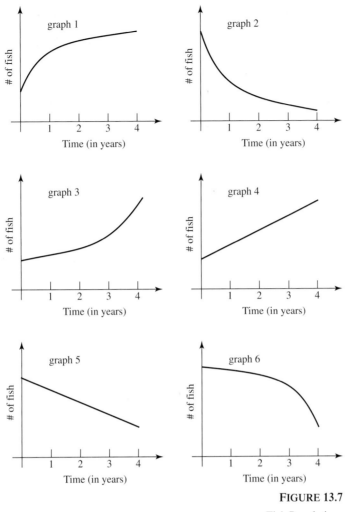

FIGURE 13.7

Fish Populations

2. Hot water is poured into a mug and left to cool. This situation gives rise to a temperature function for which the input is the time elapsed since pouring the water into the mug and the output is the temperature of the water at that time. The graph of this function is shown. What can you tell about the temperature of the water based on this graph? Does the water cool more rapidly right after it is poured, or later on? Explain how the shape of the graph helps you answer this question.

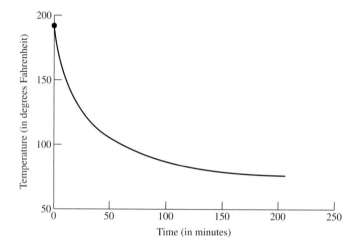

3. A tagged manatee swims up a river, away from a dock. Meanwhile, the manatee's tag transmits its distance from the dock. This situation gives rise to a distance function for which the input is the time since the manatee first swam away from the dock and the output is the manatee's distance from the dock at that time. The graph of this distance function is shown.

  Write a story about the manatee that fits with this graph. Explain how features of the graph fit with your story.

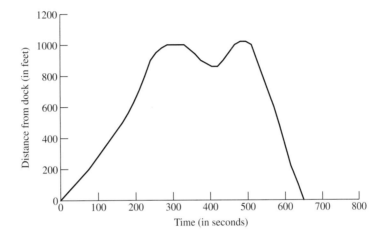

4. Carl started to drive from Providence to Boston, but after leaving, he realized that he had forgotten something and drove back to Providence. Then Carl got back in his car and drove straight to Boston. This scenario gives rise to a distance function whose input is time elapsed since Carl first started to drive to Boston and whose output is Carl's distance from Providence. Could the next graph be the graph of the distance function described? Why or why not? If not, draw a different graph that could be the graph of the distance function. (Boston is 50 miles from Providence.)

13.6 Linear Functions

CLASS ACTIVITY 13V: Comparing the Way Functions Change

(a)

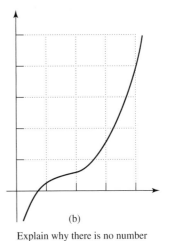

(b)

Fill in the blank to make a
true statement about graph (a):
"Whenever the input increases by 1
the output _____ "
Explain why the statement is true.

Explain why there is no number
you can place in the blank to
make a true statement about
graph (b):
"Whenever the input increases by 1
the output increases by _____ "

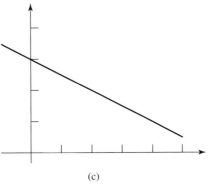

(c)

Fill in the blank to make a true statement about graph (c):
"Whenever the input increases by 1 the output _____ "
Explain why the statement is true.

CLASS ACTIVITY 13W: Functions for Which the Ratio of Change in Input to Change in Output Is Always the Same

You will need graph paper for parts of this activity.

1. Consider a function that has the following properties:
   - When the input is 1, the output is 5.

   - Whenever the input increases by 1, the output increases by 3.
   a. Make a table and draw the graph of a function that has the properties described.

   b. Explain how the properties in the two bulleted items above are reflected in the graph of the function.

   c. Find a formula for a function that has the properties described.

2. Consider a function that has the following properties:
   - When the input is 0, the output is 0.

   - Whenever the input increases by 3, the output increases by 7.
   a. Make a table and draw the graph of a function that has the properties described.

   b. Explain how the properties in the two bulleted items above are reflected in the graph of the function.

   c. Find a formula for a function that has the properties described.

3. To make a certain shade of pink paint, for every 2 cups of white paint you will produce 5 cups of pink paint (by adding 3 cups of red paint to the white paint). This situation gives rise to a "pink-paint function" for which the input is the number of cups of white paint and the output is the number of cups of pink paint produced for that amount of white paint.

    a. Make a table and draw a graph of the pink-paint function described. Be sure to label your axes appropriately.

    b. Fill in the blank to make a true statement about the pink-paint function: "Whenever the input increases by 2, the output _____." Explain how this statement is reflected in the graph of the pink-paint function.

    c. Fill in the blank to make a true statement about the pink-paint function: "Whenever the input increases by 1, the output _____." Explain how this statement is reflected in the graph of the pink-paint function.

    d. Let x stand for the number of cups of white paint. Let P be the pink-paint function, so that $P(x)$ is the number of cups of pink paint when x cups of white paint are used. Write a formula for $P(x)$ and explain how this formula is related to your answer for part (c).

CLASS ACTIVITY 13X: Story Problems for Linear Functions

You will need graph paper for part 1(b).

1. Sherri's monthly bill for phone service is $20. If Sherri calls her sister in France, then she pays an additional $0.15 per minute of phone call.
    a. Describe a function that arises from this situation.

    b. Make a table and draw a graph of your function in part (a).

    c. Find a formula for your function in part (a) and explain why your formula is valid.

2. Write a story problem which gives rise to a function, f, that has the formula $f(x) = 3x + 5$. Explain why your function has that formula.

3. Write a story problem which gives rise to a function, g, that has the formula $g(x) = \frac{3}{5}x$.

Chapter 14

Statistics

14.1 Designing Investigations and Gathering Data

CLASS ACTIVITY 14A: Challenges in Conducting Good Surveys

1. Lincoln Elementary School would like to add soup to its school lunch menu. The school staff decides to poll the students to learn about the soups they like. Compare the questions in (a) through (e). How might the data that the school would collect be different for the different questions? What are the advantages and disadvantages of each question?

   a. What is your favorite soup?

   b. If you had to pick a soup to eat right now, what soup would you pick?

   c. Vote for one of the following soups you like to eat:
      - tomato
      - chicken noodle
      - vegetable
      - other

   d. Circle all of the following soups you like to eat:
      - tomato
      - chicken noodle
      - vegetable

   e. (Write your own question.)

2. A college newspaper wants to find out how the students at the college would answer a specific question of importance to the student body. There are too many students for the newspaper staff to ask them all. So the staff decides to choose a sample of students to ask. Discuss the advantages and disadvantages of each of the following ways that the newspaper staff could gather data from a sample:

a. ask their friends

b. ask as many of their classmates as they can

c. stand outside the buildings their classes are in and ask as many people as they can who come by

d. stand outside the student union or other common meeting area and try to pick people who they think are representative of the students at their institution to ask their question

e. generate a list of random numbers between 1 and the number of students at their college. (Many calculators can generate random numbers; random numbers can also be generated on the Internet, see www.aw-bc.com/beckmann.) Pick names out of the student phone book corresponding to the random numbers (for example, for 123, pick the 123rd name), and contact that person by phone or by e-mail.

CLASS ACTIVITY 14B: **Which Experiment Is Better?**

Suppose a class wants to do an experiment to see if a fertilizer makes bean plants grow faster. Which of the following designs for this experiment will be better, which will be worse, and why?

1. Fill two identical trays with soil from the same bag. Mix the fertilizer with the soil in one of the trays. Plant half of the bean seeds in each tray. Give one tray to the class next door. Keep one tray in your class. Observe and water the bean plants every day. Once they sprout, measure how tall they are.

2. Same as problem 1 except that you keep both trays in your class at windows on two different walls.

3. Same as problem 2 except that you keep both trays side by side at the same window.

4. Fill identical paper cups with soil. Put fertilizer in half of the cups. Label each cup to show whether or not it has fertilizer. Plant seeds in the cups. Put the cups at a window, alternating between fertilized and unfertilized. Observe and water the bean plants every day. Once they sprout, measure how tall they are.

5. Same as problem 4 except that the paper cups are labeled on the bottom (so that you can't see which is which) and the cups are arranged randomly at the window.

6. Same as problem 5 but make additional collections of cups with seeds and put them at different windows and in different classrooms.

CLASS ACTIVITY 14C: Using Random Samples

1. At a factory that produces computer chips, a batch of 5000 computer chips has just been produced. To check the quality of the computer chips, a random sample of 100 computer chips are selected to test for defects. Out of these 100 chips, 3 were found to be defective. Based on these results, what is the best estimate you can give for the number of defective computer chips in the batch of 5000? Find several different ways to solve this problem, including ways that elementary school children might be able to develop.

2. At a factory that produces locks, a batch of 2500 ball bearings has just been produced. To check the quality of the ball bearings, a random sample of 75 ball bearings are selected to test for defects. Out of these 75 ball bearings, 2 were found to be defective. Based on these results, what is the best estimate you can give for the number of defective ball bearings in the batch of 2500? Explain your reasoning.

CLASS ACTIVITY 14D: Using Random Samples to Estimate Population Size by Marking (Capture-Recapture)

You will need a bag filled with a large number (at least 100) of small, identical paper strips or other small objects that can be marked (such as beads that can be colored with a marker).

Pretend that the paper slips are fish in a lake. You will estimate the number of fish in the lake without counting them all by using a method called *capture-recapture*.

1. Go "fishing:" pick about 20 or 30 "fish" out of your bag. Count the number of fish you caught and label each fish with a distinctive mark. Then throw your fish back in the lake (the bag) and mix them thoroughly.

2. Go fishing again: randomly pick about 20 or 30 fish out of your bag. Count the total number of fish you caught this time and count how many of the fish are marked.

3. Use your counts from part 2 to estimate the number of "fish" in your bag. Explain your reasoning.

4. When Ms. Wade used the method described in parts 1 through 3, she picked 30 "fish" at first, marked them, and put them back in the bag. Ms. Wade thoroughly mixed the fish in the bag and randomly picked out 40 fish. Out of these 40 fish, 5 were marked. The children in Ms. Wade's class had several different ideas for how to determine the total number of fish in the bag. For each of the following initial ideas, discuss the idea and describe how to use the idea to determine approximately how many fish are in the bag.

a.

$$
\begin{array}{cccccc}
40 & 40 & 40 & 40 & 40 & 40 \\
\downarrow & \downarrow & \downarrow & \downarrow & \downarrow & \downarrow \\
5 & 5 & 5 & 5 & 5 & 5
\end{array}
$$

b.

$$
\begin{array}{rcl}
40 & \rightarrow & 5 \\
80 & \rightarrow & 10 \\
120 & \rightarrow & 15 \\
160 & \rightarrow & 20 \\
200 & \rightarrow & 25 \\
240 & \rightarrow & 30
\end{array}
$$

c. $\frac{1}{8}$ of the fish are marked.

d. There are 6 sets of 5 in 30, so . . .

e. There are 8 sets of 5 in 40, so . . .

f.

$$
\frac{5}{40} = \frac{10}{80} = \frac{15}{120} = \frac{20}{160} = \frac{25}{200} = \frac{30}{240}
$$

5. When Lillie used the method described in parts 1 through 3, she picked 25 "fish" at first, marked them, and put them back in the bag. Lillie thoroughly mixed the fish in the bag and randomly picked out 30 fish. Out of these 30 fish, 4 were marked. Based on Lillie's sample, what is the best estimate you can give for the number of fish in Lillie's bag? Explain your reasoning.

14.2   Displaying Data and Interpreting Data Displays

CLASS ACTIVITY 14E: Three Levels of Questions about Graphs

Recall that the three levels of graph comprehension described by Frances Curcio in [2, p. 7] are as follows:

READING THE DATA. This level of comprehension requires a literal reading of the graph. The reader simply "lifts" the facts explicitly stated in the graph, or the information found in the graph title and axes labels, directly from the graph. There is no interpretation at this level.

READING BETWEEN THE DATA. This level of comprehension includes the interpretation and integration of the data in the graph. It requires the ability to compare quantities (e.g., greater than, tallest, smallest) and the use of other mathematical concepts and skills (e.g., addition, subtraction, multiplication, division) that allow the reader to combine and integrate data and identify the mathematical relationships expressed in the graph.

READING BEYOND THE DATA. This level of comprehension requires the reader to predict or infer from the data by tapping existing schemata (i.e., background knowledge, knowledge in memory) for information that is neither explicitly nor implicitly stated in the graph.

The following examples are questions at the different graph-reading levels. All questions are about a bar graph that shows the heights of children in a class ([2, p. 35]):

- What would be a good title for this graph? [Read between the data]

- How tall is (insert a name)? [Read the data]

- Who is the tallest of the students on the graph? [Read between the data]

- Who do you think is the oldest? Why? Can this be answered directly from the graph? [Read beyond the data]

- Who do you think has the smallest shoe size? Why? Can this be answered directly from the graph? [Read beyond the data]

- Who do you think weighs the least? Why? [Read beyond the data]

Now design your own data graphing activity that you could use with elementary school children; include a list of questions to foster the different levels of graph-reading comprehension:

1. Describe an activity in which children will gather data and create a graph.

2. Show roughly what the data display from part 1 might look like.

3. Write a list of questions at the three different graph-reading levels. Label each question with its level.

CLASS ACTIVITY 14F: What Do You Learn from the Display?

For each of the data displays in this activity, pose questions about the data display at the three levels of graph reading: "read the data," "read between the data," and "read beyond the data." Answer each of your questions (to the extent possible).

1. The next graph is about the physical activity of adolescents and was taken from a website of the Center for Disease Control and Prevention (CDC) (see www.aw-bc.com/beckmann).

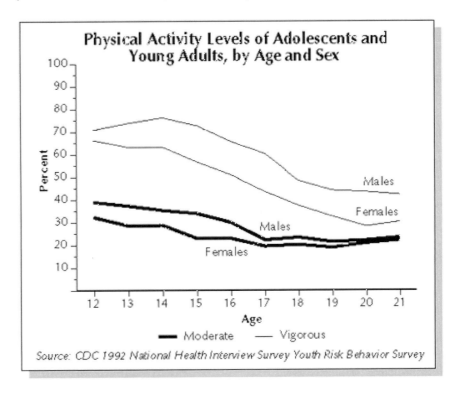

"Read the data" questions:

"Read between the data" questions:

"Read beyond the data" questions:

2. The next bar chart was created with statistics from the U.S. Department of Education, National Center for Education Statistics, National Household Education Survey, 1993, 1999. These statistics can be found in the report *Home Literacy Activities and Signs of Children's Emerging Literacy, 1993 and 1999.* See www.aw-bc.com/beckmann.

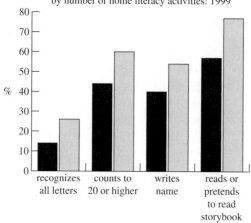

Percentage of 3- to 5-year-old children not yet enrolled in kindergarten with specific reported school readiness skills, by number of home literacy activities: 1999

□ read to 3 or more times in past week

■ read to fewer than 3 times in past week

"Read the data" questions:

"Read between the data" questions:

"Read beyond the data" questions:

3. The next pie chart was created from a table available on the Internet based on data collected by the Current Population Survey. (This is a monthly survey conducted for the Bureau of Labor Statistics by the U.S. Census Bureau.) See www.aw-bc.com/beckmann.

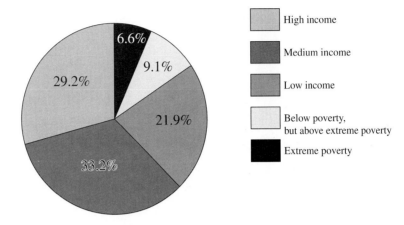

Percentage of children under age 18 living with relatives
by family income relative to the poverty line, 2001

"Read the data" questions:

"Read between the data" questions:

"Read beyond the data" questions:

CLASS ACTIVITY 14G: What Is Wrong with These Displays?

1. Ryan grabbed a handful of small plastic animals and made a pictograph like the following:

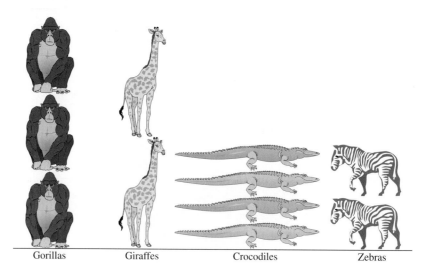

Gorillas   Giraffes   Crocodiles   Zebras

What is a problem with Ryan's pictograph?

2. The line graph for this problem was created from data about children's eating that was available on the Internet. See www.aw-bc.com/beckmann. What is wrong with this display? Show how to fix it.

Percent of children ages 7 to10 meeting dietary recommendations of selected components of the Healthy Eating Index, 1994–96 average

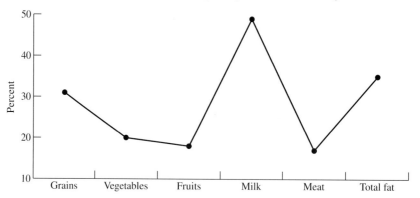

3. The next table on children's eating habits is based on a table found at www.aw-bc.com/beckmann.

FOOD	PERCENT OF 4–6 YEAR OLDS MEETING THE DIETARY RECOMMENDATION FOR THE FOOD
Grains	27%
Vegetables	16%
Fruits	29%
Saturated fat	28%

Would it be appropriate to use a single pie graph to display this information? Explain your answer.

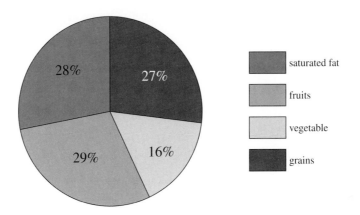

4. The line graph shown was created from data about children's smoking that was available on the Internet. See www.aw-bc.com/beckmann.

Based on this display, would it be correct to say that the percentage of 8th graders who reported smoking cigarettes daily in the previous 30 days was about twice as high in 1996 as it was in 1993? Why or why not?

Percent of eighth graders who reported smoking cigarettes daily in the previous 30 days, 1991–2000

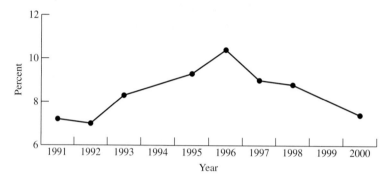

CLASS ACTIVITY 14H: Display These Data

1. A class collected information about the pets they have at home, as shown in the following table:

NAME	PETS AT HOME
Michelle	1 dog, 2 cats
Tyler	3 dogs, 1 salamander, 2 snakes
Antrice	hamster
Yoon-He	cat
Anne	none
Peter	2 dogs
Brandon	guinea pig
Brittany	1 dog, 1 cat
Orlando	none
Chelsey	2 dogs, 10 fish
Sarah	1 rabbit
Adam	none
Lauren	2 dogs
Letitia	3 cats
Jarvis	1 dog

For each of the following questions, use the data from the table to create a graph that could help the class answer the question:

a. Are dogs our most popular pet?

b. How many pets do most people have?

c. How many people have more than one pet?

d. Are most of our pets mammals?

2. Three third-grade classes are having a contest to see which class can read more pages during the month of February. The classes want to create a display, to be posted in the hall, that will show their progress. What do you recommend? Be specific, and make sure your recommendation can be carried out realistically. Draw a picture of what the display might look like at some point during February.

3. For this problem, the class should divide into about 5 teams.
   a. Together with your teammates, write a question that you can use to survey your classmates. Your question should have several different answers that your classmates should come up with on their own. So, your question should not be a yes/no question, and you should not give your classmates a list of answers to choose from.

   b. Send one of your teammates to survey the class and to record all the answers to your team's question. (Or take turns sending different team members.)

   c. Look for different ways to display the results of your survey. For at least one of your ways, create categories into which to fit the different answers to your survey question. For example, if your survey question was about foods, you could have categories such as: snack food, dessert, and meat.

   d. Interpret the results of your survey and use one of your displays to help you make a convincing case for your interpretation.

CLASS ACTIVITY 14I: How Accurately Do Random Samples Reflect the Full Population?

For this activity, you will need a large collection of small objects that are identical except that they come in two different colors. These objects could be poker chips, small cubes, or even slips of paper. Let's say that the two colors are red and black. Thirty percent of the objects in the bag should be red and 70% should be black. Think of the objects in the bag as representing a group of people, and the two colors as representing each person's answer to a certain yes/no question: red for "yes," and black for "no."

If you pick a random sample of the population, will it necessarily be the case that 30% of the sample will answer yes to the question and 70% will answer no? Carry out the following experiment and see what happens.

1. You will pick a random sample of 10 from your bag, record the number in your sample that were red, put your sample back in the bag, mix well, and repeat the whole process, repeatedly picking samples of 10. You will record your results in a line plot later. Before you start, use the first line plot at the top of the next page to predict what you think your actual line plot may look like. Explain why you think your line plot may come out that way.

2. Thoroughly mix the objects in your bag and randomly pick a sample of 10. Record the number that are red by putting the appropriate mark in the line plot on the next page. Put your sample back in the bag, mix well, and repeat the whole process many times, repeatedly picking samples of 10.

3. Discuss what your actual line plot shows. How is the fact that 30% of the objects are red reflected in the line plot?

   Is your actual line plot significantly different from your predicted line plot? If so, why do you think it is?

4. Suppose you were to pick the same number of samples as you did in part 2, but this time picking samples of 20 instead of 10. How do you think the line plot you would create would be different from your line plot in part 2 and how do you think it would be similar? On the next page, create a predicted line plot for samples of 20 and explain why you think your line plot might come out that way.

prediction:

0   1   2   3   4   5   6   7   8   9   10

The number of reds in samples of 10

actual:

0   1   2   3   4   5   6   7   8   9   10

The number of reds in samples of 10

prediction:

0 1 2 3 4 5 6 7 8 9 10 11 12 13 14 15 16 17 18 19 20

The number of reds in samples of 20

14.3 The Center of Data: Mean, Median, and Mode

CLASS ACTIVITY 14J: The Average as "Making Even" or "Leveling Out"

In this class activity you will use physical objects to help you see the average as "making groups even". This point of view can be useful in calculations involving averages.

1. Using blocks, snap cubes, pennies, or other small objects, make towers with the following number of objects in the towers, using a different color (or type of coin) for each tower:

2,   5,   4,   1

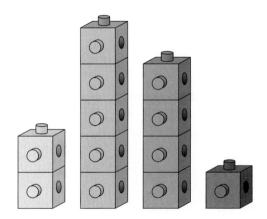

Determine the average of the list numbers 2, 5, 4, 1 by "leveling out" the block towers, or making them even. That is, redistribute the blocks among your block towers until all 4 towers have the same number of blocks in them. This common number of blocks in each of the 4 towers is the average of the list 2, 5, 4, 1.

2. Use the process of making block towers even in order to determine the averages of each of the lists of numbers shown. In some cases you may have to imagine cutting your blocks into smaller pieces.

List 1:   1,   3,   3,   2,   1
List 2:   2,   3,   4,   3,   4
List 3:   2,   3,   1,   5
List 4:   3,   4,   4,   3,   4

3. To calculate the average of a list of numbers *numerically* we add the numbers and divide the sum by the number of numbers in the list. So, to calculate the average of the list 2, 5, 4, 1, we calculate

$$(2 + 5 + 4 + 1) \div 4$$

Interpret the *numerical* process for calculating an average in terms of 4 block towers built of 2 blocks, 5 blocks, 4 blocks, and 1 block. When we add the numbers, what does that correspond to with the blocks? When we divide by 4, what does that correspond to with the blocks?

Explain why the process of determining an average physically by making block towers even must give us the same answer as the numerical procedure for calculating the average.

4. Suppose you have made 3 block towers: one 3 blocks tall, one 6 blocks tall, and one 2 blocks tall. Describe some ways to make two more towers so that there is an average of 4 blocks in all 5 towers.

   Solve this problem in several ways and explain your solutions.

5. If you run 3 miles every day for 5 days, how many miles will you need to run on the sixth day in order to have run an average of 4 miles per day over the 6 days?

   Solve this problem in several ways and explain your solutions.

6. The average of 7 numbers is 12.1. An eighth number, 12.9, is included in the list. What is the average of the 8 numbers?

   Solve this problem in several ways and explain your solutions.

7. Explain how you can quickly calculate the average of the following list of test scores without adding the numbers:

$$81, \quad 78, \quad 79, \quad 83$$

8. If you run an average of 3 miles a day over one week and an average of 4 miles a day over the next two weeks, then what is your average daily run distance over that 3-week period?

   Before you solve this problem, explain why it makes sense that your average daily run distance over the 3-week period is *not* just the average of 3 and 4, namely 3.5. Should your average daily run distance over the 3 weeks be greater than 3.5 or less than 3.5? Explain how to answer this without a precise calculation.

   Now determine the exact average daily run distance over the 3-week period. Explain your solution.

CLASS ACTIVITY 14K: The Average as "Balance Point"

In this class activity you will use physical objects to help you see the average of a list of numbers as the "balance point" among the numbers. You will need the following:

- a 12 inch ruler

- a block or tile on which to balance the ruler—a thin rhombus from a set of pattern tiles is ideal

- small objects, such as pattern tiles, that are stable when placed on the ruler

1. Make a see-saw by balancing the ruler on a tile or a block, checking that it balances at the number 6 (more or less).

2. Holding the ruler steady, place one object on the see-saw for each of the following numbers:

    3,   4,   11

    In each case, place the object centered on that number, as shown in the previous figure. Check that the see-saw still balances at the number 6 (more or less). Check that the average of the numbers is also 6.

3. Repeat 1 with other lists of numbers, *that have an average of 6,* such as

    1,   1,   10

    and

    2,   3,   4,   9

    In each case, verify that the ruler balances at 6.

    For lists of numbers whose average is not 6, the ruler will not balance at the average due to the different weights of the parts of the ruler on either side of the fulcrum (the point where the ruler balances). If it were possible to make a weightless ruler, then the ruler would always balance at the average of the numbers.

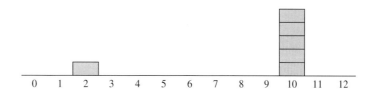

4. The three see-saws in the previous figure represent the following three lists of numbers:

List 1:   1,   2,   2,   3,   3,   3,   4,   4,   5,   8,   9
List 2:   3,   3,   4,   4,   4,   8,   8,   9
List 3:   2,   10,   10,   10,   10,   10

For each list, predict the average by guessing where the corresponding see-saw (made out of a weightless ruler) would balance. Check your predictions by calculating the averages of the lists.

CLASS ACTIVITY 14L: Same Median, Different Average

In most cases, the median of a list of numbers is not the same as its average. In this activity, you will alter a data set to keep the same median but vary the average.

The pennies along the number line at the top of Figure 14.1 are arranged to represent the following data set:

4,   5,   5,   6,   6,   6,   7,   7,   8

Arrange real pennies along the number line at the bottom of Figure 14.1 to represent the same data set.

1. Rearrange your pennies so that they represent new lists of numbers that still have median 6, but have averages *less than* 6. To help you do this, think about the average as the "balance point." Draw pictures of your penny arrangements.

2. Rearrange your pennies so that they represent new lists of numbers that still have median 6, but have averages *greater than* 6. To help you do this, think about the average as the "balance point." Draw pictures of your penny arrangements.

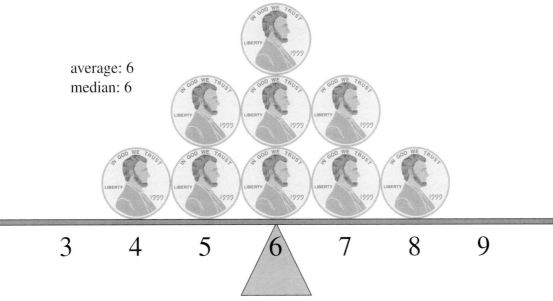

average: 6
median: 6

3   4   5   6   7   8   9

Show data sets with the same median, different averages:

3   4   5   6   7   8   9

FIGURE 14.1
Same Medians, Different Averages

CLASS ACTIVITY 14M: Can More Than Half Be above Average?

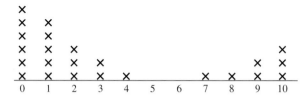

1. **a.** For each of the line plots shown, decide which is greater without calculating: the median or the average of the data.

   b. Calculate the medians and averages of the data in the two line plots. Verify that your answers in part 1 were correct.

2. A teacher gives a test to a class of 20 children.

   Is it possible that 90% of the class scores above average? If so, give an example of test scores for which this is the case. If not, explain why not.

   Is it possible that 90% of the class scores below average? If so, give an example of test scores for which this is the case. If not, explain why not.

3. A radio program describes a fictional town in which "all the children are above average." In what sense is it possible that all the children are above average? In what sense is it not possible that all the children are above average?

14.4 The Spread of Data: Percentiles

CLASS ACTIVITY 14N: Determining Percentiles

1. Determine the 25th, 50th, and 75th percentiles for each of the hypothetical test data shown in the following:

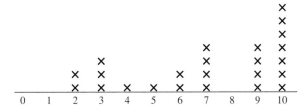

2. Suppose that a 400-point test is given to third graders at three different schools. The bar graphs in Figure 14.2 show hypothetical test results.

   a. Using the bar graphs, determine approximately the 20th, 40th, 60th, and 80th percentiles at each of the schools. Explain your reasoning.

   b. Describe qualitative differences in test performance at the three schools and explain how these qualitative differences are reflected in the percentile scores.

   c. At each of the three schools, consider a third grader who scored at the 60th percentile. In each case, approximately what score did such a third grader probably get? Did such third graders get 60% correct, more than 60% correct, or less than 60% correct on the test?

FIGURE 14.2

Bar Graphs of Hypothetical Test Scores

CLASS ACTIVITY 140: Percentiles versus Percent Correct

1. What is the difference between getting 90% correct on a test and being in the 90th percentile on a test? Give some specific examples to illustrate.

2. Mrs. Smith makes an appointment to talk to Johnny's teacher. Johnny has been getting As in math, but on the standardized test he took, he was in the 80th percentile. Mrs. Smith is concerned that this means Johnny is really doing B work in math, not A work. If you were Johnny's teacher, what could you tell Mrs. Smith?

CLASS ACTIVITY 14P: How Percentiles Inform You about Data Spread: The Case of Household Income

You will need scissors and glue or tape for this activity.

If you know several different percentiles for a set of data, then you have information about how the data are distributed. In particular, you can determine the approximate shape of a bar graph for the data. In this activity, you will see a way to construct an approximate bar graph based on percentile data.

1. The percentile data in the next table on household incomes in the U.S. in 2000 were taken from a table provided by the U.S. Census Bureau. See www.aw-bc.com/beckmann.

Year	HOUSEHOLD INCOME LIMITS BY PERCENTILE					
	10th	20th	50th	80th	90th	95th
2000	$10,600	$17,955	$42,000	$81,960	$111,602	$145,526

Do the following to construct an approximate pictograph for household income. Cut out the square picture on page 629. Think of the 100 houses in this picture as representing 100% of all households in the year 2000. Distribute and glue or tape the 100 houses so as to create a pictograph in Figure 14.3 on page 507. Your pictograph must be consistent with the percentile information about household income in the table. Note: it may be easiest to cut the square of houses into vertical strips first, and then cut houses away from the vertical strips as needed. (To determine what 1 house in the pictograph represents you would need to look up the total number of households in 2000.)

Discuss what the percentile data and your bar graph tell you about household income in the U.S. in the year 2000.

2. What if the household income percentiles were different? Construct approximate household income pictographs for the hypothetical data in the next table. Show your graphs in Figures 14.4 and 14.5 on pages 508 and 509. Use the squares of houses on pages 631 and 633 in the manner of problem 1.

	HOUSEHOLD INCOME LIMITS BY PERCENTILE					
	10TH	20TH	50TH	80TH	90TH	95TH
Hypothetical 1	$20,000	$25,000	$40,000	$55,000	$60,000	$65,000
Hypothetical 2	$10,000	$30,000	$40,000	$80,000	$120,000	$145,000

Discuss how society might be different if one or the other of the hypothetical data situations were accurate.

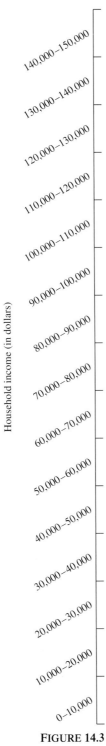

FIGURE 14.3

Create a Pictograph
of Household Income

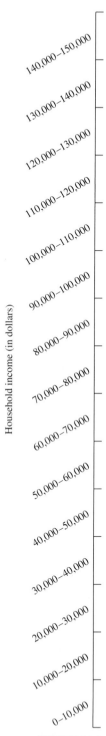

FIGURE 14.4

Create a Pictograph
of Hypothetical
Household Income

FIGURE 14.5

Create a Pictograph
of Hypothetical
Household Income

CLASS ACTIVITY 14Q: More about Household Income

The next table was created from U.S. Census Bureau data.   See
www.aw-bc.com/beckmann. The table shows various household income
percentiles for selected years. All dollar values are in year 2000 dollars, so that
dollar values can be compared across years.

	HOUSEHOLD INCOME LIMITS BY PERCENTILE					
YEAR	10TH	20TH	50TH	80TH	90TH	95TH
2000	$10,600	$17,955	$42,000	$81,960	$111,602	$145,526
1990	9,376	16,050	38,446	70,882	95,828	121,654
1980	8,954	15,035	35,238	63,075	81,580	102,472
1970	7,944	14,245	33,746	56,646	72,251	89,553

1. Examine the data in the table. What strikes you about these data? Try to
   find qualitative and quantitative statements to make about these data.

2. Based on the table, determine roughly what percent of the households had
   incomes of $15,000 or less in 2000, 1990, 1980, and 1970.

3. Based on the table, determine roughly what percent of households had
   incomes of $50,000 or more in 2000, 1990, 1980, and 1970.

4. Based on the table, determine roughly what percent of households had
   incomes between $30,000 and $80,000 in 2000, 1990, 1980, and 1970.

Chapter 15

Probability

15.1 Basic Principles and Calculation Methods of Probability

CLASS ACTIVITY 15A: Comparing Probabilities

1. Many children's games use "spinners." You can make a simple spinner by placing the tip of a pencil through a paper clip and holding the pencil so that its tip is at the center of the circle as shown. The paper clip should spin freely around the pencil tip.

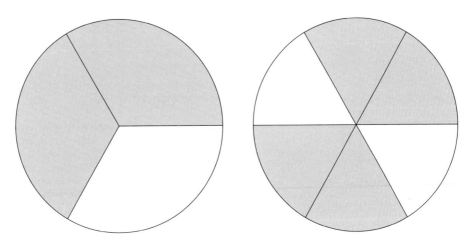

    The next problem is similar to a problem in an activity book for grades 1 – 3, see [5]. Compare the two spinners shown. For which spinner is a paper clip most likely to point into a shaded region? Explain your answer.

2. Compare the next two spinners. For which spinner is the paper clip that spins around a pencil point held at the indicated center point most likely to land in a shaded region? Explain your answer.

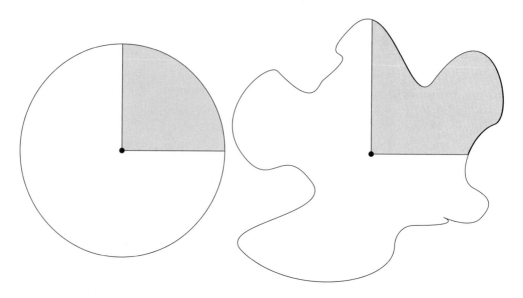

3. A family math night at school features the following game: There are two opaque bags, each containing red blocks and yellow blocks. Bag 1 contains 2 red blocks and 4 yellow blocks. Bag 2 contains 4 red blocks and 16 yellow blocks. To play the game, you pick a bag and then you pick a block out of the bag without looking. You win a prize if you pick a red block. Eva thinks she should pick from bag 2 because it has more red blocks than yellow blocks. Is Eva more likely to pick a red block if she picks from bag 2 than from bag 1? Why or why not?

CLASS ACTIVITY 15B: If You Flip 10 Pennies Should Half Come Up Heads?

You will need a bag, 10 pennies, and some sticky notes for this activity.

1. Make a guess: what do you think the probability is of getting exactly 5 heads on 10 pennies when you dump the 10 pennies out of a bag?

2. Put the 10 pennies in the bag, shake them up, and dump them out. Record the number of heads on a sticky note. Repeat this for a total of 10 times, using a new sticky note each time. Out of these 10 tries, how many times did you get 5 heads? Therefore, what is the experimental probability of getting 5 heads based on your 10 trials?

3. Now work with a large group (e.g., the whole class). Collect the whole group's data on the sticky notes from part 2. Find a way to display these data so that you can see how often the whole group got 5 heads and other numbers of heads.

4. Is the probability of getting exactly 5 heads from 10 coins 50%? What does your data display from part 3 suggest?

CLASS ACTIVITY 15C: Experimental versus Theoretical Probability: Picking Cubes From a Bag

Each person (or small group) will need an opaque bag, 3 red cubes, 7 blue cubes, and a sticky note. In this activity you will compare experimental and theoretical probabilities of picking a red cube from a bag containing 3 red and 7 blue cubes.

1. Put the 10 cubes in the bag, mix them up, and randomly pick a cube from the bag without looking. Record the color of the cube and put the cube back in the bag. Repeat until you have picked 10 cubes. Record the number of red cubes you picked on your sticky note. Calculate the experimental probability of picking a red cube based on your 10 picks. Is it the same as the theoretical probability of picking red?

2. Now work with a large group (e.g., the whole class). Collect the sticky notes of part 1 from the full group. Determine the total number of reds picked and the total number of picks among the large group. Use these results to determine the experimental probability of picking a red cube obtained by the large group. Compare this experimental probability to the theoretical probability of picking red.

3. Use the sticky notes of part 1 to create a line plot. How is the fact that there are 3 red cubes and 7 blue cubes in the bag reflected in the line plot?

CLASS ACTIVITY 15D: Guess the Colors of Cubes in a Bag

This activity is a game that you play with a partner. You will need two opaque bags and 8 cubes, 4 in each of two different colors. Let's say the two colors are red and black.

THE GAME: Take turns being the "bag filler" and the "guesser." Play 5 times each. The person with the highest score wins.

To start, place all 8 cubes in one bag, the "reserve bag." The other bag will be the "guessing bag." Without letting the guesser see, the bag filler takes 4 cubes from the reserve bag and puts them in the guessing bag. All four cubes may be one color, or they can be a combination of the two colors, but there must be 4 cubes in the guessing bag.

Without looking into the bag, the guesser picks one cube out of the guessing bag, records its color, and puts it back in the bag. The guesser does this 6 times and then stops to make a guess about what is in the bag. The guesser continues to pick 4 more times and then makes a final guess about what is in the bag. Finally, the bag filler reveals what is in the bag.

SCORING: Only the guesser scores points.

If the guesser guessed the correct number of red cubes in the bag after 6 cube-picks she gets 2 points.

If the guesser guessed the correct number of red cubes in the bag after 10 cube-picks she gets (another) 1 point.

If both guesses were incorrect, then the guesser gets 0 points.

While you are playing, keep track of how often a person guesses correctly on 6 picks and how often a person guesses correctly on 10 picks.

Answer the following questions when you are done playing:

What percent of the time did a person guess correctly on 6 picks? What percent of the time did a person guess correctly on 10 picks? How many times do you think you would need to pick a cube to be fairly certain about what is in the bag?

CLASS ACTIVITY 15E: Some Probability Misconceptions

Discuss the misconceptions listed next. What might their origins be? What activities or problems could you give someone who has these misconceptions?

1. Simone has been flipping a coin and has just flipped 5 heads in a row. Simone says that because she has just gotten so many heads, she is more likely to get tails than heads the next time she flips. Is Simone correct? What is the probability that Simone's next flip will be a tail? Does the answer depend on what the previous flips were?

2. There is a brown paper bag with 2 red bears and 3 blue bears in it. Michael says that if you reach in the bag 5 times and pick a bear without looking, putting the bear back after checking its color, you will pick out 2 red bears and 3 blue bears. Is this correct?

3. There are two opaque bags, each containing red blocks and yellow blocks. Bag 1 contains 1 red block and 3 yellow blocks. Bag 2 contains 3 red blocks and 12 yellow blocks. Tom says he is more likely to pick a red block out of bag 2 than out of bag 1 because bag 2 has more red blocks than bag 1. Is this correct?

4. Let's say you flip two coins simultaneously. There are three possible outcomes: Both are heads, both are tails, or one is heads and the other is tails. Does this mean that the probability of getting one head and one tail is $\frac{1}{3}$?

5. Kevin has a bag that is filled with 2 red balls and 1 white ball. Kevin says that because there are two different colors he could pick from the bag, the probability of picking the red ball is $\frac{1}{2}$. Is this correct?

CLASS ACTIVITY 15F: Picking Two Marbles from a Bag of 1 Black and 3 Red Marbles

You will need an opaque bag, 3 red marbles, and 1 black marble for this activity. Put the marbles in the bag.

If you reach in without looking and randomly pick out two marbles, what is the probability that one of the two marbles you pick is black? You will study this question in this activity.

1. Before you continue, make a guess: What do you think the probability of picking the black marble is when you randomly pick two marbles out of the four marbles (3 red, 1 black) in the bag?

2. Pick 2 marbles out of the bag. Repeat this many times, recording what you pick each time. What fraction of the times did you pick the black marble?

3. Now calculate the probability theoretically using a tree diagram. For the purpose of computing the probability, think of first picking one marble, then (without putting this marble back in the bag) picking a second marble. From this point of view, draw a tree diagram that will show all possible outcomes for picking the two marbles. But draw this tree diagram in a special way, *so that all outcomes shown by your tree diagram are equally likely.*

   Hints: the first stage of the tree should show all possible outcomes for your first pick. Remember that all branches you show should be equally likely. In the second stage, the branches you draw should depend on what happened in the first stage. For instance, if the first pick was the black marble, then the second pick must be one of the three red marbles.

   a. How many total outcomes for picking two marbles, one at a time, out of the bag of four (3 red, 1 black) does your tree diagram show?

   b. In how many outcomes is the black marble picked (on one of the two picks)?

   c. Use your answers to 3(a) and 3(b) and the basic principles of probability to calculate the probability of picking the black marble when you pick two marbles out of a bag filled with one black and three red marbles.

4. Why was it important to draw the tree diagram so that all outcomes were equally likely?

5. Here's another method for calculating the probability of picking the black marble when you pick two marbles out of a bag filled with one black and three red marbles:

   a. How many pairs of marbles can be made from the four marbles in the bag?

   b. How many of those pairs of marbles in 5(a) contain the black marble? (Use your common sense.)

   c. Use 5(a) and 5(b) and basic principles of probability to determine the probability of picking the black marble when you pick two marbles out of a bag containing one black and three red marbles.

6. Compare your answers with 3(a) and 5(a) and compare your answers with 3(b) and 5(b). How and why are they different?

CLASS ACTIVITY 15G: A Dice Rolling Game

Maya, James, Kaitlyn, and Juan are playing a game in which they take turns rolling a pair of dice. Each child has chosen a "special number" between 2 and 12, and receives 8 points whenever the total number of dots on the two dice is their special number. (They receive their points regardless of who rolled the dice. Their teacher picked 8 points so that the children would practice counting by 8s.)

Maya's special number is 7.

James's special number is 10.

Kaitlyn's special number is 12.

Juan's special number is 4.

The first person to get to 100 points or more wins. The children have played several times, each time using the same special numbers. They notice that Maya wins most of the time. They are wondering why.

1. Roll a pair of dice many times and record the total number of dots each time. Display your data so that you can compare how many times each possible number between 2 and 12 has occurred. What do you notice?

2. Draw an array showing all possible outcomes on each die when a pair of dice are rolled. (Think of the pair as *die 1* and *die 2*.)

   For which outcomes is the total number of dots 7? 10? 12? 4?

   What is the probability of getting 7 total dots on a roll of two dice? What is the probability of getting 10 total dots on a roll of two dice? What about for 12 and 4?

   Is it surprising that Maya kept winning?

15.2 Calculating Probabilities by Considering the Ideal Outcome in a Large Number of Trials

CLASS ACTIVITY 15H: Using the Meaning of Fraction Multiplication to Calculate a Probability

Use the circle in Figure 15.1, a pencil, and a paper clip to make a spinner as follows: Put the pencil through the paper clip and put the point of the pencil on the center of the circle. The paper clip will now be able to spin freely around the circle.

1. What is the probability of the spinner pointing to blue? Why?

2. To win a game, Jill needs to spin a blue followed by a red in her next two spins.
   a. What do you think Jill's probability of winning is? (Make a guess.)

   b. Carry out the experiment of spinning the spinner twice in a row 20 times. (In other words, spin the spinner 40 times, but each experiment consists of 2 spins.) Out of those 20 times, how often does Jill win? What fraction of 20 does this represent? Is this close to your guess in part (a)?

   c. Calculate Jill's probability of winning theoretically as follows: Imagine that Jill carries out the experiment of spinning the spinner twice in a row many times. In the ideal, what fraction of those times should the first spin be blue? _____

   In the ideal, what fraction of those times when the first spin is blue should the second spin be red? _____

   In the ideal, what fraction of pairs of spins should Jill spin first a blue and then a red? Therefore what is Jill's probability of winning? _____

3. Think of some other probability questions about the spinner in Figure 15.1. Try to answer your questions both by carrying out a number of experiments and by using a theoretical calculation.

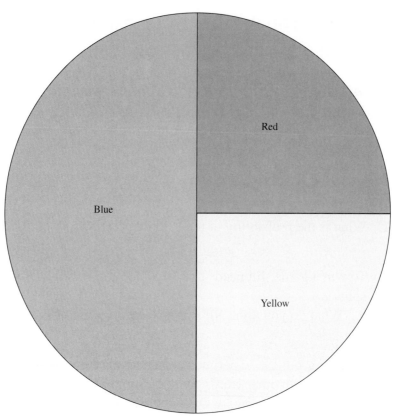

FIGURE 15.1

A Spinner

Bibliography

[1] George W. Bright. Helping elementary- and middle-grades preservice teachers understand and develop mathematical reasoning. In *Developing Mathematical Reasoning in Grades K-12*, pages 256–269. National Council of Teachers of Mathematics, 1999.

[2] Frances Curcio. *Developing Data-Graph Comprehension in Grades K-8*. National Council of Teachers of Mathematics, second edition, 2001.

[3] Singapore Curriculum Planning and Development Division, Ministry of Education. *Primary Mathematics Workbook*, volume 1A – 6B. Times Media Private Limited, Singapore, third edition, 2000. Available at http://www.singaporemath.com.

[4] Singapore Curriculum Planning and Development Division, Ministry of Education. *Primary Mathematics Workbook*, volume 1A – 6B. Times Media Private Limited, Singapore, third edition, 2000. Available at http://www.singaporemath.com.

[5] Graham Jones and Carol Thornton. *Data, Chance, and Probability, Grades 1 – 3 Activity Book*. Learning Resources, 1992.

[6] Edward Manfre, James Moser, Joanne Lobato, and Lorna Morrow. *Heath Mathematics Connections*. D. C. Heath and Company, 1994.

[7] National Council of Teachers of Mathematics. *Navigating through Algebra in Prekindergarten – Grade 2*. National Council of Teachers of Mathematics, 2001.

[8] A. M. O'Reilley. Understanding teaching/ teaching for understanding. In Deborah Schifter, editor, *What's Happening in Math Class?*, volume 2: Reconstructing Professional Identities, pages 65–73. Teachers College Press, 1996.

[9] Dav Pilkey. *Captain Underpants and the Attack of the Talking Toilets*. Scholastic, 1999.

Index

1 object

FIGURE A.1

A Rectangle Showing 2.3 × 1.8 for Class Activity 6I on Page 148

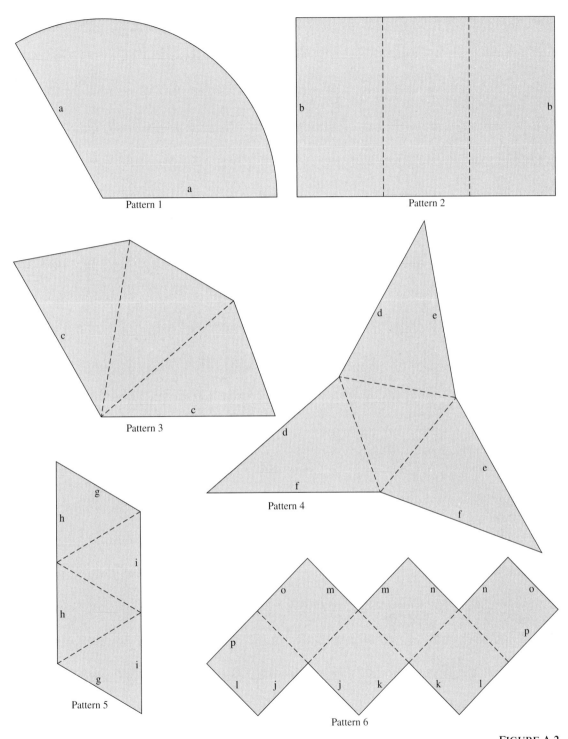

Pattern 1

Pattern 2

Pattern 3

Pattern 4

Pattern 5

Pattern 6

FIGURE A.2

Patterns for Shapes for Class Activity 8D on Page 213

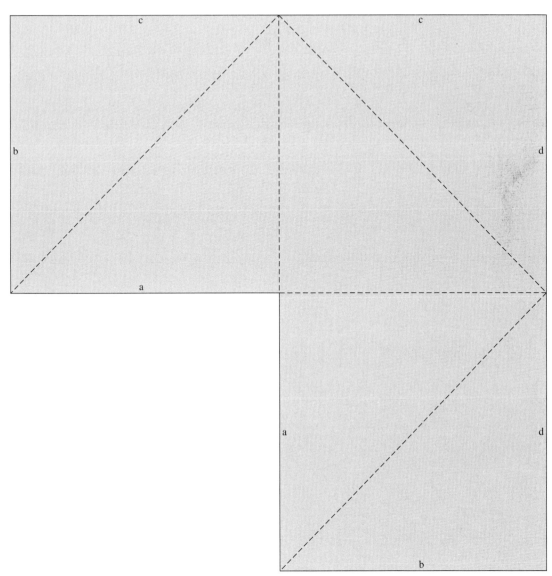

FIGURE A.3

A Pattern for a Shape for Class Activity 8H on Page 220

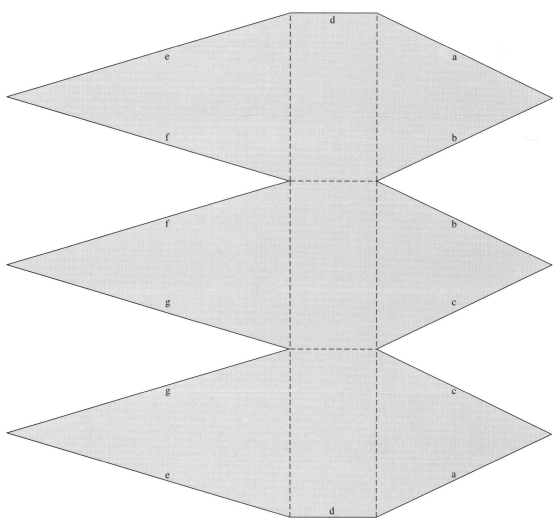

FIGURE A.4
A Pattern for a Shape for Class Activity 8H on Page 220

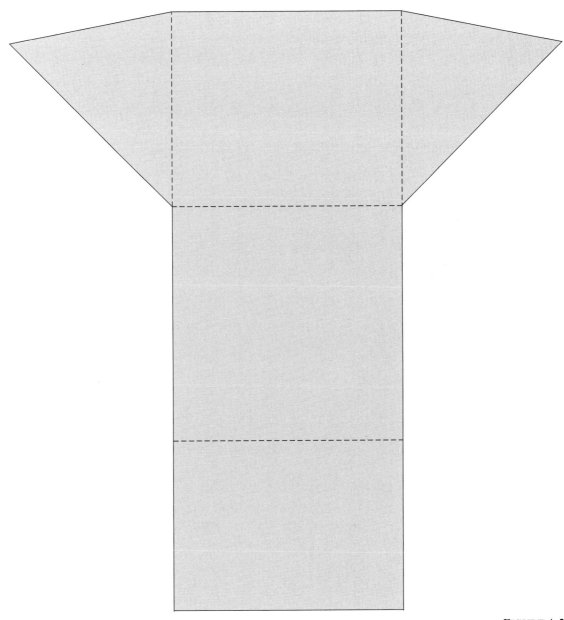

FIGURE A.5
For Class Activity 8OO on Page 271

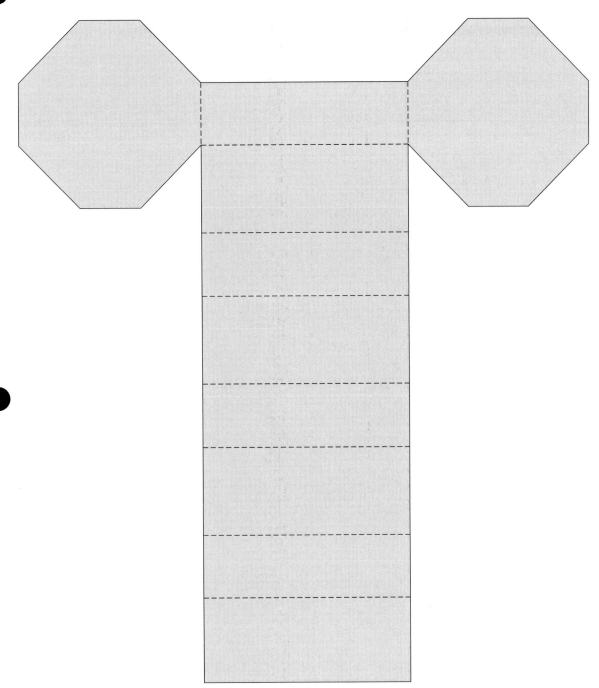

FIGURE A.6

For Class Activity 8OO on Page 271

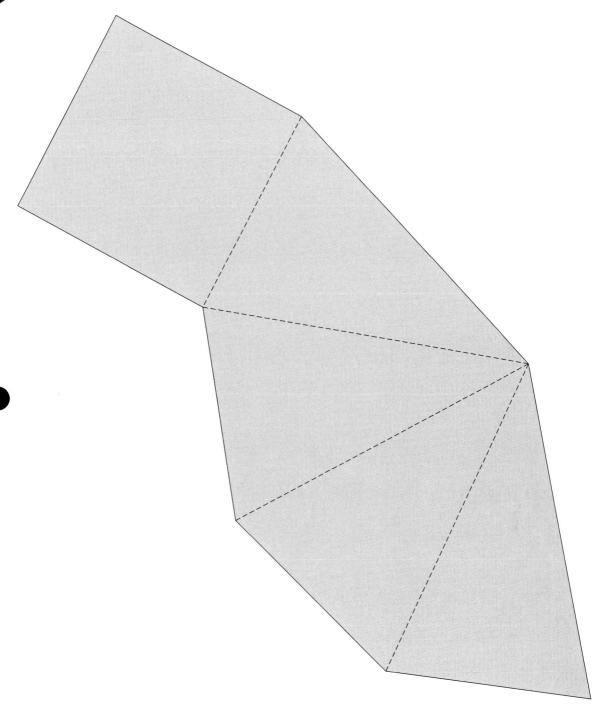

FIGURE A.7
For Class Activity 8OO on Page 271

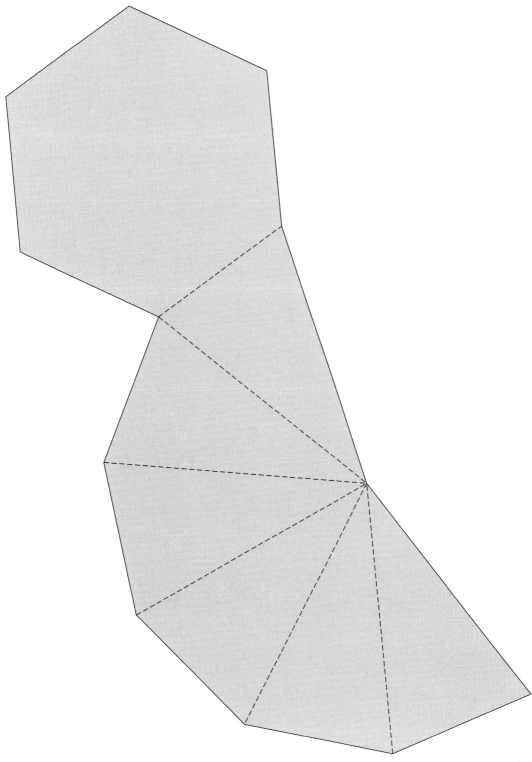

FIGURE A.8
For Class Activity 8OO on Page 271

FIGURE A.9

For Class Activities 8TT and 8RR on Pages 277 and 275

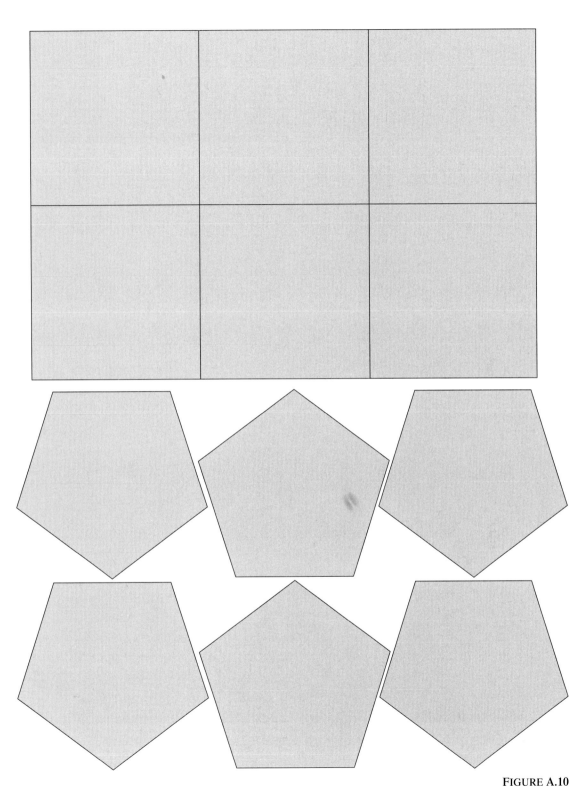

FIGURE A.10
For Class Activity 8TT on Page 277

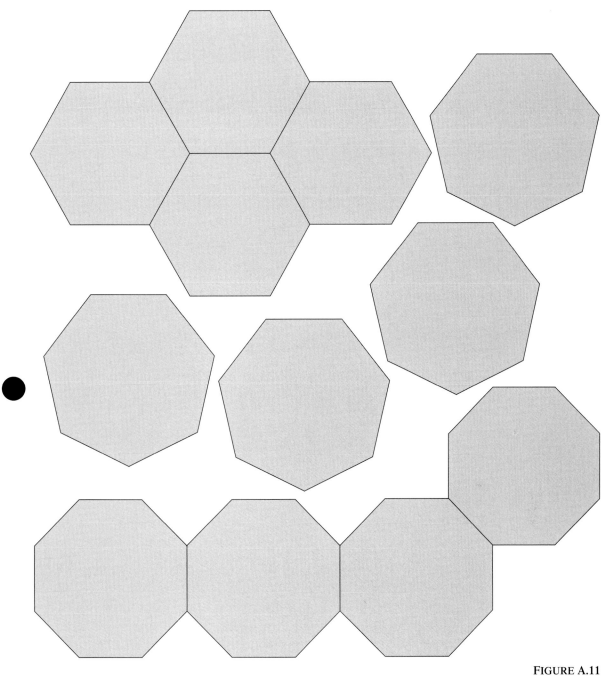

FIGURE A.11
For Class Activity 8TT on Page 277

FIGURE A.12
A Circle and Two Shapes for Class Activities 9D and 9E on pages 285 and 286

Imagine the curlicues repeating forever to the right and left.

FIGURE A.13

Five Designs for Class Activity 9G on page 289

Imagine the curlicues repeating forever to the right and left.

FIGURE A.14

Second Copy of Five Designs for Class Activity 9G on page 289

FIGURE A.15

Four Frieze Patterns for Class Activity 9H on Page 290

FIGURE A.16
Copy of Four Frieze Patterns for Class Activity 9H on Page 290

FIGURE A.17

Three Frieze Patterns for Class Activity 9H on Page 290

FIGURE A.18

Copy of Three Frieze Patterns for Class Activity 9H on Page 290

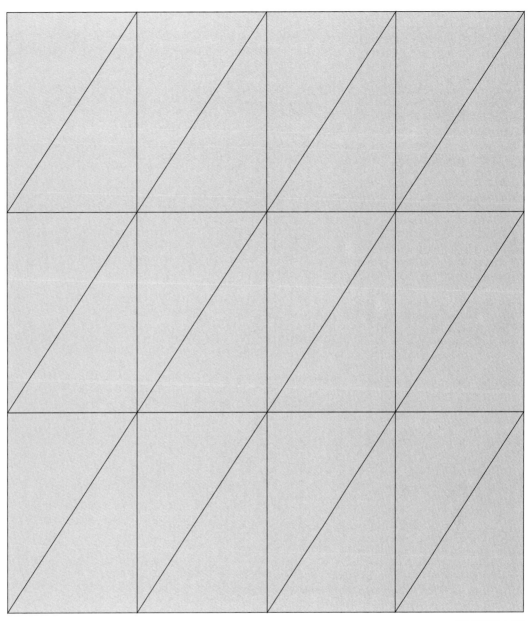

FIGURE A.19

Use These Triangles to Create Symmetrical Designs for Class Activity 9J on Page 292

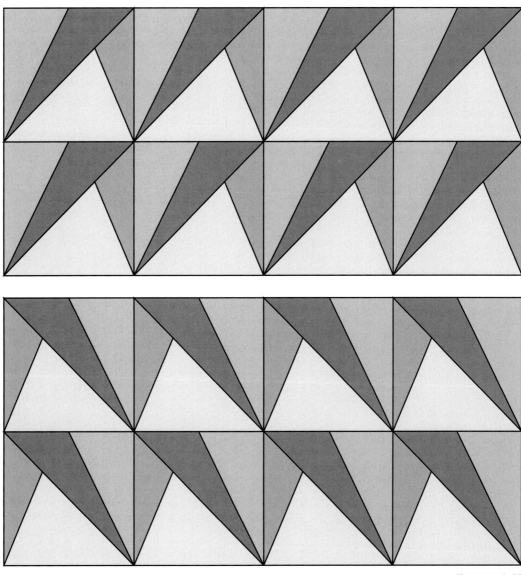

FIGURE A.20

Square Designs for Class Activity 9L on Page 294 on Analyzing Designs

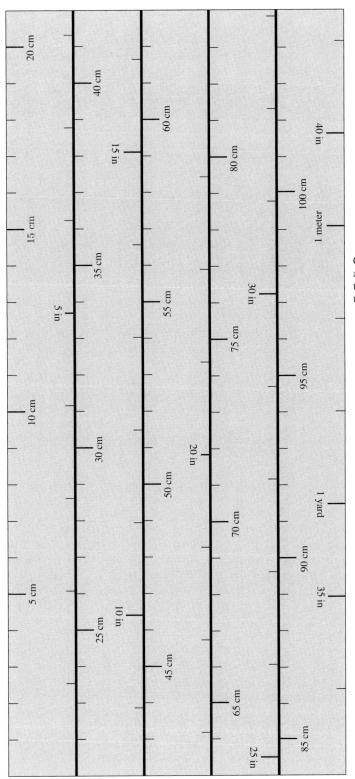

Cut out these strips and tape them end to end to make a tape measure.

FIGURE A.21
A Tape Measure to Cut Out for Class Activity 10B on Page 312

FIGURE A.22
Centimeter Graph Paper for Class Activity 10F on Page 319

FIGURE A.23

To Cut Out for Class Activity 10I on Page 323

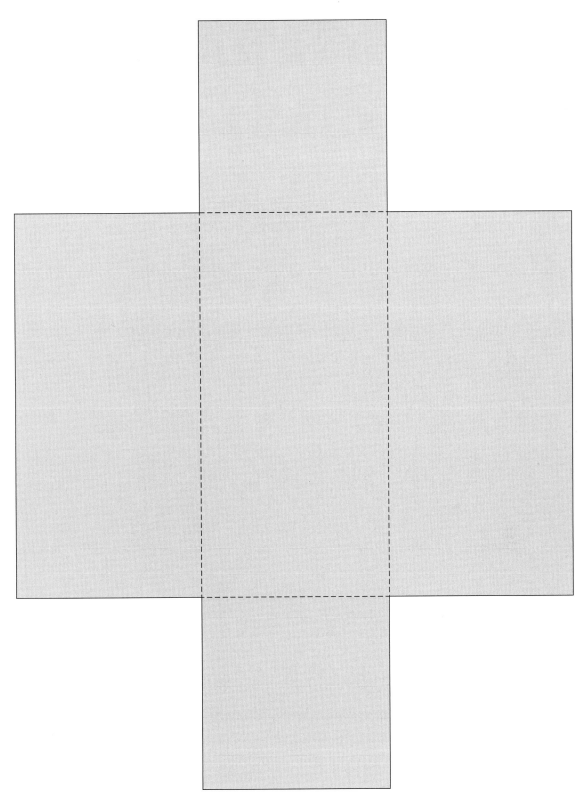

FIGURE A.24
Box Pattern for Class Activity 10J on Page 324

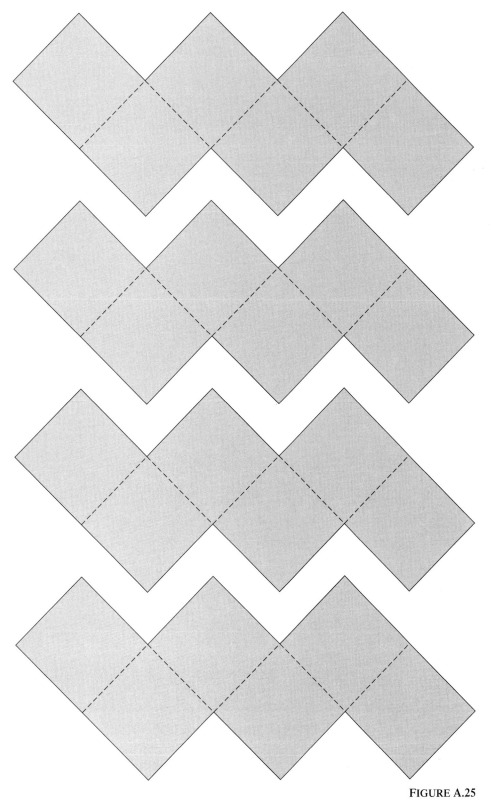

FIGURE A.25
Cube Patterns for Class Activity 10J on Page 324

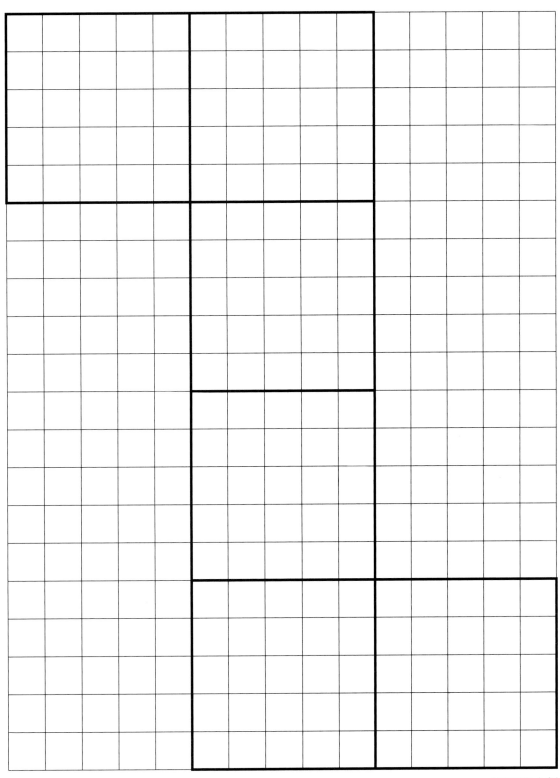

FIGURE A.26
A Pattern for a Box for Class Activity 10L on Page 327

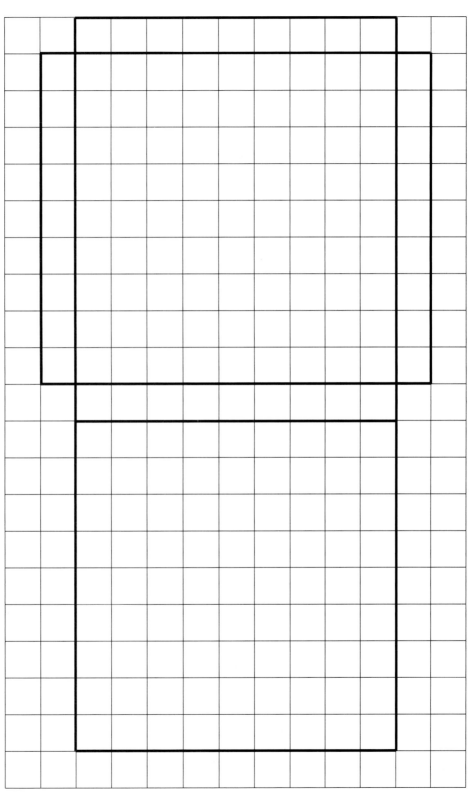

FIGURE A.27

A Pattern for a Box for Class Activity 10L on Page 327

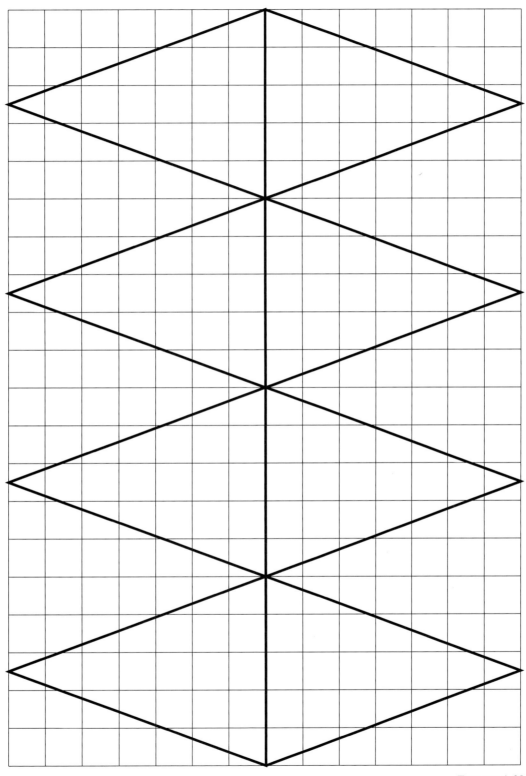

FIGURE A.28

Triangles for an Octahedron for Class Activity 11C on Page 337

15 cm

10 cm

10 cm

15 cm

FIGURE A.29

Rectangles for Class Activity 11A on Page 333

15 cm

10 cm

10 cm

15 cm

FIGURE A.30

Rectangles for Class Activity 11A on Page 333

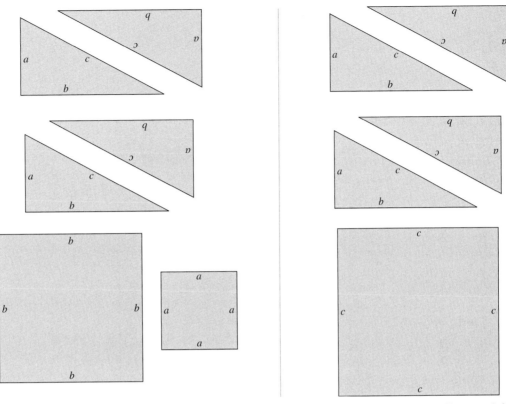

FIGURE A.31

To Cut Out for Class Activity 11F on Page 340

FIGURE A.32

A Triangle to Shear for Class Activity 11K on Page 348

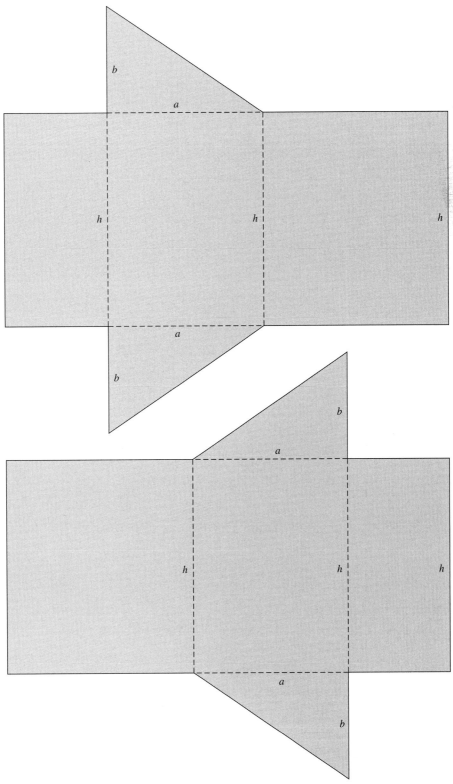

FIGURE A.33

Patterns for Prisms with Triangle Bases for Class Activity 11W on Page 369

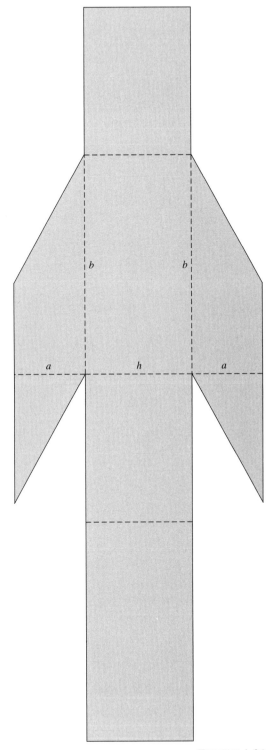

FIGURE A.34

A Pattern for a Prism with Parallelogram Base for
Class Activity 11W on Page 369

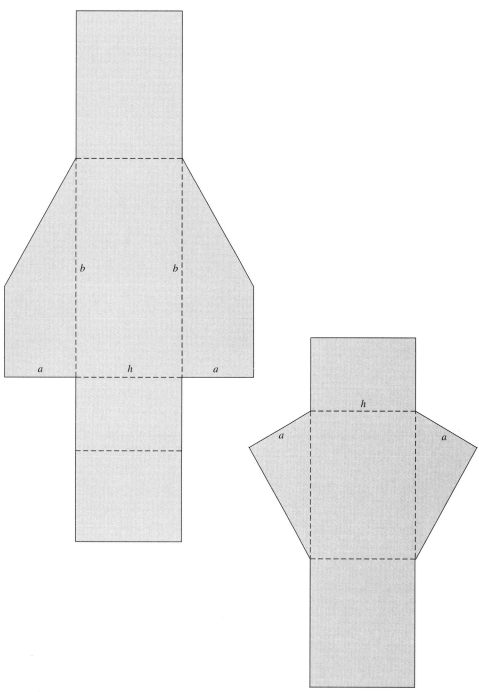

FIGURE A.35

Patterns for Prisms with Trapezoid and Triagular Bases for Class Activity 11W on Page 369

FIGURE A.36

A Centimeter Tape Measure for Class Activity 11X on Page 372

FIGURE A.37
A Pattern for a Rectangular Prism for Class Activity 11Z on Page 374

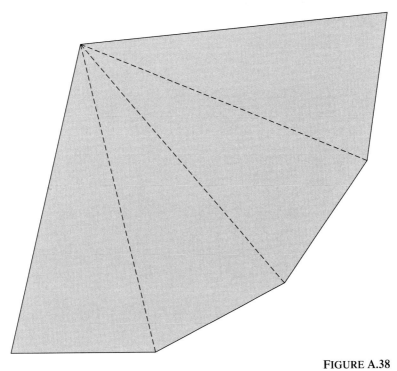

FIGURE A.38

A Pattern for a Rectangular Prism for Class Activity 11Z on Page 374

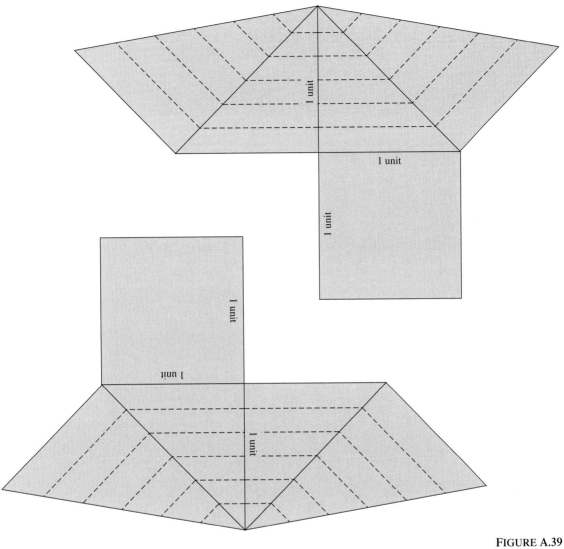

FIGURE A.39

Patterns for Oblique Pyramids for Class Activity 11AA on Page 375

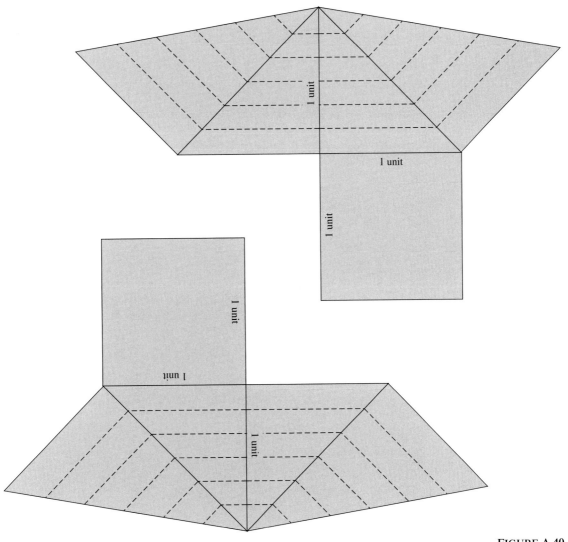

FIGURE A.40

Patterns for Oblique Pyramids for Class Activity 11AA on Page 375

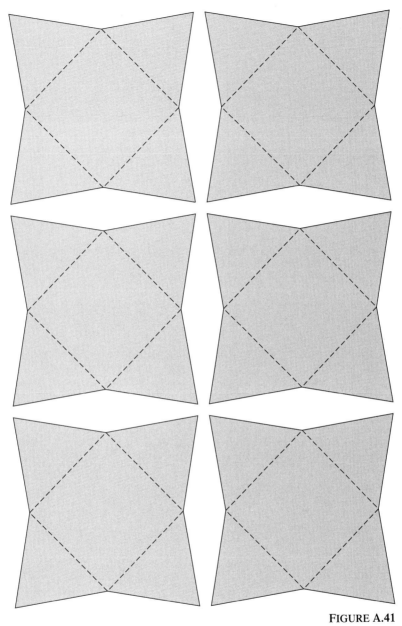

FIGURE A.41

Patterns for 6 Pyramids for Class Activity 11BB on Page 377

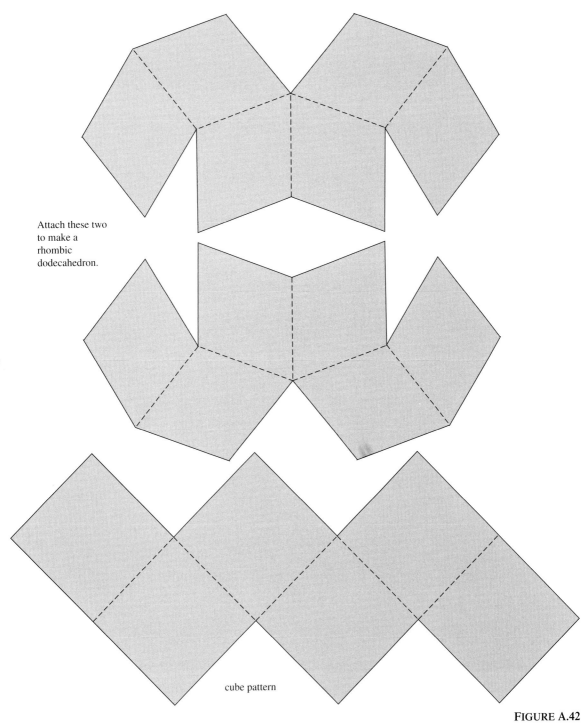

Attach these two to make a rhombic dodecahedron.

cube pattern

FIGURE A.42

Patterns for a Rhombic Dodecahedron and a Cube for Class Activity 11BB on Page 377

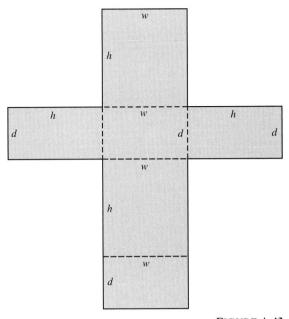

FIGURE A.43

A Pattern for a Small Box for Class Activity 11CC on
Page 378

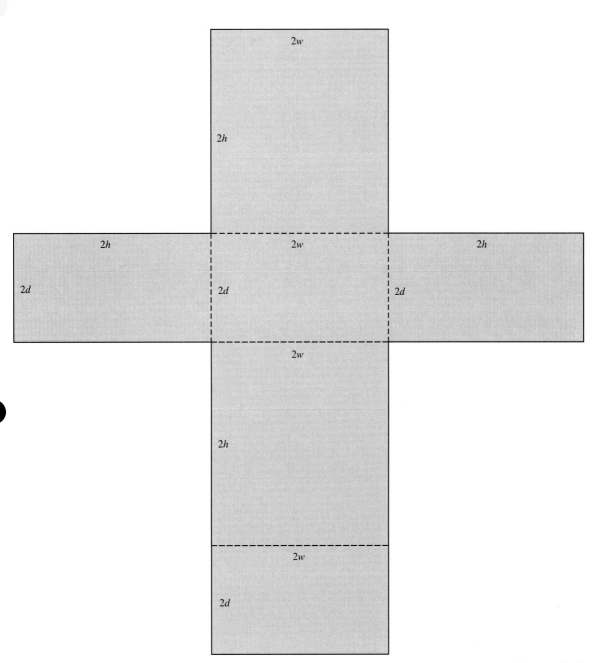

FIGURE A.44

A Pattern for a Big Box for Class Activity 11CC on Page 378

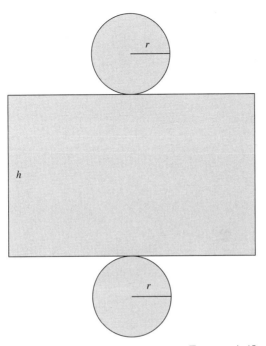

FIGURE A.45

A Pattern for a Small Cylinder for Class
Activity 11DD on Page 380

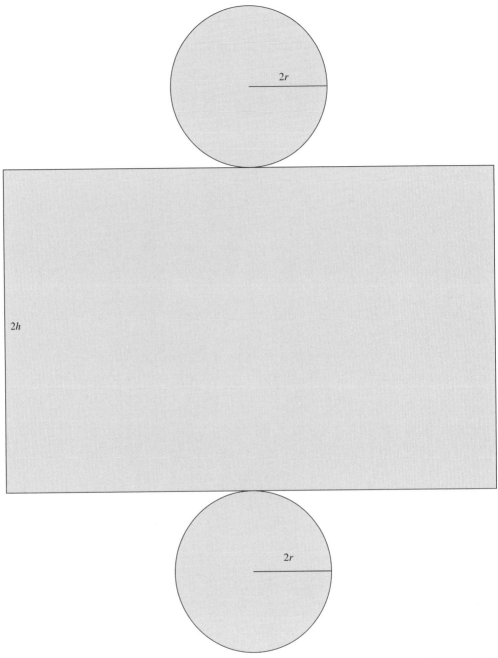

FIGURE A.46
A Pattern for a Large Cylinder for Class Activity 11DD on Page 380

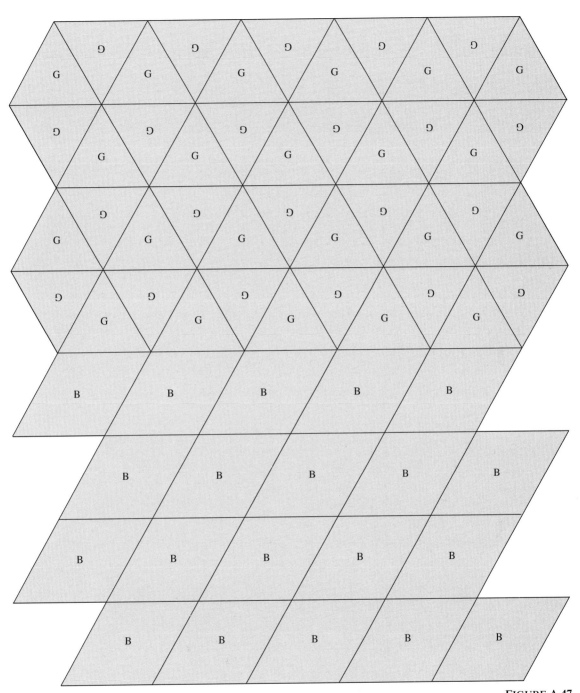

FIGURE A.47

Pattern Tiles for Class Activity 12T on Page 417

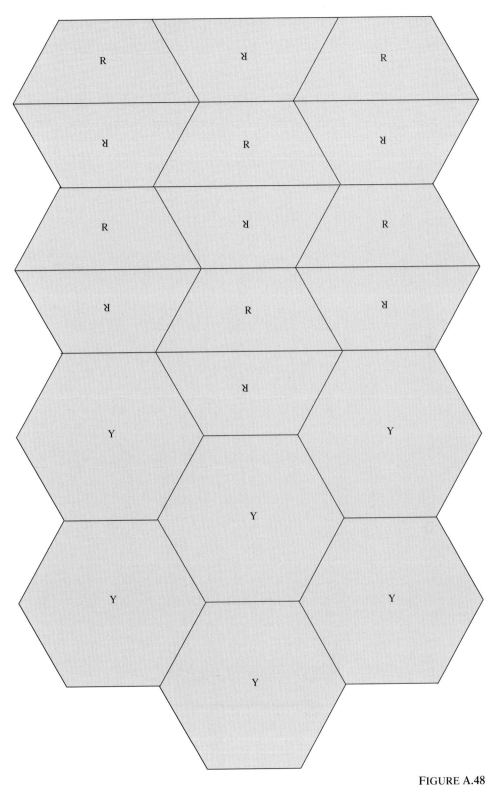

FIGURE A.48

Pattern Tiles for Class Activity 12T on Page 417

FIGURE A.49
Pattern Tiles for Class Activity 12T on Page 417

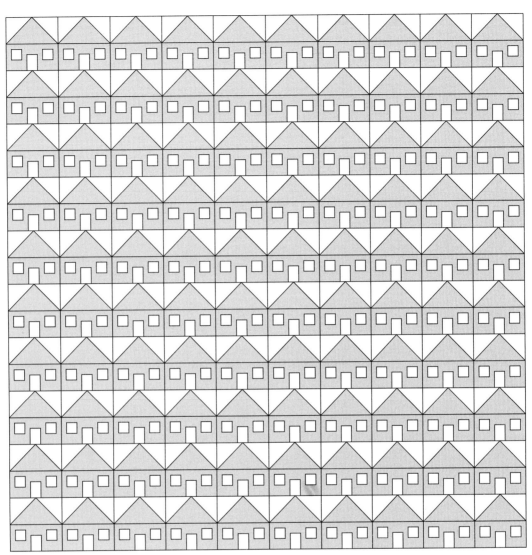

FIGURE A.50

First Cutout for Pictograph for Class Activity 14P on Page 505

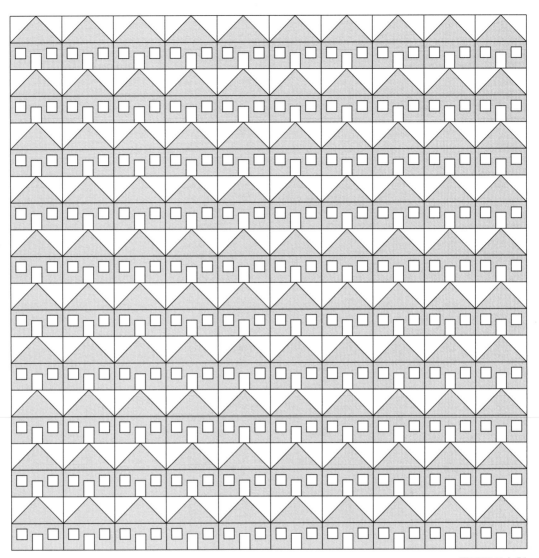

FIGURE A.51

Second Cutout for Pictograph for Class Activity 14P on Page 505

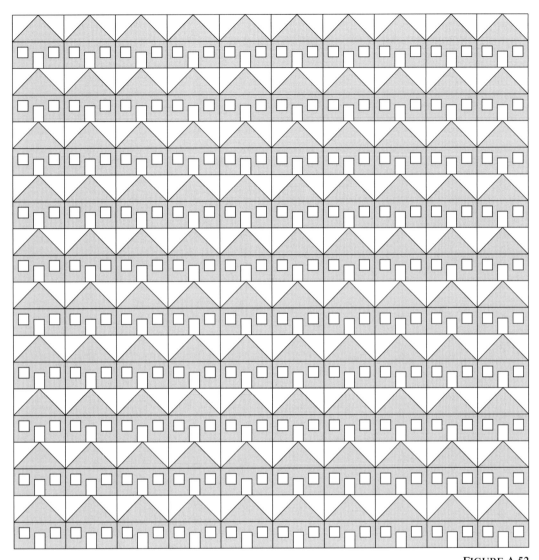

FIGURE A.52

Third Cutout for Pictograph for Class Activity 14P on Page 505